Rando

Nonlinear Stochastic
Operator Equations

Nonlinear Stochastic Operator Equations

GEORGE ADOMIAN

CENTER FOR APPLIED MATHEMATICS
UNIVERSITY OF GEORGIA
ATHENS, GEORGIA

1986

ACADEMIC PRESS, INC.

Harcourt Brace Jovanovich, Publishers

Orlando   San Diego   New York   Austin
Boston   London   Sydney   Tokyo   Toronto

ACADEMIC PRESS, INC.
Orlando, Florida 32887

United Kingdom Edition published by
ACADEMIC PRESS INC. (LONDON) LTD.
24–28 Oval Road, London NW1 7DX

Library of Congress Cataloging in Publication Data

Adomian, G.
  Nonlinear stochastic operator equations.

  Includes index.
  1. Stochastic systems. 2. Nonlinear theories.
3. Operator equations. I. Title.
QA402.A29 1986   003   85-26655
ISBN 0-12-044375-9 (alk. paper)

PRINTED IN THE UNITED STATES OF AMERICA

86 87 88 89   9 8 7 6 5 4 3 2 1

*Dedicated to the Class of 1911
of the University of Georgia*

Contents

Foreword

A previous volume, *Stochastic Systems* (1983), was the first systematic book bringing nonlinear and stochastic equations within the reach of engineers and physicists concerned with the difficulties of real systems and frontier problems in which conventional techniques such as linearization and perturbation are not sufficient or realistic.

This volume increases very substantially the scope of the work to cover very wide classes of equations. It is a simple and powerful method applicable to the solution of a multitude of problems in physics, engineering, operations research, systems analysis, economics, biology, medicine, and other fields.

Forthcoming volumes will deal with applications to physics and engineering. Previously, either such problems were not realistically formulated or the approximations made and the methods used made the results either unrealistic or misleading. This work will necessitate the rewriting of the mathematics and physics books since mathematics deals largely with linear operator theory and physics with perturbation. In my view, this overall work will have a profound impact on mathematics and on the modeling of problems of physics, engineering, economics, biology, and medicine and may well be viewed in retrospect as one of the significant contributions of this century. This work is a scientific breakthrough. The importance of it cannot be overemphasized.

RICHARD E. BELLMAN

In Memoriam

Richard Bellman's scientific contributions and service to mathematics were cut short just before this book finally went to the publisher. My hope is that the book will serve as another testimonial to his motivation and encouragement of so many people.

G. ADOMIAN

Preface

This book addresses the need for realistic solutions of the nonlinear stochastic equations arising in the modeling of frontier problems in every area of science. This includes linear or deterministic models or both as special cases. What makes this methodology* different is the avoidance of perturbation, linearization, truncation, discretization, or the assumption of unphysical processes. Thus the solution sought is that of the problem at hand, rather than one tailored to machine computation or the use of existing theorems of mathematics. Although there is much that is new which should be of interest to researchers, this material is still considered to be within the grasp of students with the normal mathematical background of senior undergraduate and graduate students in mathematical, physical, and engineering sciences.

---

* A short bibliography at the end of each chapter lists only those works that are felt to be particularly relevant and necessary to this approach, rather than all work in the area.

Acknowledgments

I would like to express my deep appreciation to Dr. Fred C. Davison, President of the University of Georgia, and to Professor Richard Bellman for support, encouragement, and confidence in my work.

I am appreciative also of the painstaking assistance and editing of Randolph Rach.

Finally, I am grateful to Arlette Revells, my secretary, who has "traveled" with me cheerfully through complex equations and multidimensional spaces for seventeen years.

CHAPTER 1

Introduction

> When confronted with a nonlinear systems engineering prob-
> lem, the first approach usually is to linearize, i.e., to try to avoid
> the nonlinear aspects of the problem. It is indeed a happy
> circumstance when a solution can be obtained in this way...
> *Wilson J. Rugh.*

In a previous volume, "*Stochastic Systems*" [*1*], we introduced an approximation method—we called it the *decomposition method*—for solving generic
operator equations of the form $\mathscr{F}u = g$, where the operator $\mathscr{F}$ may be
nonlinear (or linear as a special case) or stochastic (or deterministic as a
special case). It seems appropriate to call the method the "decomposition"
method, even though the word is used in other connections relating to the
theory of factorization and decomposition of dynamic systems. In Galois
theory, the representability of the roots of a polynomial in radicals is
considered in terms of factorizations of the group of automorphisms of the
decomposition field of the polynomial.

Decomposition has also been used in large-scale system theory where if
state spaces of subsystems are disjoint, decomposition into those subsystems
is an effective approach to simplify the system and if state spaces overlap, the
original system is expanded into a larger state space, including the original
system, such that overlapping subsystems appear as disjoint; then analysis
can be carried out using standard disjoint decomposition [*2*].

We discussed primarily differential equations but will now show that this
work is more general. Here $\mathscr{F}$ may be a partial differential operator, a
differential operator, a differential-delay operator, or an algebraic operator.
The term g may be a function of t or x, or x and t, or x, y, z, t, or even $x, y, z, t,$
ω where $\omega \in (\Omega, F, \mu)$ a probability space. Thus the inhomogeneous term, as
well as initial or boundary conditions, and coefficients in the operator may be
stochastic processes. The boundary conditions may be simple or quite
complicated (nonlinear, coupled, or random). The equation may be linear or
nonlinear, and deterministic or stochastic.

1

Basically two techniques are involved. First, any nonlinearities in the equation to be solved are written in terms of the author's A_n polynomials, a special set of polynomials which can be generated for the specific nonlinearity. Second, the assumed solution $u = \mathscr{F}^{-1}g$ is decomposed into components to be determined such that the first component is the solution for the linear deterministic part of $\mathscr{F}$, or of a suitable invertible part, including conditions on u. The other components are then found in terms of preceding components.

In the stochastic case, the method yields a natural statistical separability so that no truncations or closure approximations become necessary as discussed in ref. 1.

Since the method is nonperturbative and does not resort to linearization or assumptions of "small" or weak nonlinearity, "small" fluctuations, or special processes, the solutions are not only quite general but more realistic as well. This is true since we can solve a model, usually or often, much closer to the physical model rather than a mathematized model to fit the mathematics at hand.

Dynamical models whether for solitons, population problems, VLSI devices, control systems, or the national economy are nonlinear and stochastic, in general. Special cases for which stochasticity vanishes or linearity assumptions are adequate are precisely that, i.e., special cases included in the general methodology. Thus, we can consider deterministic linear systems, deterministic nonlinear systems, stochastic linear systems, and stochastic nonlinear systems in a unified framework. Cases involving stochasticity involve only an additional step of determining appropriate statistical measures, and deterministic cases are not more difficult by embedding in a general framework. The method was evolved to achieve statistical separability and avoid truncations but is valuable in the deterministic case as well!

A tremendous variety of applications exist: plasmas, high-current beams, propagation in random media, laser technology, turbulence, control theory for nonlinear stochastic or adaptive systems, chemical and biological oscillators, and many others. A number of important applications are dealt with elsewhere [3].

Finally, we should mention that in some areas, the work is preliminary and not a final document, in other words, it is an active research area. I hope it will strike creative sparks in many dissertations.

REFERENCES

1. G. Adomian, "Stochastic Systems." Academic Press, New York, 1983.
2. M. Ikeda, D. D. Siljak, and E. E. White, *IEEE Trans. Automatic Control* **AC-29**, 244–249.
3. G. Adomian, Applications of Nonlinear Stochastic Systems Theory to Physics, in press.

CHAPTER 2

Operator Equations and the Decomposition Method

There must be a simpler way.

R. E. Bellman

2.1. MODELING, APPROXIMATION, AND REALITY

Frontier problems exist in physics, engineering, biology, medicine, astrophysics, and other disciplines and in applications ranging from nuclear reactors, the fusion process, lasers, typhoons, tsunamis, computer chips, radar, turbulence, internal waves, solitons, compartmental analyses in medicine, behavior of the national economy, and many more which require sophisticated mathematical methods to even attempt to formulate, let alone solve.

Their solutions—when appropriate models can be constructed—may depend on equations for which present mathematical methods in general use may require supercomputers and even so, possibly yield solutions which simply are not correct or realistic. (A gigaflop computer could conceivably give wrong answers much faster.)

The equations modeling these applications may be ordinary algebraic (polynomial) equations starting from the quadratic equations familiar to school students to high-order polynomials, transcendental and exponential equations, differential equations or systems of such equations, delay-differential equations, partial differential equations, or systems of partial differential equations. The coefficients of these differential equations may be not only space and time dependent but may be random processes. Finally, the equations may be nonlinear.

If the latter two effects are relatively insignificant, then existing methods are adequate. In general, these effects are not insignificant. Even mathematicians are sometimes unaware that the methodology in constant use for

3

decades can yield results departing significantly from actual behavior. Why is this so?

Modeling any real problem involves approximation. One attempts to retain essential factors while keeping within the bounds of mathematical tractability. Thus, in modeling a complex dynamical system we must seek a sufficiently simplified abstraction or model so that we can understand and analyze the behavior while the analytical results still conform sufficiently to actual system behavior. This involves great difficulties.

Real nonlinear systems are very sensitive to small changes in functions or in initial conditions. Consider, for example, the equation $dy/dx = (y - 1)^2$, $y(0) = 1$ for which the solution is a *constant*, $y = 1$. Then consider $dy/dx = y^2 - 2y + 1.01 = (y - 1)^2 + 0.01$ whose solution is $y = 1 + \frac{1}{10}\tan(x/10)$ which has vertical asymptotes at $(2k + 1)(5\pi)$, $k = 0, \pm 1, \pm 2, \ldots$ and is periodic. Finally, consider $dy/dx = (y - 1)^2$ with $y(0) = 1.01$ instead of 1.0 whose solution is $y = 1 - 1/(x - 100)$ which represents a hyperbola with one vertical asymptote. Yet it is difficult or impossible in the modeling of a physical problem to determine functions or initial conditions with such precision. Thus, anomalies arise as a result of the modeling.

The decomposition method [1] cannot answer all such difficulties; they are inherent in modeling, and it is clear that wherever nonlinearity and/or stochasticity is involved, serious new looks at models now used without question are in order. The earlier models would be an excellent guide. We first seek gross understanding with linearized deterministic or perturbative models. After analysis and tests against reality, we can consider more sophisticated models and seek deeper understanding.

Any physical system is nonlinear in general. Even a slight (or "small") nonlinearity can produce new and possibly intolerable effects as every high-fidelity music enthusiast realizes when pure tone inputs produce harmonics. Linearity is a very special case corresponding to a linear or straight-line relationship between output and input. If we limit our attention to a very small portion of such an output–input graph, we can approximate the curve by a straight line and represent the performance as linear; otherwise we cannot. There is an even worse complexity to consider. Real systems involve randomness or stochastic behavior. Thus, a general system may be *stochastic* as well as *nonlinear*.

When the resulting nonlinear stochastic equations are solved by the usual methods in common use (perturbation, linearizations, averagings, closure approximations, assumptions of white noise or Markov or Wiener behavior, quasi-monochromatic approximations, Picard method, Newton's method, finite differences, Runge–Kutta, etc.), all of which have now become commonplace and no longer even to be questioned, the resulting solutions may depart significantly from the actual physical behavior. The mathematical solution is then the solution of the mathematized or mathematically simplified problem and not of the actual physical problem.

We must note that for some nonlinear systems, exact linearization is possible, in which by clever transformations of dependent and independent variables, the equations become linear and solvable. Unfortunately, this is only occasionally possible and usually we must resort to ad hoc methods and perturbative methods.

In systems that involve stochastic parameters, e.g., in differential equations involving stochastic process coefficients (the stochastic operator case), usual analyses employ either perturbation or hierarchy methods, either of which means the fluctuations are assumed to be small.

Another common restrictive assumption is the requirement of a very special nature or behavior for the stochastic processes involved. Again such assumptions are made for mathematical and not for physical reasons. The literature abounds with unrealistic (i.e., unphysical) assumptions and approximations such as "white noise," the monochromatic approximation, and "local independence."

These limitations, restrictions, and assumptions are made, of course, for mathematical tractability and use of existing theory. Yet, if we can solve models which more accurately represent phenomena of interest [accounting in a realistic way for the nonlinear and stochastic behavior, and for retarded effects (delays), coupled or random boundary conditions] and if we can solve equations whether they are algebraic, differential, partial differential, or systems of equations, i.e., if we are less constrained by the severe requirement of tractability, then the modeling can be more realistic. Our resulting solutions will then be much more accurate and closely in correspondence with actual physical results. All modeling, of course, is approximate since we abstract the reality and decide to neglect certain factors.

Real-world application of mathematics, i.e., to physical problems, requires making a reasonable model. This means making one that is realistic as well as solvable. Since models must be tractable (i.e., mathematically solvable) to be useful, they have tended to be linear and deterministic, or, at least, almost so, because of the limitations of the available applicable mathematics. However, all real dynamical systems whether physical, biological, or economic are quite generally nonlinear and often stochastic as well. Linearity is a special case of nonlinearity and deterministic is a special case of stochastic. Of course, in many problems it may be sufficient to assume weak non-linearity, small fluctuations, or special fluctuations, such as white noise, or to neglect coupling terms; this approach has led to considerable progress. Yet, it certainly is not realistic or adequate in all cases. Thus, our objective must be to solve nonlinear stochastic dynamical systems.

Because of widespread use of standard methods for many years we tend to be frozen into various approaches. It is not always wise to follow over-zealously the footsteps of the masters. Itô's famous equation, for example, is based on Wiener's study of Brownian motion. However, the Wiener process is not a process that occurs in nature; it is a mathematical process.

The Itô equation is written as $dy = f(y, t) dt + g(y, t) dw$, where w is a Weiner process, a nondifferentiable process. It is interpreted as an integral equation involving the white noise dw. Suppose $z(t, \omega)$ is a general stochastic process. If it has zero mean, we can write it as the canonical expansion or sum of "elementary random functions" of the form $v_\nu \phi_\nu$. Here $z = \sum_\nu v_\nu(\omega)\phi_\nu(t)$, where the $v_\nu(\omega)$ are uncorrelated random variables with zero expected values and $\phi_\nu(t)$ are ordinary (deterministic) functions of time. Analogously we write $z = \int w(\omega, \lambda)\phi(t, \lambda) d\lambda$, where w is a white-noise variation of the parameter λ and $\phi(t, \lambda)$ is deterministic with parameter t and argument λ. The integral corresponds to the sum and each uncorrelated elementary random function is $w(\omega, \lambda)\phi(t, \lambda) d\lambda$. Thus the integral is a representation of a stochastic process in terms of a white noise. Note that if $\phi(t, \lambda) = \delta(t - \lambda)$, then $z = \int w(\omega, \lambda)\delta(t - \lambda) d\lambda = w(\omega, t)$. Thus the Itô equation would preferably, in our view, be written $dy = f(y, t) dt + g(y, t) dz$ or as

$$dy/dt = f(y, t) + g(y, t) dz/dt$$
$$= f(y, t) + g(y, t)\alpha(t, \omega)$$

or $\mathscr{F} y = x$ in our standard form. The Itô equation is for a system whose input is an elementary random function—a *single* component of a canonical expansion of a real stochastic process; and only for the singular case where $\phi = \delta(t - \lambda)$ does it and, therefore, the question of differentiation of w ever arise.

A very wide range of problems including all of the above can indeed be solved by an approximation method we have called the decomposition method. In view of the modeling approximations and simplifications discussed above, *such "approximate" solutions solving nonlinear random equations without first mathematically changing the problem, may well be more exact than so-called "exact" methods.*

We are interested in developing the ability to solve any general nonlinear stochastic dynamical system equations not only because the modeling of frontier problems often leads to such equations, but because the simpler linear or deterministic cases are special cases solvable by the same methodology which becomes a very convenient and rather general computational method for problems.

Certainly, it is important to know that attempts to compute solutions will be successful. Mathematically this means the problem is well-set, (e.g., in the sense of Hadamard)—that an operator exists which uniquely and continuously takes elements in a suitable class of initial data into a class of solutions. Statement of the precise mathematical conditions unfortunately requires a complicated symbolism, but the meaning is simple enough. Solutions should exist for reasonable input data and each solution should be unique so it can serve as a physical approximation and depend continuously without jumps on the given conditions. Also, it is reasonable to say small changes in parameters of the model should cause no more than small changes in our solutions. However, to talk of a problem as being well-set and then to neglect the nonlinear (or stochastic) effects or to approximate them to first order means that the "solution" is only a mathematical solution and not the real solution. Nonlinear equations can be very sensitive to small input changes. If we linearize a strongly nonlinear equation in our model, then precisely define conditions under which a mathematical solution to the simplified equation is valid, the solution of the model retaining nonlinearity seems preferable (even if we know merely that $u(x, 0) = g(x)$ and not that $g(x)$ belongs to a Sobolev space of L_2 functions with generalized first derivatives also in L_2). After all, g represents a physical quantity. We are dealing with physical problems; the physical system has a solution, and the parameters are generally well defined without discontinuities. This and the fact that our general forms are for *operator* equations in which the operator may be algebraic, differential, or partial differential, allows us to conceive of solving problems in wide ranging applications.

2.2. THE OPERATOR EQUATIONS

A general dynamical system will be viewed as nonlinear and stochastic (without the common qualification as being weakly nonlinear or involving "small" nonlinearities or random fluctuations). It will be represented by the operator equation

$$\mathscr{F}u = g \tag{2.2.1}$$

where g may be a stochastic process or simply a function, and $\mathscr{F}$ represents a nonlinear stochastic operator which may be a differential or algebraic operator. (It is convenient to defer precise mathematical definition now for good reasons.) Script letters will denote stochasticity for an operator. Since $\mathscr{F}u$ may have linear and nonlinear parts we will write (2.1.1) in a more detailed form as

$$\mathscr{L}u + \mathscr{N}u = g \tag{2.2.2}$$

Here, $\mathscr{L}$ denotes a linear (stochastic) operator and $\mathscr{N}u$ a nonlinear (stochastic) term. If both operators are deterministic, (2.1.2) is written as

$$Lu + Nu = g \tag{2.2.3}$$

where g again may be deterministic or stochastic. In (2.1.2), the linear operator $\mathscr{L}$ may be decomposed into deterministic and stochastic (linear) operators, thus

$$\mathscr{L} = L + \mathscr{R} \tag{2.2.4}$$

It may be convenient to use L as the average of $\mathscr{L}$ (i.e., $L = \langle \mathscr{L} \rangle$). Then $\mathscr{R} = \mathscr{L} - L$ is a zero-mean random operator. If, for example, our independent variable is t and $\mathscr{L}$ is an nth order differential (stochastic) operator given by

$$\mathscr{L} = \sum_{v=0}^{n} a_v(t, \omega) \, d^v/dt^v \tag{2.2.5}$$

where the $a_v(t, \omega)$ may be stochastic processes defined on a suitable probability space,[1] then

$$L = \sum_{v=0}^{n} \langle a_v(t, \omega) \rangle \, d^v/dt^v \tag{2.2.6}$$

and

$$\mathscr{R} = \sum_{v=0}^{n-1} \alpha_v(t, \omega) \, d^v/dt^v \tag{2.2.7}$$

where the fluctuating component α_v of each coefficient a_v is given by

$$\alpha_v(t, \omega) = a_v - \langle a_v \rangle \tag{2.2.8}$$

Since it is necessary that L be invertible (as we shall see) and the choice of $L = \langle \mathscr{L} \rangle$ may make the determination of the Green's function difficult, we can choose a simpler L more easily invertible such as L equal to the highest-ordered derivative only. In this case, we have

$$\mathscr{L} = L + R + \mathscr{R}$$

where $\mathscr{R}$ is again a random operator and the deterministic operator is written as $L + R$, where R is simply the *remainder operator* or remaining part of the operator when L is specified as the highest-ordered term and $\mathscr{R}$ is the term containing random processes.

It now occurs to us that $\mathscr{N}u$, the nonlinear part, may be deterministic (written Nu) or it may also have a stochastic part which we identify as $\mathscr{M}u$ (i.e., $\mathscr{N}u = Nu + \mathscr{M}u$).

Assume now that Nu is a (nonlinear) function $f(u)$. Later, we will consider expressions where the nonlinear term is a function of u and one or more

---

[1] We will assume the coefficient of the highest-ordered derivative is not stochastic, but any of the other coefficients can be stochastic. We usually take $a_n = 1$.

derivatives of u such as $f(u, u')$ and various composite and product functions such as $u^2 u'^3$, uu'', or $f(u, u', \ldots, u^m)$. The operator $\mathscr{F}$ may involve derivatives with respect to one or more independent variables such as x, y, z, t, or mixed derivatives. We will defer these cases. We will assume the same probability space for each process; it is easy enough to make them different, but it obscures notational convenience.

If the independent variable is t, then L may be d^2/dt^2, for example, or $d^2/dt^2 + \alpha(t) \, d/dt + \beta(t)$. If independent variables are x, y, z, t, then we may have $L = L_x + L_y + L_z + L_t$, where, for example, $L_x = \partial^2/\partial x^2$, $L_y = \partial/\partial y$, etc. Until we treat multidimensional equations we consider a single independent variable t.

We now have the operator equation

$$\mathscr{F} u = g$$

or $\mathscr{L} u + \mathscr{N} u = g$ or finally

$$L u + R u + \mathscr{R} u + N u + \mathscr{M} u = g \tag{2.2.9}$$

where, of the five terms on the left, any one, two, three, or four may vanish; so we include a very wide range of possibilities in the single equation (2.2.9) whose solution we will consider in detail in the following chapter.

Our approach, as developed in "Stochastic Systems" [1], will be first to solve the operator equation for Lu and, second, to write any nonlinear term in terms of the author's A_n polynomials. Thus $N u = \sum_{n=0}^{\infty} A_n$, a special set of polynomials generated for the particular nonlinearity $N u = f(u)$. (If we also have $\mathscr{M} u$, we can write $\sum_{n=0}^{\infty} A'_n$ or $\sum_{n=0}^{\infty} B_n$.) These polynomials have been calculated for general classes of nonlinearities and explicit formulas have been developed. Their calculation is as simple as writing down a set of Hermite or Legendre polynomials. They depend, of course, on the particular nonlinearity and we will see how to calculate them. Third, we assume decomposition of u into $\sum_{n=0}^{\infty} u_n$ or, equivalently, of $\mathscr{F}^{-1} g$ into $\sum_{n=0}^{\infty} \mathscr{F}_n^{-1} g$ to determine individual components with $u_0 = \mathscr{F}_0^{-1} g$ determined as the complete solution of $L u = g$. Each $\mathscr{F}_{n+1}^{-1} g$ now depends on $\mathscr{F}_n^{-1} g$ (and therefore ultimately on $\mathscr{F}_0^{-1} g$) and is calculable. Hence $\mathscr{F}^{-1}$, the inverse of the (stochastic nonlinear) operator $\mathscr{F}$ is determined. Our solution will not be the complete series for u but the n-term approximation $\phi_n = \sum_{i=0}^{n-1} u_i$ for a suitable n.

If stochasticity is involved, the above series involves stochastic processes. It is then averaged to get $\langle u \rangle$ or multiplied and averaged to form the correlation $\langle u(t_1) \overset{*}{u}(t_2) \rangle = R_u(t_1, t_2)$ as discussed in [1]. Thus, the solution statistics (statistical measures) are obtained when appropriate statistical knowledge of the input random quantities is available.

Summarizing, the solution process for the output of a physical system is decomposed into additive components—the first being the solution of a simplified linear deterministic system which takes account of initial conditions or boundary conditions. Each of the other components is then found in terms of a *preceding* component and thus ultimately in terms of the first.

The usual statistical separability problems requiring closure approximations are eliminated with the reasonable assumption of statistical independence of the system *input* and the system itself! Quasi-monochromaticity assumptions are unnecessary and processes can be assumed to be general physical processes rather than white noise. White noise is not a physical process! Physical inputs are neither unbounded nor do they have zero correlation times. In any event, the results can be obtained as a special case. If fluctuations are small, the results of perturbation theory are exactly obtained [1], but again this is a special case, as are the diagrammatic methods of physicists.

Just as spectral spreading terms are lost by a quasi-monochromatic approximation when a random or scattering medium is involved, or terms are lost in the use of closure approximations, Boussinesq approximations, and replacement of stochastic quantities by their expectations, significant terms may be lost by the usual linearizations, unless, of course, the behavior is actually close to linear.

One hopes, therefore, that physically more realistic and accurate results and predictions will be obtained in many physical problems by this method of solution, as well as interesting new mathematics from the study of such operators and relevant analysis. The easy computability and accuracy of the method are its principal features and its potential applicability to a very wide range of problems in physics, engineering, economics, and biology is substantial. A number of applications in physics and engineering are dealt with in forthcoming publications. Let us consider now the solution we have indicated.

2.3.   THE DECOMPOSITION METHOD

We begin with the operator equation $\mathscr{F}u = g$ in the form

$$Lu + Ru + \mathscr{R}u + Nu + \mathscr{M}u = g \tag{2.3.1}$$

where g denotes a function of t or a stochastic process $g(t, \omega)$, and the linear operator $\mathscr{L}$ has been decomposed into components L, R, and $\mathscr{R}$, where L is invertible, R is the remaining portion of the deterministic operator in L, and $\mathscr{R}$ is the random part. The nonlinear terms denoted by $\mathscr{N}u$ are written explicitly as $Nu + \mathscr{M}u$, where a nonlinear portion that is deterministic is symbolized by Nu and a nonlinear portion that is stochastic is symbolized by

$\mathcal{M}u$. If the last two terms on the left are zero, we have a linear stochastic equation. If the second, third, and fifth terms vanish, we have an ordinary (deterministic) nonlinear equation. Now write (2.3.1) as

$$Lu = g - Ru - \mathcal{R}u - Nu - \mathcal{M}u \qquad (2.3.2)$$

and since we assumed invertible L

$$L^{-1}Lu = L^{-1}g - L^{-1}Ru - L^{-1}\mathcal{R}u - L^{-1}Nu - L^{-1}\mathcal{M}u \qquad (2.3.3)$$

We must now specify whether we are dealing with initial-value problems or boundary-value problems.

2.4.   EVALUATION OF THE INVERSE OPERATOR L^{-1} AND THE y_0 TERM OF THE DECOMPOSITION FOR INITIAL OR BOUNDARY CONDITIONS

Consider a second-order differential operator $\mathcal{F}$ (we can generalize later to nth-order differential operators and multidimensional differential operators). Assume that the independent variable is t and the highest-ordered linear operator is symbolized by L. We need not be concerned now about other terms such as R. Thus, we now consider a simple linear differential equation $Ly(t) = x(t)$ with $L = d^2/dt^2$ for this discussion (later we will let $L = d^n/dt^n$).

Since $L^{-1}x(t) = \int_0^t G(t, \tau)x(\tau)\,d\tau$, where G is the Green's function [i.e., L^{-1} is an integral operator whose kernel is $G(t, \tau)$] and since the Green's function satisfies

$$d^2G(t, \tau)/dt^2 = \delta(t - \tau) \qquad (2.4.1)$$

we can find G by solving this equation. Here δ, of course, is the Dirac delta function, and in the sense of distribution theory and symbolic functions, there is no mathematical difficulty in verifying that $Ly = x$ is solved by $y(t) = \int G(t, \tau)x(\tau)\,d\tau$. Integration of (2.4.1) results in

$$dG/dt = H(t - \tau) + \alpha(\tau) \qquad (2.4.2)$$

where H is the Heaviside function and α is an arbitrary function. This approach is discussed in numerous references, some listed at the end of the chapter. A second integration yields

$$G(t, \tau) = (t - \tau)H(t - \tau) + t\alpha(\tau) + \beta(\tau) \qquad (2.4.3)$$

then

$$y(t) = L^{-1}x(t) = \int G(t, \tau)x(\tau)\,d\tau$$

$$= \int (t - \tau)H(t - \tau)x(\tau)\,d\tau + t \int \alpha(\tau)x(\tau)\,d\tau + \int \beta(\tau)x(\tau)\,d\tau \qquad (2.4.4)$$

The arbitrary functions α and β must be evaluated using the specified initial or boundary conditions on the solution. Let us consider some possibilities.

(a) **Homogeneous Boundary Conditions** $y(0) = y(1) = 0$: Substitution into (2.4.4) of the given conditions results in

$$-\int \tau H(-\tau)x(\tau)\,d\tau + \int \beta(\tau)x(\tau)\,d\tau = 0$$

$$\int (1-\tau)H(1-\tau)x(\tau)\,d\tau + \int \alpha(\tau)x(\tau)\,d\tau + \int \beta(\tau)x(\tau)\,d\tau = 0$$

Consequently,

$$\beta(\tau) = \tau H(-\tau)$$

$$(1-\tau)H(1-\tau) + \alpha(\tau) + \tau H(-\tau) = 0$$

$$\alpha(\tau) = (\tau - 1)H(1-\tau) - \tau H(-\tau)$$

so that

$$G(t, \tau) = (t - \tau)H(t - \tau) + t(\tau - 1)H(1 - \tau) + \tau(1 - t)H(-\tau)$$

We observe that $H(1 - \tau)$ is positive if $\tau < 1$, which must be the case in the $[0, 1]$ interval considered. The last term vanishes since τ cannot be negative in $[0, 1]$. The first term vanishes except when $t > \tau$, i.e., for $\tau < t < 1$. Therefore,

$$G(t, \tau) = t - \tau + t\tau - t = \tau(t - 1)$$

for $t > \tau$ and

$$G(t, \tau) = t(\tau - 1)$$

for $t < \tau$.

We can also apply the boundary conditions directly to G as a function of t. Thus,

$$G(0, \tau) = -\tau H(-\tau) + \beta(\tau) = 0$$
$$G(1, \tau) = (1 - \tau)H(1 - \tau) + \alpha(\tau) + \beta(\tau) = 0$$

(2.4.5)

which yields the same results.

Still another way of doing this problem is to realize that for $t < \tau$, a solution satisfying the left boundary condition is proportional to t. For $t > \tau$, the solution of the homogeneous equation satisfying the right boundary condition, $G(1, \tau) = 0$, is proportional to $1 - t$. However, if we use

$$G = \begin{cases} t & \text{for } t < \tau \\ 1 - t & \text{for } t > \tau \end{cases}$$

the Green's function will not be continuous at $t = \tau$ as it must. To make it continuous, we simply multiply the first expression by the value of the second at $t = \tau$ and vice versa. Then

$$G(t, \tau) = \begin{cases} t(1 - \tau) & \text{for} \quad t < \tau \\ (1 - t)\tau & \text{for} \quad t > \tau \end{cases}$$

Now we have the required continuity at $t = \tau$ and the appropriate jump in the derivative as the reader can easily verify. The result can be written as

$$G(t, \tau) = t(1 - \tau)H(\tau - t) + (1 - t)\tau H(t - \tau) \qquad (2.4.6)$$

and with this Green's function,

$$y(t) = \int_0^1 G(t, \tau)x(\tau) \, d\tau$$

solves $Ly = x$.

(b) Given Boundary Conditions on Interval $[0, a]$: $y(0) = y(a) = 0$: Since this is a trivial generalization, we will derive results a little differently in order to keep it interesting. Since G must satisfy the boundary conditions, we have $G(0, \tau) = G(a, \tau) = 0$ from which α and β can be evaluated as before. Instead now, we will use the fact that except at $t = \tau$, $G(t, \tau)$ satisfies the homogeneous equation $Ly = 0$. Consequently, G satisfies $d^2G/dt^2 = 0$ except at $t = \tau$. Therefore, integration results in $G = At + B$.

In the region $0 \leq t < \tau$, $B = 0$ since $G(0, \tau) = 0$. In the region $\tau < t \leq a$, since $G(a, \tau) = 0$, $G = Ct + D$ becomes $Ca + D = 0$ so $D = -Ca$. Thus $G(t, \tau) = C(t - a)$. At the point $t = \tau$, the Green's function must be continuous. Hence $A\tau = C(\tau - a)$ requiring that $C = A\tau/(\tau - a)$. Finally then,

$$G(t, \tau) = \begin{cases} At & \text{for} \quad t < \tau \\ A\tau(t - a)/(\tau - a) & \text{for} \quad t > \tau \end{cases}$$

At $t = \tau$, the discontinuity in the derivative yields

$$\frac{dG(\tau + 0, \tau)}{dt} - \frac{dG(\tau - 0, \tau)}{dt} = 1$$

$$\frac{A\tau}{(\tau - a)} - A = 1$$

$$A = \frac{(\tau - a)}{a}$$

Hence,

$$G(t, \tau) = (\tau - a)t/a, \qquad 0 \leq t < \tau$$

$$G(t, \tau) = \tau(t - a)/a, \qquad \tau < t \leq a$$

Equivalently,

$$G(t, \tau) = \frac{(\tau - a)t}{a} H(\tau - t) + \frac{\tau(t - a)}{a} H(t - \tau) \qquad (2.4.7)$$

for all t. If $a = 1$,

$$G(t, \tau) = (\tau - 1)tH(\tau - t) + \tau(t - 1)H(t - \tau)$$

or

$$G(t, \tau) = \begin{cases} (\tau - 1)t & \text{for } t < \tau \\ \tau(t - 1) & \text{for } t > \tau \end{cases}$$

which is the previous result as expected.

(c) **Initial Conditions** $y(0) = y'(0) = 0$: We have $d^2G(t, \tau)/dt^2 = \delta(t - \tau)$, $G(0, \tau) = 0$, and $G'(0, \tau)$ (or better $G_t(0, \tau)$, $= 0$). The Green's function is the solution of the homogeneous equation except at $t = \tau$. At the point $t = \tau$, G must be continuous and have a discontinuity of -1 in its derivative. The initial conditions imply that for $t < \tau$, $G = 0$. For $t > \tau$, assume $G = At + b$. The condition on the derivative requires that $A = -1$. Since G is continuous at $t = \tau$, $B = \tau$. Therefore, $G = -(t - \tau)$ for $t > \tau$ or

$$G(t, \tau) = -(t - \tau)H(t - \tau)$$

for all t. If we now consider $L^{-1}Ly$ or $L^{-1} d^2y/dt^2$ we have

$$L^{-1}Ly = \int G(t, \tau) \frac{d^2y(\tau)}{d\tau^2} d\tau$$

and integrating by parts twice we get

$$L^{-1}Ly = G(t, \tau)y'(\tau)\Big|_0^t - G'(t, \tau)y(\tau)\Big|_0^t + \int G''y(\tau) \, d\tau$$

The last term is simply $y(t)$ since G'' is $\delta(t - \tau)$. Hence,

$$L^{-1}Ly = G(t, t)y'(t) - G(t, 0)y'(0) - G'(t, t)y(t) + G'(t, 0)y(0) + y(t)$$

From our given Green's function, $G(t, t) = 0$, $G'(t, t) = 0$, $G'(t, 0) = 1$, and $y(0)$ and $y'(0)$ were given as zero. Thus,

$$L^{-1}Ly = y(t)$$

Now let us consider nonhomogeneous conditions.

(d) **Nonzero Initial Conditions:** To correlate with previous work (in [1] and many papers) when we solved equations by decomposition we kept only the Ly term on the left-hand side, then operated on both sides with L^{-1}.

(There is no difficulty in determining the Green's function or assuming existence of L^{-1} because of the way we choose L.) The left-hand side was $y(t) - y(0) - ty'(0)$ for second-order operators. We take the terms after $y(t)$ to the right so

$$y(t) = y(0) + ty'(0)$$

and identify $y(0) + ty'(0)$ as the y_0 term of the decomposition if the forcing term $x(t) = 0$. More generally, $y_0 = y(0) + ty'(0) + L^{-1}x$. If $L = d^n/dt^n$, then

$$y_0 = y(0) + ty'(0) + \cdots + (t^{n-1}/(n-1)!)y^{(n-1)}(0) + L^{-1}x.$$

The result is obtained by integrating from 0 to t as many times as there are differentiations in the L operator. For $L = d^2/dt^2$, $L^{-1}Ly$ means integrating the quantity d^2y/dt^2 twice from 0 to t. The first integration yields $y'(t) - y'(0)$. The second yields $y(t) - y(0) - ty'(0)$. We easily extend the result to higher derivatives. We now wish to consider this problem in such a way that we can evaluate y_0 terms for all given conditions and begin with this case in which we know what to expect.

Let us begin with the general form of G for $L = d^2/dt^2$, i.e.,

$$G(t, \tau) = (t - \tau)H(t - \tau) + t\alpha(\tau) + \beta(\tau)$$

$$G'(t, \tau) = H(t - \tau) + \alpha(\tau)$$

and determine α and β if $y(0)$ and $y'(0)$ are given nonzero constants. For convenience write $y(0) = a$, $y'(0) = b$. Write $y = y_1 + y_2$, where y_1 satisfies $Ly_1 = x$ with $y_1(0) = y'_1(0) = 0$ and y_2 satisfies $Ly_2 = 0$ with $y_2(0) = a$ and $y'_2(0) = b$. For the homogeneous conditions, i.e., for y_1, clearly $G_1(0, \tau)$ and $G'_1(0, \tau)$ are zero; hence,

$$-\tau H(-\tau) + \beta(\tau) = 0$$

$$H(-\tau) + \alpha(\tau) = 0$$

and

$$G(t, \tau) = (t - \tau)H(t - \tau) - tH(-\tau) + \tau H(-\tau)$$

and

$$G'(t, \tau) = H(t - \tau) - H(-\tau)$$

For y_2 we have $d^2y_2/dt^2 = 0$; hence, $y_2 = At + B$. Since $y'_2(0) = b$, $y_2(0) = a$ and $y_2 = bt + a$. Consequently,

$$y = y_1 + y_2 = \int_0^t [(t - \tau)H(t - \tau) - tH(-\tau) + \tau H(-\tau)]x(\tau)\, d\tau + bt + a$$

$$= \int_0^t (t - \tau)H(t - \tau)x(\tau)\, d\tau + bt + a$$

which we can write as

$$y = y(0) + ty'(0) + L^{-1}x \tag{2.4.8}$$

where $L^{-1}x = \int_0^t (t - \tau)H(t - \tau)x(\tau)\, d\tau$ for $t > \tau$. The first two terms are exactly what we used before. The $L^{-1}x$ term is different; it is a single integration, not a double integration. The double integration, however, is preferred for the $L^{-1}x$ term and other following terms of the decomposition because it has a unity kernel and, therefore, a simple integrand.

It is easy to verify, if we choose a particular $x(t)$, that the two forms of L^{-1} give the same result. Suppose $x = 1$. Integrating twice from 0 to t gives the result $L^{-1}x = t^2/2$. The single integral form of $L^{-1}x$ is

$$\int_0^t (t - \tau)H(t - \tau)x(\tau)\, d\tau = \int_0^t (t - \tau)H(t - \tau)\, d\tau.$$

Integrate by parts with $u = H(t - \tau)$, $dv = (t - \tau)d\tau$ to get

$$-H(t - \tau)\frac{(t - \tau)^2}{2}\bigg|_0^t + \int_0^t \frac{(t - \tau)^2}{2}\delta(t - \tau)\, d\tau$$

$$= -H(0)[0] + H(t)\frac{t^2}{2} + 0 = \frac{t^2}{2}$$

so both forms yield the same result.

Again, let $x(t) = t^2$. Then

$$\int_0^t H(t - \tau)(t - \tau)\tau^2\, d\tau = H(t - \tau)\left[\frac{t\tau^3}{3} - \frac{\tau^4}{4}\right]\bigg|_0^t$$

$$+ \int\left[\frac{t\tau^3}{3} - \frac{\tau^4}{4}\right]\delta(t - \tau)\, d\tau$$

$$= H(0)\left[\frac{t^4}{3} - \frac{t^4}{4}\right] - H(t)[0] + \frac{t^4}{3} - \frac{t^4}{4}$$

Since the first two terms are zero, we have $t^4/12$. Using the double integrals, $\int_0^t (\int_0^t t^2\, dt)\, dt = t^4/12$ immediately. Our objective then is only to identify the part of the y_0 term excluding the forcing term—in this case, simply $y(0) + ty'(0)$.

(e) **Inhomogeneous Boundary Conditions** $y(0) = a$, $y(1) = b$:   Again, using $L = d^2/dt^2$ in $Ly = x$ with the above given conditions, we reduce the problem to the earlier problem of homogeneous conditions by writing $y = y_1 + y_2$ such that $Ly_1 = x$ so that $y_1 = \int_0^1 G_1(t, \tau)x(\tau)\, d\tau$ satisfies $y_1(0) = y_1(1) = 0$ and y_2 is the solution of $Ly_2 = 0$ with $y_2(0) = a$ and $y_2(1) = b$. We have as before

$$G(t, \tau) = (t - \tau)H(t - \tau) + t\alpha(\tau) + \beta(\tau).$$

Since y_1 satisfies homogeneous conditions, G_1 does also, and we have

$$G_1(0, \tau) = -\tau H(-\tau) + \beta(\tau) = 0$$

$$G_1(1, \tau) = (1 - \tau)H(1 - \tau) + \alpha(\tau) + \beta(\tau) = 0$$

From the first condition, $\beta(\tau) = \tau H(-\tau)$. From the second condition, $\alpha(\tau) = -\tau H(-\tau) - (1 - \tau)H(1 - \tau)$ so that

$$G_1(t, \tau) = (t - \tau)H(t - \tau) - t[\tau H(-\tau) + (1 - \tau)H(1 - \tau)] + \tau H(-\tau)$$
$$= (t - \tau)H(t - \tau)$$

Since y_2 satisfies $Ly_2 = 0$ or $d^2y_2/dt^2 = 0$, $y_2 = At + b$. From the first condition on y_2, $B = a$. From the second condition, $A + B = b$ or $A + a = b$ or $A = b - a$. Hence,

$$y_2 = a + (b - a)t = y(0) + t[y(1) - y(0)] \tag{2.4.9}$$

The complete solution is $y = \int_0^1 G_1(t, \tau)x(\tau) + y(0) + t[y(1) - y(0)]$, and we are interested in the last two terms.

To extend this to conditions $y(0) = a$ and $y(l) = b$ we can use the previous section to write $y_2 = At + B = a + t(b - a)/l$ or

$$y(0) + t\,\frac{y(l) - y(0)}{l} \tag{2.4.10}$$

(f) **Mixed Conditions** $y(0) = a$, $y'(1) = b$: Write $y = y_1 + y_2$ with $Ly_1 = x$, $y_1(0) = 0$, $y_1'(1) = 0$ and $Ly_2 = 0$, $y_2(0) = a$, $y_2'(1) = b$. From $Ly_2 = 0$ or $d^2y_2/dt^2 = 0$ we have $y_2 = At + B$. Satisfying the specified conditions for y_2 requires that

$$y_2 = a + t(b - a) = y(0) + t[y'(1) - y(0)]$$

Thus, $y = y(0) + t[y'(1) - y(0)] + L^{-1}x$, where the Green's function for L^{-1} satisfies $G(0, \tau) = 0$ and $G'(1, \tau) = 0$ from which α and β are easily evaluated although we need only the terms preceding $L^{-1}x$.

REFERENCES

1. G. Adomian, "Stochastic Systems," Academic Press, New York, 1983.

SUGGESTED FURTHER READING

A. G. Butkovsky, "Green's Functions and Transfer Functions Handbook." Ellis Horwood, Ltd., Chichester, U.K., 1982.
B. Friedman, "Principles and Techniques of Applied Mathematics." Wiley, New York, 1956.
I. M. Gel'fand and G. E. Shilov, "Generalized Functions," Vol. 1. Academic Press, New York, 1964.

M. D. Greenberg, "Applications of Green's Functions in Science and Engineering." Prentice Hall, Englewood Cliffs, New Jersey, 1971.

C. Lanczos, "Linear Differentiable Operators." Van Nostrand-Reinhold, New York, 1961.

L. Zadeh and E. Pollak, "System Theory." McGraw-Hill, New York, 1969.

A. Zemanian, "Distribution Theory and Transform Analysis." McGraw-Hill, New York, 1965.

CHAPTER 3

Expansion of Nonlinear Terms: The A_n Polynomials

3.1. INTRODUCTION

Nonlinear behavior is an inherent feature of real systems. Examples occur readily in nuclear reactors, plasmas, propagation, control, signal processing, physiological systems, cellular or population growth, black holes, behavior of the national economy, the equations of a free electron laser, and a gyrotron. Modeling leads immediately to nonlinear differential, partial differential, or sets of nonlinear (and possibly stochastic) equations. The significance of nonlinear systems is well recognized; however, the prevalent methods are inadequate to the general problem. There are, of course, cases in which by clever transformations of dependent and independent variables, an *exact linearization* can be accomplished (i.e., the nonlinear equation can be transformed into a linear equation in which superposition can be used). This is not generally possible and even when it is, it is difficult to determine the necessary transformations. The general (nonlinear stochastic) operator in an equation $\mathscr{F}y = x$ is partitioned into linear and nonlinear components represented by $\mathscr{L}$ and $\mathscr{N}$ with $\mathscr{L} = L + \mathscr{R}$ or $L + R + \mathscr{R}$ and $\mathscr{N}y = Ny + \mathscr{M}y$ as previously discussed. Thus $\mathscr{F}y = Ly + Ry + \mathscr{R}y + Ny + \mathscr{M}y = x$, where L is linear, deterministic, and invertible. The general solution process $y = \mathscr{F}^{-1}x$ is decomposed into the sum $y = \sum_{n=0}^{\infty} y_n$ or equivalently $y = \sum_{n=0}^{\infty} \mathscr{F}_n^{-1}x$ with $y_0 = F_0^{-1}x = L^{-1}x$ plus the homogeneous solution, and $F_{n+1}^{-1}x$ involving the A_n polynomials for the nonlinear terms. These polynomials can be viewed as expansions of the nonlinearities. The desired statistical measures of the solution, if it is stochastic, are then computed by appropriate ensemble averages. Because of the importance of direct calculation of the A_n polynomials, the remainder of this chapter is focused on their systematic computation, first considering the deterministic case to simplify discussion.

19

3.2. CALCULATION OF THE A_n POLYNOMIALS FOR SIMPLE NONLINEAR OPERATORS

Let N be a nonlinear deterministic operator not involving differentials such that Ny is an ordinary function $f(y)$ such as y^2, y^4, e^y, $\sin y, \ldots$. These will be referred to as simple nonlinear operators. We can also have operators such that the result of the operation is $f(y, y')$, $f(y, y', y'')$, etc. Examples are

$$Ny = [(d^0/dt^0)y][(d^1/dt^1)y] = yy' = f(y, y')$$

We will consider such cases later in this chapter.

We assume now an operator equation of the form $Fy = x$, where $x = x(t)$ and F is a deterministic differential operator with linear and nonlinear parts such that $Fy = Ly + Ny$ (with L a linear differential operator and Ny a nonlinear part or function $f(y)$). N is a simple nonlinear operator, and L must be invertible. If it is not, we use L to symbolize the invertible part of the linear differential operator and write $L + R$ with R representing the remaining part of the linear operator. We are interested here in physical systems so inputs are bounded. Nonphysical processes, such as delta-correlated processes and Wiener processes, are excluded with no loss of generality. Basically, as we have seen, the decomposition method solves the differential equation in the form $y = F^{-1}x$ writing $y = \sum_{n=0}^{\infty} y_n$ and taking y_0 to be the solution of the linear part.

In order to calculate the A_n we will introduce a parameter λ into the decomposition and write $y = \sum_{n=0}^{\infty} \lambda^n y_n = \sum_{n=0}^{\infty} \lambda^n F_n^{-1}x$ (where λ is not a "small" parameter). The F_n^{-1} are to be determined, and λ is a parameter for grouping terms, not a perturbation parameter. Thus, we view the operator F^{-1} in $y = F^{-1}x$ to have been decomposed into component operators F_n^{-1} to be determined.

The key to the solution in the nonlinear case is to represent the nonlinear term Ny as the expansion $\sum_{n=0}^{\infty} A_n \lambda^n$, i.e., $f(y)$, or $f(y(\lambda))$, is assumed to be analytic in λ so we write $f(y) = f(y(\lambda)) = \sum_{n=0}^{\infty} A_n \lambda^n$. The A_n are the polynomials defined by Adomian [1]. These are defined such that each A_n depends only on $y_0, y_1, \ldots, y_n$. Thus, $A_0 = A_0(y_0)$, $A_1 = A_1(y_0, y_1)$, $A_2 = A_2(y_0, y_1, y_2)$, etc.

In the resulting series for the solution $y = \sum_{n=0}^{\infty} \lambda^n y_n$, each y_n will be calculable from the preceding term y_{n-1} only. The y_0 term involves only the linear invertible part of the equation, the initial (or boundary) conditions, and the input or forcing function term. The y_{n+1} term is dependent on y_n, and the highest term in A_n is y_n so the system is calculable without perturbation or closure approximation. The difficult part is to see how the A_n polynomials can be obtained. Once obtained, they can be viewed as a special convenient set of polynomials like Hermite's polynomials or Legendre's polynomials and can become even more familiar because of the global nature of the methodology, as we will see in the following chapters. They can be calculated from the following expression:

$$A_n = (1/n!)(d^n/d\lambda^n)f(y(\lambda))|_{\lambda=0} \qquad (3.2.1)$$

If we write $D = d/d\lambda$ we can write (3.2.1) simply as

$$A_n = (1/n!)D^n f|_{\lambda=0}$$

We have now a systematic scheme with $D = d/d\lambda = (dy/d\lambda)(d/dy)$ since $f = f(y)$ and $y = y(\lambda)$. Each $D^n f$ is evaluated at $\lambda = 0$ and divided by $n!$. Since $y = y_0 + \lambda y_1 + \lambda^2 y_2 + \ldots$, the following are useful relations:

$$(d^n/d\lambda^n)y(\lambda)|_{\lambda=0} = n! \, y_n$$

$$(d^n/dy^n)f(y(\lambda))|_{\lambda=0} = \frac{d^n f}{dy_n} = h_n(y_0) \qquad (3.2.2)$$

[Since $d^n f/dy_n$ is a function of y_0, we have written it as $h_n(y_0)$.]

The $D^n f$ term for $n > 0$ can be written as a sum from $v = 1$ to n of terms $d^v f/dy^v$ with coefficients which are polynomials in the $d^v y/d\lambda^v$. Thus,

$$D^1 f = (df/dy)(dy/d\lambda)$$

$$D^2 f = (d^2 f/dy^2)(dy/d\lambda)^2 + (df/dy)(d^2 y/d\lambda^2)$$

$$D^3 f = (d^3 f/dy^3)(dy/d\lambda)^3 + 3(d^2 f/dy^2)(dy/d\lambda)(d^2 y/d\lambda^2) + (df/dy)(d^3 y/d\lambda^3)$$

$$\vdots \qquad (3.2.3)$$

If for the nth derivative $D^n f$, we denote the vth coefficient by $c(v, n)$ we can write

$$D^n f = \sum_{v=1}^{n} c(v, n)F(v) \qquad (3.2.4)$$

where $F(v) = d^v f/dy^v$. Here $D^3 f$, for example, is given by

$$D^3 f = c(1, 3)F(1) + c(2, 3)F(2) + c(3, 3)F(3).$$

The second index in the $c(v, n)$ term is the order of the derivative, and the first index progresses from 1 to n along with the index of F.

These coefficients can be calculated in a number of ways. The first calculations were done by developing a recurrence relation which can be given as follows: For $1 \leq i, j \leq n$,

$$c(i, j) = \frac{d}{d\lambda}[c(i, j - 1)] + \frac{dy}{d\lambda}[c(i - 1, j - 1)]. \qquad (3.2.5)$$

with $c(0, 0) = 1$ and $c(1, 0) = 0$. The second condition is true because $c(i, j) = 0$ for $i > j$. The fact that the coefficient $c(0, 0) = 1$ is seen by comparison of $D^0 f = c(0, 0) d^0 f/dy^0 = f$, i.e., $A_0 = f|_{\lambda=0} = f(y_0)$.

The notation

$$\psi(i, j) = (d^i y/d\lambda^i)^j, \qquad F(i) = d^i f/dy^i \qquad (3.2.6)$$

will be convenient because these quantities are explicit derivatives and the implicit differentiations of (3.2.1) are cumbersome.

Now (3.2.4) can be given in terms of the c terms or the ψ terms, for example,

$$D^3 f = c(1, 3)F(1) + c(2, 3)F(2) + c(3, 3)F(3)$$

or

$$D^3 f = \psi(3, 1)F(1) + 3\psi(1, 1)\psi(2, 1)F(2) + \psi(1, 3)F(3)$$
$$= (d^3 y/d\lambda^3)(df/dy) + 3(dy/d\lambda)(d^2 y/d\lambda^2)(d^2 f/dy^2) + (dy/d\lambda)^3(d^3 f/dy^3)$$

While we can now derive the A_n polynomials quickly or simply present generating forms, we will go into detail for the benefit of mathematical researchers or persons seeking dissertation topics. Let us consider the $c(i, j)$ coefficients:

$$c(0, 0) = \psi(1, 0) = 1$$

$$c(1, 1) = \frac{d}{d\lambda} \{c(1, 0)\} + \psi(1, 1)\{c(0, 0)\}$$

$$= \frac{d}{d\lambda} \{0\} + \psi(1, 1)\{1\} = \psi(1, 1)$$

Noting that $c(0, j) = 0$ for $j > 0$,

$$c(2, 2) = \frac{d}{d\lambda} \{c(2, 1)\} + \psi(1, 1)\{c(1, 1)\}$$

$$= \frac{d}{d\lambda} \{0\} + \psi(1, 1)\psi(1, 1) = \psi(1, 2)$$

$$c(1, 2) = \frac{d}{d\lambda} \{c(1, 1)\} + \psi(1, 1)\{c(0, 1)\}$$

$$= \frac{d}{d\lambda} \psi(1, 1) + \psi(1, 1)\{0\} = \psi(2, 1)$$

$$c(3, 3) = \frac{d}{d\lambda} \{c(3, 2)\} + \psi(1, 1)\{c(2, 2)\}$$

$$= \psi(1, 1)\psi(1, 2) = \psi(1, 3)$$

$$c(2, 3) = \frac{d}{d\lambda}\{c(2, 2)\} + \psi(1, 1)\{c(1, 2)\}$$

$$= \frac{d}{d\lambda}\psi(1, 2) + \psi(1, 1)\psi(2, 1)$$

$$= 2\psi(1, 1)\psi(2, 1) + \psi(1, 1)\psi(2, 1)$$

$$= 3\psi(1, 1)\psi(2, 1)$$

$$c(1, 3) = \frac{d}{d\lambda}\{c(1, 2)\} = \frac{d}{d\lambda}\psi(2, 1) = \psi(3, 1)$$

$$\vdots$$

To calculate any $D^n f$ we need only to multiply the $c(v, n)$ coefficients by $F(v)$ for the range from 1 to n and sum. The A_n polynomials are then given by

$$A_n = (1/n!)D^n f|_{\lambda = 0}$$

Thus, remembering the definition from Eq. (3.2.2), i.e.,

$$h_n(y_0) = (d^n/dy^n)f(y(\lambda))|_{\lambda = 0}$$

$$A_0 = (1/0!)D^0 f|_{\lambda = 0} = f(y_0) = h_0(y_0)$$

$$A_1 = (1/1!)D'f|_{\lambda = 0}$$

$$= c(1, 1)h_1(y_0) = \psi(1, 1)h_1(y_0) = h_1(y_0)y_1$$

$$A_2 = (1/2!)D^2 f|_{\lambda = 0}$$

$$= \tfrac{1}{2}\{c(1, 2)h_1 + c(2, 2)h_2\}$$

$$= \tfrac{1}{2}\{\psi(2, 1)h_1 + \psi(1, 2)h_2\}$$

$$= \tfrac{1}{2}\{2y_2 h_1 + y_1^2 h_2\}$$

$$= \tfrac{1}{2}\{h_2(y_0)y_1^2 + 2h_1(y_0)y_2\}$$

$$= h_1(y_0)y_2 + h_2(y_0)\tfrac{1}{2}y_1^2$$

we show various arrangements for convenience. Continuing in this manner,

$$A_3 = (1/3!)\{c(1, 3)h_1 + c(2, 3)h_2 + c(3, 3)h_3\}$$

$$= (1/3!)\{\psi(3, 1)h_1 + 3\psi(1, 1)\psi(2, 1)h_2 + \psi(1, 3)h_3\}$$

$$= (1/3!)\{(3!)y_3 h_1 + (3!)y_1 y_2 h_2 + y_1^3 h_3\}$$

$$= (1/3!)\{h_3(y_0)y_1^3 + 6h_2(y_0)y_1 y_2 + 6h_1(y_0)y_3\}$$

$$= h_1(y_0)y_3 + h_2(y_0)y_1 y_2 + h_3(y_0)\tfrac{1}{6}y_1^3$$

$$A_4 = (1/4!)\{h_4(y_0)y_1^4 + 12h_3(y_0)y_1^2 y_2$$

$$+ h_2(y_0)[12y_2^2 + 24y_1 y_3] + 24h_1(y_0)y_4\}$$

$$= h_1(y_0)y_4 + h_2(y_0)[\tfrac{1}{2}y_2^2 + y_1 y_3]$$

$$+ h_3(y_0)[\tfrac{1}{2}y_1^2 y_2] + h_4(y_0)\tfrac{1}{24}y_1^4$$

$$A_5 = h_1(y_0)y_5 + h_2(y_0)[y_2y_3 + y_1y_4]$$
$$+ h_3(y_0)[\tfrac{1}{2}y_1y_2^2 + \tfrac{1}{2}y_1^2y_3]$$

$$+ h_4(y_0)\tfrac{1}{6}y_1^3y_2 + h_5(y_0)\tfrac{1}{120}y_1^5$$
$$A_6 = h_1(y_0)y_6 + h_2(y_0)[\tfrac{1}{2}y_3^2 + y_2y_4 + y_1y_5]$$
$$+ h_3(y_0)[\tfrac{1}{6}y_2^3 + y_1y_2y_3 + \tfrac{1}{2}y_1^2y_4]$$
$$+ h_4(y_0)[\tfrac{1}{4}y_1^2y_2^2 + \tfrac{1}{6}y_1^3y_3]$$
$$+ h_5(y_0)\tfrac{1}{24}y_1^4y_2 + h_6(y_0)\tfrac{1}{720}y_1^6$$
$$\vdots$$

The next section discusses this further.

We observe that when $f(y)$ is chosen to be simply y, i.e., the linear limit, the $A_n = y_n$ and we get precisely earlier results [1] for the linear case. Thus, $f(y) = y$ results in $h_0 = y_1$, $h_1 = 1$, and $h_i = 0$ for $i \geq 2$; and, as a consequence, $A_0 = y_0$, $A_1 = y_1, \ldots, A_n = y_n$.

Alternatively, since $y = \sum_{n=0}^{\infty} \lambda^n y_n$ and $n!\, y_n = d^n y/d\lambda^n|_{\lambda=0}$,

$$A_n = (1/n!)D^n f(y)|_{\lambda=0}$$
$$= (1/n!)D^n y|_{\lambda=0} = (1/n!)d^n y/d\lambda^n|_{\lambda=0}$$
$$= (1/n!)\{n!\, y_n\} = y_n$$

When an equation $Ly + Ny = x$ is considered in the limit $Ny = y$ we have

$$Ly + y = x,$$

$$Ly = x - y$$

$$y = y_0 - L^{-1}\sum_{n=0}^{\infty} A_n = y_0 + y_1 + y_2 + \cdots$$

Thus, $y_{n+1} = y_{n+1}(y_n)$ so that in the linear case y_{n+1} depends only on the term preceding it as first demonstrated by the author. In the nonlinear case, $y_{n+1} = y_{n+1}(y_0, y_1, \ldots, y_n)$.

3.3.   THE A_n POLYNOMIALS FOR DIFFERENTIAL NONLINEAR OPERATORS

Consider the nonlinear operator $Ny = f(y, y^{(1)}, \ldots, y^{(n)})$. We assume that f is analytic in λ and $y, y^{(1)}, \ldots, y^{(n)}$ are also analytic in λ. We are concerned with two important subcases of the *differential nonlinear operator* N which are

(1)   the sum of nonlinear functions of the time derivatives of y, with each nonlinear function dependent on a single derivative:

$$Ny = \sum_{i=0}^{n} N_i y = \sum_{i=0}^{n} f_i(y^{(i)})$$

(2)   a sum of products of nonlinear functions of y, each dependent on a single derivative. As an example consider $f(y, y') = y^2 y'^3$.

Obviously, if $Ny = f(y)$, we have the simple nonlinearity for which we have previously found expansion coefficients, and we must obtain identical results for this limiting case. We, therefore, define the A_n for the general differential nonlinear operator Ny to be defined by

$$A_m = (1/m!)D^m\{f(y, y', \ldots, y^{(n)})\}|_{\lambda=0}$$

where $y, y', \ldots, y^{(n)}$ are assumed analytic functions of λ.

Case 1:   The first subcase of our general class was specified by $Ny = f(y, y', \ldots, y^{(n)}) = \sum_{i=0}^{n} f_i(y^{(i)})$, which we will call a sum decomposition. The A_n are given by

$$A_m = \sum_{i=0}^{n} [(1/m!)D^m f_i(y^{(i)})|_{\lambda=0}] = \sum_{i=0}^{n} A_{im}$$

because

$$f(y, y', \ldots, y^{(n)}) = \sum_{m=0}^{\infty} \lambda^m A_m = \sum_{i=0}^{n} f_i(y^{(i)})$$

and each $f_i(y^{(i)}) = \sum_{m=0}^{\infty} \lambda^m A_{im}$. This leads to

$$f(y, y', \ldots, y^{(n)}) = \sum_{i=0}^{n} \sum_{m=0}^{\infty} \lambda^m A_{im} = \sum_{m=0}^{\infty} \left[\sum_{i=0}^{n} A_{im} \right] \lambda^m$$

therefore, $A_m = \sum_{i=0}^{n} A_{im}$.

Case 2:   The second subcase, the product decomposition of the nonlinear operator, decomposes $Ny = f(y, y', \ldots, y^{(n)})$ into a sum of products. Let us first take pairwise products such as $f(y, y') = f_0(y)f_1(y') = \prod_{i=0}^{1} f_i(y^{(i)})$ so we can consider nonlinearities such as $y^2 y'^3$. Now the A_n are given by

$$A_m = (1/m!)D^m\{f_0(y^{(0)}(\lambda))f_1(y^{(1)}(\lambda))\}|_{\lambda=0}$$

$$= (1/m!) \sum_{k=0}^{m} \binom{m}{k} [D^{m-k}f_0(y^{(0)}(\lambda))][D^k f_1(y^{(1)}(\lambda))]|_{\lambda=0}$$

This leads to

$$A_m = \sum_{k=0}^{m} A_{0,m-k} A_{1,k}$$

since

$$f(y, y') = \sum_{m=0}^{\infty} A_m \lambda^m = \prod_{i=0}^{1} f_i(y^{(i)})$$

and, as before, $f_i(y^{(i)}(\lambda)) = \sum_{m=0}^{\infty} A_{im} \lambda^m$. This implies

$$\Gamma(y, y') = \left(\sum_{m=0}^{\infty} A_{0m} \lambda^m \right) \left(\sum_{m=0}^{\infty} A_{im} \lambda^m \right) = \sum_{m=0}^{\infty} \left[\sum_{k=0}^{m} A_{0,m-k} A_{1,k} \right] \lambda^m,$$

which also gives us the result of Case 2. An extended Leibnitz rule in terms of multinomial coefficients can handle products of n factors, that is $f(y, y', \ldots, y^{(n)}) = \prod_{i=0}^{n} f_i(y^{(i)})$.

3.4.   CONVENIENT COMPUTATIONAL FORMS FOR THE A_n POLYNOMIALS

It is possible to find simple symmetry rules for writing the A_n polynomials quickly to high orders. Using the A_n, there is no need for mathematically inadequate and physically unrealistic approximations or linearizations. Thus, if the modeling retains the inherent nonlinearities, we may expect solutions conforming much more closely to actual behavior. We will consider here simple nonlinear operators not involving differentials, i.e., of the form $Ny = f(y)$. In the preceding section, we gave $A_n = (1/n!) \sum_{\nu=1}^{n} c(\nu, n) h_\nu(y_0)$ with $h_\nu(y_0) = (d^\nu/dy^\nu) f(y(\lambda))|_{\lambda=0}$ with the $c(\nu, n)$ specified by a recurrence rule.

Noticing that the symmetrized version of our computation of the y_n terms for polynomial nonlinearities makes it simpler and easier to remember, it was suggested by Rach [2] that the A_n being sums of various products of the y_i up to $i = n$ could also be written in symmetrized form as before but for a wider class of nonlinearities. This is obviously the case, again a convenience for memory. We remind the reader (see [1]) that if we have $Ny = y^2 = \sum_{n=0}^{\infty} A_n$, $A_0 = y_0^2$, $A_1 = 2y_0 y_1$, $A_2 = y_1^2 + 2y_0 y_2$, etc.; but we can write this as $A_0 = y_0 y_0$, $A_1 = y_0 y_1 + y_1 y_0$, $A_2 = y_0 y_2 + y_1 y_1 + y_2 y_0$, etc., i.e., the first subscript goes from 0 to n, and the second is chosen such that the sum of subscripts is n.

In extending this to the forms we have just developed for the A_n, we begin by noticing that to get $h_\nu(y_0)$ for $\nu = 1, 2, \ldots, n$, we differentiate $f(y)$ ν times with respect to y and evaluate at $\lambda = 0$. Then, for example, A_3 would involve h_1, h_2, h_3. From the previous section $A_3 = c(1, 3) h_1/3! + c(2, 3) h_2/3! + c(3, 3) h_3/3!$. To get the $c(\nu, n)/n!$ term we simply ask how many combinations (not permutations) of ν integers add to n.[1] Thus $c(\nu, n)$ will mean the sum

---

[1] We can write $C(\nu, n) = c(\nu, n)/n!$

(from 1 to v) of the products of v of the y_i terms whose subscripts add to n. To get $c(2, 3)$, we see two integers can add to 3 only if one integer is 1 and the other is 2 (if zero is excluded). Hence, we write $c(2, 3) = y_1 y_2$. To get $c(1, 3)$, the coefficient of $h_1(y_0)$, we have one y_i and its subscript must be 3, hence $c(1, 3) = y_3$. What about $c(3, 3)$, the coefficient of $h_3(y_0)$? Now we need 3 factors y_i with subscripts summing to 3, hence each subscript must be 1 and $c(3, 3) = y_1 y_1 y_1 = y_1^3$. This is not quite right, and we add another heuristic rule. If we have repetitions of subscripts, we divide by the factorial of the number of repetitions. Then, $c(3, 3) = (1/3!)y_1^3$. We now have

$$A_3 = h_1(y_0)y_3 + h_2(y_0)y_1 y_2 + h_3(y_0)(1/3!)y_1^3$$

To write A_6, for example, we need the coefficients for the terms $h_v(y_0)$ for v from 1 to 6. The coefficient of h_6 must involve six integers adding to 6 or y_1^6 hence the coefficient of $h_6(y_0)$ is $(1/6!)y_1^6$. What about the coefficient for $h_2(y_0)$ in A_6 or $v = 2$, $n = 6$? Clearly we need two integers that sum to 6. These are $(1, 5)$, $(2, 4)$, and $(3, 3)$. Thus, the coefficient $c(2, 6)$ is $(1/2!)y_3^2 + y_2 y_4 + y_1 y_5$. The terms involve $\prod_{i=1}^{v} y_{k_i}$ with $\sum_{i=1}^{n} k_i = n$, and if we have j repeated subscripts, we divide by $j!$:

$$A_0 = h_0(y_0)$$

$$A_1 = h_1(y_0)y_1$$

$$A_2 = h_1(y_0)y_2 + h_2(y_0)(1/2!)y_1^2$$

$$A_3 = h_1(y_0)y_3 + h_2(y_0)y_1 y_2 + h_3(y_0)(1/3!)y_1^3$$

$$A_4 = h_1(y_0)y_4 + h_2(y_0)[(1/2!)y_2^2 + y_1 y_3] \\ + h_3(y_0)(1/2!)y_1^2 y_2 + h_4(y_0)(1/4!)y_1^4$$

$$A_5 = h_1(y_0)y_5 + h_2(y_0)[y_2 y_3 + y_1 y_4] \\ + h_3(y_0)[y_1(1/2!)y_2^2 + (1/2!)y_1^2 y_3] \\ + h_4(y_0)(1/3!)y_1^3 y_2 + h_5(y_0)(1/5!)y_1^5$$

$$A_6 = h_1(y_0)y_6 + h_2(y_0)[(1/2!)y_3^2 + y_2 y_4 + y_1 y_5] \\ + h_3(y_0)[(1/3!)y_2^3 + y_1 y_2 y_3 + (1/2!)y_1^2 y_4] \\ + h_4(y_0)[(1/2!)y_1^2(1/2!)y_2^2 + (1/3!)y_1^3 y_3] \\ + h_5(y_0)(1/4!)y_1^4 y_2 + h_6(y_0)(1/6!)y_1^6$$

$$A_7 = h_1(y_0)y_7 + h_2(y_0)[y_3 y_4 + y_2 y_5 + y_1 y_6] \\ + h_3(y_0)[(1/2!)y_2^2 y_3 + y_1(1/2!)y_3^2 + y_1 y_2 y_4 + (1/2!)y_1^2 y_5] \\ + h_4(y_0)[y_1(1/3!)y_2^3 + (1/2!)y_1^2 y_2 y_3 + (1/3!)y_1^3 y_4] \\ + h_5(y_0)[(1/3!)y_1^3(1/2!)y_2^2 + (1/4!)y_1^4 y_3] \\ + h_6(y_0)(1/5!)y_1^5 y_2 + h_7(y_0)(1/7!)y_1^7$$

$$A_8 = h_1(y_0)y_8 + h_2(y_0)[(1/2!)y_4^2 + y_3y_5 + y_2y_6 + y_1y_7]$$
$$+ h_3(y_0)[y_2(1/2!)y_3^2 + (1/2!)y_2^2y_4 + y_1y_3y_4 + y_1y_2y_5 + (1/2!)y_1^2y_6]$$
$$+ h_4(y_0)[(1/4!)y_2^4 + y_1(1/2!)y_2^2y_3 + (1/2!)y_1^2(1/2!)y_3^2$$
$$+ (1/2!)y_1^2y_2y_4 + (1/3!)y_1^3y_5]$$
$$+ h_5(y_0)[(1/2!)y_1^2(1/3!)y_2^3 + (1/3!)y_1^3y_2y_3 + (1/4!)y_1^4y_4]$$
$$+ h_6(y_0)[(1/4!)y_1^4(1/2!)y_2^2 + (1/5!)y_1^5y_3]$$
$$+ h_7(y_0)(1/6!)y_1^6y_2 + h_8(y_0)(1/8!)y_1^8$$

$$A_9 = h_1(y_0)y_9 + h_2(y_0)[y_4y_5 + y_3y_6 + y_2y_7 + y_1y_8]$$
$$+ h_3(y_0)[(1/3!)y_3^3 + y_2y_3y_4 + (1/2!)y_2^2y_5 + y_1(1/2!)y_4^2$$
$$+ y_1y_3y_5 + y_1y_2y_6 + (1/2!)y_1^2y_7]$$
$$+ h_4(y_0)[(1/3!)y_2^3y_3 + y_1y_2(1/2!)y_3^2 + y_1(1/2!)y_2^2y_4$$
$$+ (1/2!)y_1^2y_3y_4 + (1/2!)y_1^2y_2y_5 + (1/3!)y_1^3y_6]$$
$$+ h_5(y_0)[y_1(1/4!)y_2^4 + (1/2!)y_1^2(1/2!)y_2^2y_3$$
$$+ (1/3!)y_1^3(1/2!)y_3^2 + (1/3!)y_1^3y_2y_4 + (1/4!)y_1^4y_5]$$
$$+ h_6(y_0)[(1/3!)y_1^3(1/3!)y_2^3 + (1/4!)y_1^4y_2y_3 + (1/5!)y_1^5y_4]$$
$$+ h_7(y_0)[(1/5!)y_1^5(1/2!)y_2^2 + (1/6!)y_1^6y_3]$$
$$+ h_8(y_0)(1/7!)y_1^7y_2 + h_9(y_0)(1/9!)y_1^9$$

$$A_{10} = h_1(y_0)y_{10} + h_2(y_0)[(1/2!)y_5^2 + y_4y_6 + y_3y_7 + y_2y_8 + y_1y_9]$$
$$+ h_3(y_0)[(1/2!)y_3^2y_4 + y_2(1/2!)y_4^2 + y_2y_3y_5 + (1/2!)y_2^2y_6$$
$$+ h_1(y_0)y_4y_5 + y_1y_3y_6 + y_1y_2y_7 + (1/2!)y_1^2y_8]$$
$$+ h_4(y_0)[(1/2!)y_2^2(1/2!)y_3^2 + (1/3!)y_2^3y_4 + y_1(1/3!)y_3^3$$
$$+ y_1y_2y_3y_4 + y_1(1/2!)y_2^2y_5 + (1/2!)y_1^2(1/2!)y_4^2$$
$$+ (1/2!)y_1^2y_3y_5 + (1/2!)y_1^2y_2y_6 + (1/3!)y_1^3y_7]$$
$$+ h_5(y_0)[(1/5!)y_2^5 + y_1(1/3!)y_2^3y_3 + (1/2!)y_1^2y_2(1/2!)y_3^2$$
$$+ (1/2!)y_1^2(1/2!)y_2^2y_4 + (1/3!)y_1^3y_3y_4$$
$$+ (1/3!)y_1^3y_2y_5 + (1/4!)y_1^4y_6]$$
$$+ h_6(y_0)[(1/2!)y_1^2(1/4!)y_2^4 + (1/3!)y_1^3(1/2!)y_2^2y_3$$
$$+ (1/4!)y_1^4(1/2!)y_3^2 + (1/4!)y_1^4y_2y_4 + (1/5!)y_1^5y_5]$$
$$+ h_7(y_0)[(1/4!)y_1^4(1/3!)y_2^3 + (1/5!)y_1^5y_2y_3 + (1/6!)y_1^6y_4]$$
$$+ h_8(y_0)[(1/6!)y_1^6(1/2!)y_2^2 + (1/7!)y_1^7y_3]$$
$$+ h_9(y_0)(1/8!)y_1^8y_2 + h_{10}(y_0)(1/10!)y_1^{10}$$

Recent studies and analyses have led to development of new computer algorithms to generate the A_n polynomials to high orders.

3.5. LINEAR LIMIT

Letting $Ny = y$ yields immediately $A_n = y_n$ for $n = 0, 1, 2, \ldots$. Since we have pointed out previously that the decomposition method applies to operator equations that are not necessarily limited to differential operators, let us consider the trivial equation $x - 8 = 0$ or $x = 8$. Let us write it as $2x - x - 8 = 0$. Let $Nx = x$ and write $2x - Nx - 8 = 0$. Then $2x = 8 + Nx$ and

$$x = \tfrac{1}{2}(8) + \tfrac{1}{2}Nx$$

$$x = 4 + \tfrac{1}{2}[A_0 + A_1 + \cdots]$$

$$x = 4 + \tfrac{1}{2}(4) + \tfrac{1}{2}(2) + \cdots$$

$$= 4 + 2 + 1 + \tfrac{1}{2} + \tfrac{1}{4} + \tfrac{1}{8} + \tfrac{1}{16} + \cdots$$

$$= 7 + \sum_{n=1}^{\infty} \left(\frac{1}{2}\right)^n$$

Thus, the approximation ϕ_7 to x is given by

$$x = 7 + \sum_{n=1}^{4} \left(\frac{1}{2}\right)^n$$

$$= 7 + \tfrac{1}{2} + \tfrac{1}{4} + \tfrac{1}{8} + \tfrac{1}{16}$$

$$= 7.93$$

as an approximation to $x = 8$ with ϕ_7, which will evidently improve with more terms.

3.6. CALCULATION OF THE A_n POLYNOMIALS FOR COMPOSITE NONLINEARITIES

Some formal definitions will be useful. Let N represent a nonlinear operator and Nx a nonlinear term in an equation to be solved by decomposition. A simple term $f(x)$, such as x^2, e^x, or $\sin x$, will be viewed as a zeroth-order composite nonlinearity $\tilde{N}_0 x$ or $N_0 u^0$, where $u^0 = x$, and expanded in the A_n polynomials. We will add a superscript corresponding to the particular nonlinear operator. Thus the A_n^0 will correspond to the N_0 operator and we have $N_0 u^0 = \sum_{n=0}^{\infty} A_n^0$.

A first-order composite nonlinearity $\tilde{N}_1 x = N_0(N_1 u^1)$ or simply $N_0 N_1 u^1$, where $u^1 = x$ and $u_0 = N_1 u^1$ with $N_0 u^0 = \sum_{n=0}^{\infty} A_n^0$ and $N_1 u^1 = \sum_{n=0}^{\infty} A_n^1$.

For example, the term $e^{-x^2} = \tilde{N}x = N_0 N_1 x$, where $N_0 u^0 = e^{-u} = \sum_{n=0}^{\infty} A_n^0$, and $u^0 = N_1 u^1 = (u^1)^2 = \sum_{n=0}^{\infty} A_n^1$, where $u^1 = x$.

We will emphasize that the superscripts are not exponents; they simply identify the variables and the A_n polynomials for the particular nonlinear operator.

A second-order composite nonlinearity

$$\tilde{N}_2 x = N_0 N_1 N_2 x \quad \text{or} \quad N_0(N_1(N_2 x))$$

where

$$N_0 u^0 = \sum_{n=0}^{\infty} A_n^0, \quad u^0 = N_1 u^1 = \sum_{n=0}^{\infty} A_n^1, \quad u^1 = N_2 u^2 = \sum_{n=0}^{\infty} A_n^2$$

and $u^2 = x$. When the decomposition is carried out

$$u^0 = \sum_{n=0}^{\infty} u_n^0, \quad u^1 = \sum_{n=0}^{\infty} u_n^1, \quad u^2 = \sum_{n=0}^{\infty} u_n^2.$$

A third-order composite nonlinearity is written

$$\tilde{N}_3 x = N_0(N_1(N_2(N_3 x))) = N_0 N_1 N_2 N_3 x$$

with

$$N_0 u^0 = \sum_{n=0}^{\infty} A_n^0, \quad N_1 u^1 = \sum_{n=0}^{\infty} A_n^1, \quad N_2 u^2 = \sum_{n=0}^{\infty} A_n^2$$

$$N_3 u^3 = \sum_{n=0}^{\infty} A_n^3 \quad \text{and} \quad u^3 = x$$

By decomposition,

$$u^0 = \sum_{n=0}^{\infty} u_n^0, \quad u^1 = \sum_{n=0}^{\infty} u_n^1$$

$$u^2 = \sum_{n=0}^{\infty} u_n^2, \quad u^3 = \sum_{n=0}^{\infty} u_n^3$$

with $u^0 = N_1 u^1$, $u^1 = N_2 u^2$, $u^2 = N_3 u^3$, and $u^3 = x$.

In general, $N_\nu u^\nu = \sum_{n=0}^{\infty} A_n = u^{\nu-1}$ for $1 \le \nu \le m$ with $u^m = x$ and $u^\nu = \sum_{n=0}^{\infty} u_n^\nu$.

An mth order composite nonlinearity

$$\tilde{N}_m(x) = N_0(N_1(N_2(\ldots(N_{m-2}(N_{m-1}(N_m(x)))))\ldots))) = N_0(u^0) = \sum A_n^0$$
$$N_1(u^1) = \sum A_n^1 = u^0$$
$$N_2(u^2) = \sum A_n^2 = u^1$$
$$\vdots$$
$$N_v(u^v) = \sum A_n^v = u^{v-1}$$
$$\vdots$$
$$N_{m-1}(u^{m-1}) = \sum A_n^{m-1} = u^{m-2}$$
$$N_m(u^m) = \sum A_n^m = u^{m-1} \quad \text{with} \quad u^m \equiv x$$

so that the u's are the variables of substitution. Equivalently, $\tilde{N}_m(x) = N_0 \cdot N_1 \cdot N_2 \cdot \ldots \cdot N_{m-1} \cdot N_m(x)$, i.e., a composition of operators.

The objective is to determine the A_n polynomials explicitly as functions of the x_n terms, i.e., $A_n(x_0, x_1, \ldots, x_n) = Nx$.

In the first-order case,

$$\begin{aligned}
A_n^0 &= A_n^0(x_0, \ldots, x_n) = A_n^0(u_0^0, \ldots, u_n^0) = A_n^0(A_0^1, \ldots, A_n^1) \\
&= A_n^0(A_0^1(x_0), \ldots, A_n^1(x_0, \ldots, x_n))
\end{aligned}$$

The second-order case yields

$$\begin{aligned}
A_n^0 &= A_n^0(u_0^0, \ldots, u_n^0) = A_n^0(A_0^1, \ldots, A_n^1) \\
&= A_n^0(A_0^1(u_0^1), \ldots, A_n^1(u_0^1, \ldots, u_n^1)) \\
&= A_n^0(A_0^1(A_0^2), \ldots, A_n^1(A_0^2, \ldots, A_n^2)) \\
&= A_n^0(A_0^1(A_0^2(x_0)), \ldots, A_n^1(A_0^2(x_0), \ldots, A_n^2(x_0, \ldots, x_n)))
\end{aligned}$$

The third-order case yields

$$\begin{aligned}
A_n^0(u_0^0, \ldots, u_n^0) &= A_n^0(A_0^1, \ldots, A_n^1) \\
&= A_n^0(A_0^1(u_0^1), \ldots, A_n^1(u_0^1, \ldots, u_n^1)) \\
&= A_n^0(A_0^1(A_0^2), \ldots, A_n^1(A_0^2, \ldots, A_n^2)) \\
&= A_n^0(A_0^1(A_0^2(u_0^2)), \ldots, A_n^1(A_0^2(u_0^2), \ldots, A_n^2(u_0^2, \ldots, u_n^2)))) \\
&= A_n^0(A_0^1(A_0^2(A_0^3)), \ldots, A_n^1(A_0^2(A_0^3), \ldots, A_n^2(A_0^3, \ldots, A_n^3))) \\
&= A_n^0(A_0^1(A_0^2(A_0^3(x_0))), \ldots, A_n^1(A_0^2(A_0^3(x_0)), \ldots, \\
&\qquad A_n^2(A_0^3(x_0), \ldots, A_n^3(x_0, \ldots, x_n))))
\end{aligned}$$

There are a number of ways to handle such composite nonlinearities, but this approach of repeated substitutions appears convenient because it subsumes the limiting (zeroth-order) case of the A_n for Nx and because it appears to be easily programmable.

For an mth order composite nonlinearity, we get

$$A_n^0 = A_n^0(A_0^1(A_0^2(A_0^3(\ldots(A_0^v(\ldots(A_0^m(x_0))\ldots))\ldots)))), \ldots,$$
$$A_n^1(A_0^2(A_0^3(\ldots(A_0^v(\ldots(A_0^m(x_0))\ldots))\ldots))), \ldots,$$
$$A_n^2(A_0^3(\ldots(A_0^v(\ldots(A_0^m(x_0))\ldots))\ldots)), \ldots,$$
$$A_n^3(\ldots(A_0^v(\ldots(A_0^m(x_0))\ldots)), \ldots,$$
$$A_n^v(\ldots(A_0^m(x_0), \ldots, A_n^m(x_0, \ldots, x_n))\ldots))\ldots))))$$

EXAMPLE: First-order $\tilde{N}_1 x = e^{-\sin(x/2)} = N_0(N_1 x)$. Let $N_0 u^0 = e^{-u^0} = \sum_{n=0}^{\infty} A_n^0(u_0^0, u_1^0, \ldots, u_n^0)$ and $N_1 u^1 = \sin(u^1/2)$, where $u^1 = x$ and $u^0 = \sum_{n=0}^{\infty} u_n^0 = N_1 x = \sin(x/2)$. Calculating the A_n^0 polynomials for the $N_0 u^0$ term [1, 2], we have

$$A_0^0 = e^{-u_0^0}$$

$$A_1^0 = e^{-u_0^0}(-u_1^0)$$

$$A_2^0 = e^{-u_0^0}(-u_2^0 + \tfrac{1}{2}(u_1^0)^2)$$

$$A_3^0 = e^{-u_0^0}(-u_3^0 + u_1^0 u_2^0 - \tfrac{1}{6}(u_1^0)^3)$$
$$\vdots$$

(If we omit the identifier superscript, we are dealing with $Nu = e^{-u} = \sum_{n=0}^{\infty} A_n$ where $A_0 = e^{-u_0}$, $A_1 = e^{-u_0}(-u_1)$, etc.) Now calculating the A_n polynomials for $N_1 x$, i.e., A_n^1, we have

$$A_0^1 = \sin(x_0/2)$$

$$A_1^1 = (x_1/2)\cos(x_0/2)$$

$$A_2^1 = (x_2/2)\cos(x_0/2) - (x_1^2/8)\sin(x_0/2)$$

$$A_3^1 = (x_3/2)\cos(x_0/2) - (x_1 x_2/4)\sin(x_0/2)$$
$$- (x_1^3/48)\cos(x_0/2)$$
$$\vdots$$

Since $N_0 u^0 = \sum_{n=0}^{\infty} A_n^0$ and $u^0 = N_1 x = \sum_{n=0}^{\infty} A_n^1$, $u^0 = \sum_{n=0}^{\infty} u_n^0 = \sum_{n=0}^{\infty} A_n^1$,

$$u_0^0 = A_0^1 = \sin(x_0/2)$$

$$u_1^0 = A_1^1 = (x_1/2)\cos(x_0/2)$$

$$u_2^0 = A_2^1 = (x_2/2)\cos(x_0/2) - (x_1^2/8)\sin(x_0/2)$$
$$\vdots$$

Now

$$N_0 u^0 = e^{-u^0} = \sum_{n=0}^{\infty} A_n^0 = A_0^0 + A_1^0 + \cdots = e^{-u_0^0} - u_1^0 e^{-u_0^0} + \cdots.$$

Thus, now dropping the unnecessary superscript,

$$A_0 = e^{-\sin(x_0/2)}$$

$$A_1 = -(x_1/2)\cos(x_0/2)e^{-\sin(x_0/2)}$$

A differential equation in the author's standard form which contains a nonlinear term $e^{-\sin(x/2)}$ is now solved by decomposition. A proof that $N_x = f(x) = \sum_{n-0}^{\infty} A_n$ is a convergent series has now been made by the author and will be published (see also Chapter 11).

EXAMPLE: Second-order $\tilde{N}_2 x = e^{-\sin^2(x/2)}$. Let $N_0 u^0 = e^{-u^0} = \sum_{n=0}^{\infty} A_n^0$, $N_1 u^1 = (u^1)^2 = \sum_{n=0}^{\infty} A_n^1 = u^0 = \sum_{n=0}^{\infty} u_n^0$, and $N_2 u^2 = N_2 x = \sin(x/2) = \sum_{n=0}^{\infty} A_n^2 = u^1 = \sum_{n=0}^{\infty} u_n^1$. The A_n^0 were specified in the previous example. The A_n^1 are given by

$$A_0^1 = (u_0^1)^2$$

$$A_1^1 = 2u_0^1 u_1^1$$

$$A_2^1 = (u_1^1)^2 + 2u_0^1 u_2^1$$

$$A_3^1 = 2u_1^1 u_2^1 + 2u_0^1 u_3^1$$

$$\vdots$$

and the A_n^2 are

$$A_0^2 = \sin(x_0/2)$$

$$A_1^2 = (x_1/2)\cos(x_0/2)$$

$$A_2^2 = (x_2/2)\cos(x_0/2) - (x_1^2/8)\sin(x_0/2)$$

$$A_3^2 = (x_3/2)\cos(x_0/2) - (x_1 x_2/4)\sin(x_0/2) - (x_1^3/48)\cos(x_0/2)$$

$$\vdots$$

REFERENCES

1. G. Adomian, "Stochastic Systems." Academic Press, New York, 1983.
2. R. Rach, A convenient computational form for the Adomian polynomials, *J. Math. Anal. Appl.* **102**, 415–419 (1984).

SUGGESTED FURTHER READING

G. Adomian, Solution of nonlinear stochastic physical problems, *Rendi. Semi. Mat., Univ. Politec. Torino*, **40**, 7–22 (1982).

G. Adomian, Convergent series solution of nonlinear equations, *J. Comput. Appl. Math.* **11**, 225–230 (1984).

M. Kac, "Statistical Independence in Probabilistic Analysis and Number Theory." Wiley, New York, 1959.

CHAPTER 4

Solution of Differential Equations

4.1. GENERAL METHOD AND EXAMPLES

In general we have the form $\mathscr{L}y + \mathscr{N}y = x$ or $\mathscr{F}y = x$, where $x(t, \omega)$ is a stochastic process defined on a suitable probability space (Ω, F, μ). $\mathscr{L}$ is an nth order linear differential operator which is conveniently written in the form $\mathscr{L} = \sum_{v=0}^{n} a_v(t, \omega) \, d^v/dt^v$ with the requirement that a_n is not stochastic. Equivalently, we consider $L = (d^n/dt^n) + \sum_{v=0}^{n-1} a_v(t, \omega) \, d^v/dt^v$, where one or more of the $a_0, a_1, \ldots, a_{n-1}$ are stochastic processes on (Ω, F, μ). (The possibility of different probability spaces has also been considered and can be included if necessary.[1]) We can write $\mathscr{L} = L + \mathscr{R}$, where

$$L = \langle \mathscr{L} \rangle = \frac{d^n}{dt^n} + \langle a_{n-1}(t, \omega) \rangle \frac{d^{n-1}}{dt^{n-1}} + \cdots + \langle a_1(t, \omega) \rangle \frac{d}{dt} + \langle a_0(t, \omega) \rangle$$

and $\mathscr{R} = \mathscr{L} - L$, i.e., each $a_v(t, \omega) = \langle a_v(t, \omega) \rangle + \alpha_v(t, \omega)$, where $\langle a_v \rangle$ exists and is continuous on T and α_v is the fluctuating part of a_v but is not restricted to be a stationary or other special process. Thus,

$$\mathscr{R} = \sum_{v=0}^{n-1} \alpha_v(t, \omega) \frac{d^v}{d\tau^v}$$

We will need L^{-1}, and this inverse may be difficult; i.e., the Green's function may not be easy to evaluate and even when it is found, the computation of the

---

[1] Each a_v can be defined on (Ω_v, F_v, μ_v) for $v = 0, 1, \ldots, n-1$; coefficients b_μ in nonlinear terms on $(\Omega_\mu, F_\mu, \mu_\mu)$; and $x(t)$ on (Ω_x, F_x, μ_x) for $t \in T$ with y defined on the Cartesian product of these spaces.

terms of the decomposition may become cumbersome. To avoid the problem we let L represent only the highest-ordered term d^n/dt^n of the linear operator and let the *remaining* deterministic part of the linear operator be denoted by R, i.e., $R = \sum_{\nu=0}^{n-1} \langle a_\nu(t, \omega) \rangle \, d^\nu/dt^\nu$, which we can call the remainder operator, and $\mathscr{R}$ is defined as before. Now $\mathscr{L} = L + R + \mathscr{R}$, where L^{-1} is always easily invertible by choice.

The nonlinear term $\mathscr{N}y$ (where $\mathscr{N}$ is a nonlinear stochastic operator) can also have deterministic and/or stochastic terms. We therefore write $\mathscr{N}y = Ny + \mathscr{M}y$ with Ny signifying a deterministic nonlinear term and $\mathscr{M}y$ meaning a stochastic nonlinear term. All sorts of complications in real problems can be handled by this simple breakdown of $\mathscr{F}y$, and it will be shown that complicated product nonlinearities and composite nonlinearities are readily handled. We therefore have the equivalent equations

$$\mathscr{F}y = x$$

$$\mathscr{L}y + \mathscr{N}y = x \qquad (4.1.1)$$

$$[L + R + \mathscr{R}]y + Ny + \mathscr{M}y = x$$

to represent a general differential equation in a single independent variable, which we have taken as t.

A deterministic nonlinear equation becomes $[L + R]y + Ny = x$. A purely nonlinear (deterministic) equation is $Ny = x$. A linear stochastic equation is $\mathscr{L}y = x$. An equation with stochastic terms in the linear part and a deterministic nonlinearity is written as $\mathscr{L}y + Ny = x$. (In Chapters 5 and 9, this scheme is extended to systems of equations and to partial differential equations.)

Finally, we remark that the coefficient processes a_ν and b_μ in any nonlinear terms [e.g., $b_\mu y^m$ or $b_\mu (y^{(\mu)})^{m_\mu}$] or any deterministic transformation $g(a_0, a_1, \ldots, a_{n-1}; b_0, b_1, \ldots)$ of the coefficient processes are assumed statistically independent from $x(t)$, which is a reasonable assumption in a very large class of problems. It is to be noted and emphasized that saying the system or black box parameters are statistically independent from the input is very different from assuming the system and its output are statistically independent as is the case in hierarchy or averaging methods. These differences are discussed in the first book, and numerical as well as theoretical comparisons show these methods are simply perturbation theories limited to small fluctuations. It is quite possible to modify even this statistical independence hypothesis where necessary. We will simply assume that all stochastic processes are continuous a.e. and sample functions are bounded; we can consider at a later time mean-square or other criteria. Alternatively one can consider all stochastic coefficient processes replaced by "equivalent" processes having, with probability one, continuous sample functions. Each $a_\nu(t)$

belongs to the class of functions $C^n(t)$ a.e. (i.e., a_v and its first n derivatives exist and are continuous on T for $\omega \in \Omega$).

The input term $x(t, \omega)$ is bounded on T a.e. and our L^{-1} has an inverse. (It is only necessary to remember that our objective is the solution of physical systems which do not have unbounded inputs and infinite outputs.)

The equation (4.1.1) is solved for the linear part Ly giving

$$Ly = x - Ry - \mathscr{R}y - \mathscr{N}y \qquad (4.1.2)$$

where we have grouped the nonlinear terms together for now. Since L is invertible, we operate on both sides with L^{-1}

$$L^{-1}Ly = L^{-1}x - L^{-1}Ry - L^{-1}\mathscr{R}y - L^{-1}\mathscr{N}y \qquad (4.1.3)$$

As discussed in Chapter 2, the left-hand side becomes $y(t)$, minus terms involving initial or boundary conditions. These terms are taken to the right and included with $L^{-1}x$ as the y_0 term. Then

$$y = y_0 - L^{-1}Ry - L^{-1}\mathscr{R}y - L^{-1}\mathscr{N}y \qquad (4.1.4)$$

which is formally also $y = \mathscr{F}^{-1}x$ with the $\mathscr{F}^{-1}$ as yet to be determined.

To avoid confusion by students in relating (4.1.4) to our earlier papers, we point out that L was taken there to be $\langle \mathscr{L} \rangle$ rather than just the highest-ordered derivative. Consequently R vanishes and

$$y = y_0 - L^{-1}\mathscr{R}y - L^{-1}\mathscr{N}y \qquad (4.1.5)$$

For the case of $L = \langle \mathscr{L} \rangle$, the inverse L^{-1} involves a Green's function $l(t, \tau)$ which may not be easily found; this is the reason for the change we have made in definition of L. With $L = \langle \mathscr{L} \rangle$ and vanishing initial conditions $L^{-1}x(t, \omega) = \int_0^t l(t, \tau)x(\tau)\, d\tau$ (4.1.5) becomes

$$y(t, \omega) = \int_0^t l(t, \tau)x(\tau, \omega)\, d\tau - \int_0^t l(t, \tau) \sum_{v=0}^{n-1} \alpha_v(\tau, \omega) \frac{d^v y(\tau, \omega)}{d\tau^v}\, d\tau$$

$$- \int_0^t l(t, \tau)[Ny(\tau, \omega)]\, d\tau$$

At this point we are not ready to discuss the nonlinear term but will consider the second term which is $-L^{-1}\mathscr{R}y$. In the case in which a_0 is the only stochastic process coefficient, $\mathscr{R}$ involves no derivatives. If other terms are stochastic, we have derivatives in $\mathscr{R}$. The stochastic Green's theorem, due to Adomian and Sibul [1], allows replacement, in this case, of the $L^{-1}\mathscr{R}y$ term with

$$\int_0^t y(\tau, \omega)\mathscr{R}^\dagger[l(t, \tau)]\, d\tau$$

(where $\mathscr{R}^\dagger$ is the adjoint operator) so that no differentiation acts on y if the stochastic bilinear concomitant vanishes. Thus $k(t, \tau) = \mathscr{R}^\dagger[l(t, \tau)]$ can be viewed as a new Green's function. The stochastic bilinear concomitant (s.b.c.) denoted by $\sigma[y; l]|_0^t$ is given by

$$\sigma[y(\tau, \omega); l(t, \tau)]\bigg|_0^t = \sum_{k=0}^{n-1}\sum_{v=0}^{k-1}(-1)^v[l(t, \tau)\alpha_k(\tau, \omega)]^{(v)}y^{(k-1-v)}(\tau, \omega)\bigg|_0^t.$$

At the upper limit the s.b.c. is zero because of the properties of Green's functions. If zero initial conditions (with probability one) are assumed, which can be stated as

$$P\{\omega: y^{(k)}(0, \omega) = 0\} = 1$$

the s.b.c. vanishes. If initial conditions are random, y and its derivatives are random variables at $t = 0$, and extra terms arise which are absorbed into the y_0 term. A convenient resolvent kernel formulation for linear problems has been discussed in an earlier book [2]. However, we need not discuss it further since we have simplified the problem of computation of the Green's function $l(t, \tau)$ by taking L as the highest-ordered term of $\langle \mathscr{L} \rangle$ rather than $\langle \mathscr{L} \rangle$ itself. Let us discuss this further.

EXAMPLE:

$$y' + 2ty = 0, \qquad y(0) = 1$$

Write $Ly = -2ty$, then $y = y(0) - 2L^{-1}ty$

$$y_0 = y(0) = 1$$
$$y_1 = -2L^{-1}ty_0 = -2L^{-1}t = -t^2$$
$$y_2 = -2L^{-1}ty_1 = -2L^{-1}t(-t^2) = t^4/2!$$
$$y_3 = -2L^{-1}ty_2 = -t^6/3!$$
$$\vdots$$
$$y = 1 - t^2 + \frac{t^4}{2!} - \frac{t^6}{3!} + \cdots = e^{-t^2}$$

EXAMPLE:

$$y'' + y = 0, \qquad y(0) = 1, \qquad y'(0) = 0$$

Write the equation as $Ly + y = 0$. Then $y = y_0 - L^{-1}y$, where $y_0 = y(0) + ty'(0) = 1$. Now $y_1 = -t^2/2!$, $y_2 = t^4/4!$, etc. and we find that

$$y = 1 - \frac{t^2}{2!} + \frac{t^4}{4!} - \cdots = \cos t$$

EXAMPLE:

$$y'' + 4y = 0, \qquad y(0) = a_0, \qquad y'(0) = a_1$$

The equation is written as $y = y(0) + ty'(0) - 4L^{-1}y$. We get

$$y_0 = a_0 + a_1 t$$

$$y_1 = -4L^{-1}y_0 = -2a_0 t^2 - \tfrac{2}{3}a_1 t^3$$

$$y_2 = -4L^{-1}y_1 = \tfrac{2}{3}a_0 t^4 + \tfrac{2}{15}a_1 t^5$$

$$\vdots$$

$$y = a_0[1 - 2t^2 + \tfrac{2}{3}t^4 - \cdots] + a_1[t - \tfrac{2}{3}t^3 + \tfrac{2}{15}t^5 - \cdots]$$

$$= a_0\left[\sum_{k=0}^{\infty} \frac{(-1)^k(2t)^{2k}}{(2k)!}\right] + \frac{1}{2}a_1\left[\sum_{k=0}^{\infty} \frac{(-1)^k(2t)^{2k+1}}{(2k+1)!}\right]$$

$$= a_0 \cos 2t + \tfrac{1}{2}a_1 \sin 2t$$

It takes much more work to get the result by power series.

EXAMPLE:

$$d^2y/dx^2 + (1 + x + x^2)y = 0, \qquad y(0) = y'(0) = 1$$

$$Ly = -(1 + x + x^2)y, \qquad L = d^2/dx^2, \qquad L^{-1}Ly = y - 1 - x$$

$$y_0 = 1 + x$$

$$y_1 = -L^{-1}(1 + x + x^2)(1 + x)$$

$$= -L^{-1}(1 + 2x + 2x^2 + x^3)$$

$$= -\left(\frac{x^2}{2} + \frac{x^3}{3} + \frac{x^4}{6} + \frac{x^5}{20}\right)$$

$$y = 1 + x - \frac{x^2}{2} - \frac{x^3}{3} - \cdots$$

Caution: We emphasize that $L^{-1}L \neq I$. We have $L^{-1}L = I$ only if all *initial conditions are zero*. Here L^{-1} is a *definite* integral and brings in the homogeneous solution that would otherwise have to be added.

4.2. CALCULATING A SIMPLE GREEN'S FUNCTION

Consider the equation $\mathscr{L}y = x$, where x is a stochastic process on $T \times \Omega$ where (Ω, F, μ) is a probability space and $\mathscr{L}$ is a stochastic operator, in this case, a linear ordinary differential stochastic operator. Since it is assumed that the stochasticity can occur in all coefficients except the highest ordered derivative, we write

$$\mathcal{L}(t, \omega) = \frac{d^n}{dt^n} + \sum_{\nu=0}^{n-1} a_\nu(t, \omega) \frac{d^\nu}{dt^\nu}$$

We choose $L = d^n/dt^n$ rather than $L = \langle \mathcal{L} \rangle$ since a simple Green's function is desirable. We still have a decomposition of $\mathcal{L}$ into deterministic and random parts but now into $L + R + \mathcal{R}$. Solving for Ly as before, R is given by $\sum_{\nu=0}^{n-1} \langle a_\nu(t, \omega) \rangle \, d^\nu/dt^\nu$ and $\mathcal{R}$ is given by $\sum_{\nu=0}^{n-1} \alpha_\nu(t, \omega) \, d^\nu/dt^\nu$, where $a_\nu = \langle a_\nu \rangle + \alpha_\nu(t, \omega)$ for $\nu = 0, 1, \ldots, n - 1$, so that $\mathcal{R}$ is zero-mean. Now

$$Ly = x - Ry - \mathcal{R}y$$

$$y = L^{-1}x - L^{-1}Ry - L^{-1}\mathcal{R}y$$

or simply

$$y = L^{-1}x - L^{-1}\mathcal{R}y \tag{4.2.1}$$

if we allow $\mathcal{R}$ to have a mean value and identify it as $\sum_{\nu=0}^{n-1} a_\nu(t, \omega) \, d^\nu/dt^\nu$. Letting $L = \langle \mathcal{L} \rangle$ was a convenience if L^{-1} was easily determinable, but it is not a restriction.

L^{-1} is an n-fold integral, hence

$$L^{-1}Ly = \int_0^t \cdots \int_0^t Ly = L^{-1}x - L^{-1}\mathcal{R}y \tag{4.2.2}$$

Let us assume that we are considering initial-value problems (other cases are discussed in Chapter 2). The left-hand side of (4.2.2) is then

$$y(t) - \sum_{\nu=0}^{n-1} (t^\nu/\nu!)y^{(\nu)}(0) \tag{4.2.3}$$

For example, if $L = d^2/dy^2$, we have $L^{-1}Ly = \int_0^t \int_0^t d^2y/dt^2$. The first integral yields $y'|_0^t = y'(t) - y'(0)$. The second yields $y(t) - y(0) - ty'(0)$. Hence (4.2.2) becomes

$$y(t) = \sum_{\nu=0}^{n-1} (t^\nu/\nu!)y^{(\nu)}(0) + L^{-1}x - L^{-1}\mathcal{R}y \tag{4.2.4}$$

If the initial conditions are zero, the first term of the solution for y by decomposition into $\sum_{i=0}^{\infty} y_i$ is $y_0 = L^{-1}x$. If not,

$$y_0 = L^{-1}x + \sum_{\nu=0}^{n-1} y^{(\nu)}(0)[t^\nu/\nu!] \tag{4.2.5}$$

(Additional terms may also appear from the stochastic bilinear concomitant term of the Adomian–Sibul theorem when an operator $\mathcal{R}$ involving derivatives is replaced by its adjoint.)

Since nonlinear equations only change the integral equation to

$$y = L^{-1}x - L^{-1}\mathscr{R}y - L^{-1}\mathscr{N}y \tag{4.2.6}$$

the same result holds for nonlinear equations.

4.3   GREEN'S FUNCTION BY DECOMPOSITION

Consider the differential equation

$$\frac{d^2y}{dt^2} + a_1(t, \omega)\frac{dy}{dt} + a_0(t, \omega)y = x(t, \omega) \tag{4.3.1}$$

$$a_0 = 1 + \alpha_0(t, \omega), \qquad \langle a_0 \rangle = 1, \qquad \langle \alpha_0 \rangle = 0$$
$$a_1 = \alpha_1(t, \omega), \qquad \langle a_1 \rangle = 0, \qquad \langle \alpha_1 \rangle = 0$$

We write the above equation as $Ly + \mathscr{R}y = x$, where $L = (d^2/dt^2) + 1$ and $\mathscr{R} = \alpha_1(d/dt) + \alpha_0$. With this L,

$$y = L^{-1}x - L^{-1}\mathscr{R}y$$

$$= \int_0^t l(t, \tau)x(\tau)\, d\tau - \int_0^t l(t, \tau)\mathscr{R}(\tau)y(\tau)\, d\tau \tag{4.3.2}$$

$$= \int_0^t l(t, \tau)x(\tau)\, d\tau - \int_0^t l(t, \tau)\left[\alpha_1(\tau, \omega)\frac{d}{d\tau} + \alpha_0(\tau, \omega)\right]y(\tau)\, d\tau$$

where $l(t, \tau)$ is the Green's function for $L = (d^2/dt^2) + 1$. We evaluate $l(t, \tau)$ as follows: the solutions of the homogeneous equation $Ly = 0$ are $\phi_0(t) = \cos t$ and $\phi_1(t) = \sin t$. The Green's function[2] is given by

$$l(t, \tau) = -\frac{1}{W(\tau)}\begin{vmatrix} \cos t & \sin t \\ \cos \tau & \sin \tau \end{vmatrix}$$

Since the Wronskian $W = 1$,

$$l(t, \tau) = \cos \tau \sin t - \sin \tau \cos t = \sin(t - \tau)$$

for $t \geq \tau$ and zero otherwise.

---

[2] See Adomian [2, p. 319]. We can write $H(t - \tau)\sin(t - \tau)$, where $H(t - \tau)$ is the Heaviside function.

Equation (4.3.1), or (4.3.2), is now solvable with this l and use of the decomposition method [2] and the adjoint operator $R^{\dagger}$

$$y = \int_0^t l(t, \tau)x(\tau) \, d\tau - \int_0^t \frac{d}{d\tau} [l(t, \tau)\alpha_1(\tau)] y(\tau) \, d\tau - \int_0^t l(t, \tau)\alpha_0(\tau)y(\tau) \, d\tau.$$

Thus,

$$y_0 = \int_0^t l(t, \tau)x(\tau) \, d\tau$$

$$y_1 = - \int \frac{d}{d\tau} [l(t, \tau)\alpha_1(\tau)] y_0(\tau) \, d\tau - \int l(t, \tau)\alpha_0(\tau)y_0(\tau) \, d\tau$$

$$y_2 = - \int \frac{d}{d\tau} [l(t, \tau)\alpha_1(\tau)] y_1(\tau) \, d\tau - \int l(t, \tau)\alpha_0(\tau)y_1(\tau) \, d\tau$$

$$\vdots$$

which will give us the solution to (4.3.1). Now let us consider our proposed solution using a simpler L. Let $L = d^2/dt^2$ and $R = 1$ with $\mathcal{R}$ remaining unchanged. The solution is now

$$y = y(0) + ty'(0) + L^{-1}x - L^{-1}Ry - L^{-1}\mathcal{R}y$$
$$= y_0 - L^{-1}y - L^{-1}\mathcal{R}y$$

where $y_0 = y(0) + ty'(0) + L^{-1}x$. It is again convenient to use the adjoint operator $\mathcal{R}^{\dagger}$, and L^{-1} is now given by $\int_0^t dt \int_0^t dt$.

Let $a_0 = 1$ and $a_1 = 0$. Then $d^2y/dt^2 + y = x$, and

$$y = \int_0^t H(\tau - t) \sin(t - \tau)x(\tau) \, d\tau$$

by finding the Green's function for $(d^2/dt^2) + 1$.

Now do this by using d^2/dt^2 for L and handling the remaining term by decomposition. To make it transparent, let $x = 1$ for both approaches.

$$Ly = x - y = 1 - y$$

$$y = L^{-1}(1) - L^{-1}y$$

$$= \frac{t^2}{2} - L^{-1}(y_0 + y_1 + \cdots)$$

$$= \frac{t^2}{2!} - \frac{t^4}{4!} + \frac{t^6}{6!} - \cdots$$

with the use of $L = d^2/dt^2$.

From the first approach,

$$\sin(t - \tau) = (t - \tau) - \frac{(t - \tau)^3}{3!} + \cdots$$

$$\int_0^t H(t - \tau) \sin(t - \tau) \, d\tau = \frac{t^2}{2} - \frac{t^4}{4!} + \cdots$$

i.e., the same result.

4.4   APPROXIMATING DIFFICULT GREEN'S FUNCTIONS

An impressive handbook [3] by Butkovsky in the USSR has recently become available for Green's functions for certain classes of equations $Ly = x$. It still can be valuable however to determine the Green's function in an easily computable series by decomposition of the differential operator into an operator with a known inverse and a second operator—with no smallness restrictions—whose effects can be determined.

Consider a differential equation $Ly = x(t)$, where L is a linear deterministic ordinary differential operator of the form $L = \sum_{v=0}^n a_v(t) \, d^v/dt^v$, where a_n is nonvanishing on the interval of interest.

Decompose L into $L_1 + L_2$, where L_1 is sufficiently simple that determination of its Green's function is trivial. Then if L_2 is zero, we have simply $y(t) = \int_0^t l(t, \tau) x(\tau) \, d\tau$, where $l(t, \tau)$ is the Green's function for the L_1 operator. If L is a second-order differential operator we may have $L_1 = d^2/dt^2$, and L_2 will be the remaining terms of L, say, $\alpha(t) d/dt + \beta(t)$. More generally, $L = \sum_{v=0}^n a_v(t) \, d^v/dt^v$, and we might take $L_1 = d^n/dt^n$ and $L_2 = \sum_{v=0}^{n-1} a_v(t) \, d^v/dt^v$. We have

$$Ly = (L_1 + L_2)y = x(t), \qquad L_1 y = x(t) - L_2 y \tag{4.4.1}$$

$$y = L_1^{-1}x - L_1^{-1}L_2 y \tag{4.4.2}$$

Now assume a decomposition $y = \sum_{i=0}^\infty y_i$ and assuming initial conditions are zero, or equivalently, ignoring the homogeneous solution, we identify y_0 as $L_1^{-1}x$ and write

$$y = L_1^{-1}x - L_1^{-1}L_2(y_0 + y_1 + \cdots) \tag{4.4.3}$$

from which we can determine the y_i, each being determinable in terms of the preceding y_{i-1}. (If the initial conditions are nonzero, they must be included in y_0.) Thus,

$$y = L_1^{-1}x - L_1^{-1}L_2 y_0 - L_1^{-1}L_2 y_1 - \cdots$$

or

$$y = L_1^{-1}x - L_1^{-1}L_2 L_1^{-1}x + L_1^{-1}L_2 L_1^{-1}L_2 L_1^{-1}x - \cdots \tag{4.4.4}$$

We have

$$y = \sum_{i=0}^{\infty} (-1)^i (L_1^{-1} L_2)^i L_1^{-1} x \tag{4.4.5}$$

thus

$$y_0 = L_1^{-1} x$$
$$y_1 = -L_1^{-1} L_2 L_1^{-1} x$$
$$y_2 = L_1^{-1} L_2 L_1^{-1} L_2 L_1^{-1} x \tag{4.4.6}$$
$$\vdots$$
$$y_i = (-1)^i (L_1^{-1} L_2)^i L_1^{-1} x$$

Hence, the inverse of the differential operator L is given by

$$L^{-1} = \sum_{i=0}^{\infty} (-1)^i (L_1^{-1} L_2)^i L_1^{-1} \tag{4.4.7}$$

Equation (4.4.2) written out explicitly in terms of the Green's function for L_1^{-1} is

$$y = \int_0^t l(t, \tau) x(\tau) \, d\tau - \int_0^t l(t, \tau) L_2[y(\tau)] \, d\tau \tag{4.4.8}$$

$$y = \int_0^t l(t, \tau) x(\tau) \, d\tau - \int_0^t L_2^{\dagger}[l(t, \tau)] y(\tau) \, d\tau^3 \tag{4.4.9}$$

$$y = \int_0^t l(t, \tau) x(\tau) \, d\tau - \int_0^t \sum_{i=0}^{n-1} (-1)^i \frac{d^i}{d\tau^i} [l(t, \tau) a_i(\tau)] y(\tau) \, d\tau \tag{4.4.10}$$

$$y(t) = \int_0^t l(t, \tau) x(\tau) \, d\tau - \int_0^t k(t, \tau) y(\tau) \, d\tau \tag{4.4.11}$$

where

$$k(t, \tau) = \sum_{i=0}^{n-1} (-1)^i \frac{d^i}{d\tau^i} [l(t, \tau) a_i(\tau)]$$

Let us choose $n = 1$ and work with the case $L = L_1 + \alpha(t)$, i.e., $L_2 = \alpha(t)$. Now

$$y(t) = L_1^{-1} x - L_1^{-1} \alpha(t) L_1^{-1} x + L_1^{-1} \alpha L_1^{-1} \alpha L_1^{-1} x - \cdots \tag{4.4.12}$$

---

[3] For zero bilinear concomitant.

i.e.,

$$y_0 = \int_0^t l(t, \tau)x(\tau)\, d\tau$$

$$y_1 = -\int_0^t l(t, \tau)a(\tau)\int_0^\tau l(\tau, \gamma)x(\gamma)\, d\gamma\, d\tau$$

$$y_2 = \int_0^t \int_0^\tau \int_0^\gamma l(t, \tau)l(\tau, \gamma)l(\gamma, \sigma)a(\tau)a(\gamma)x(\sigma)\, d\gamma\, d\tau\, d\sigma$$
$$\vdots$$

or equivalently

$$y(t) = \int_0^t l(t, \tau)x(\tau)\, d\tau - \int_0^t k(t, \tau)y(\tau)\, d\tau \qquad (4.4.13)$$

where $k(t, \tau) = l(t, \tau)a(\tau)$. Hence,

$$y(t) = \int_0^t l(t, \tau)x(\tau)\, d\tau - \int_0^t k(t, \tau)y_0(\tau)\, d\tau$$
$$+ \int_0^t k(t, \tau)y_1(\tau)\, d\tau + \cdots$$

If we let $F(t) = L_1^{-1}x = \int_0^t l(t, \tau)x(\tau)\, d\tau$, then we can write

$$y(t) = F(t) - \int_0^t k(t, \tau)F(\tau)\, d\tau + \int_0^t d\tau \int_0^\tau d\gamma\, k(t, \tau)k(\tau, \gamma)F(\gamma)$$
$$- \int_0^t d\tau \int_0^\tau d\gamma \int_0^\gamma d\sigma\, k(t, \tau)k(\tau, \gamma)k(\gamma, \sigma)F(\sigma) + \cdots \qquad (4.4.14)$$

If L_1 has constant coefficients, $l(t, \tau) = l(t - \tau)$. For simplicity and clarity, let us consider the example $L = L_1 + \alpha$ with α a constant and $L_1^{-1} = \int dt$ and the Green's function $l = 1$.

Our objective is to determine the Green's function $G(t, \tau)$ for L. Here G satisfies $LG(t, \tau) = \delta(t - \tau)$ or

$$(L_1 + L_2)G = \delta(t - \tau) \qquad (4.4.15)$$

Thus, G can be found from the preceding equations by replacing x by the δ function. For the last example $L = d/dt + \alpha$

$$(d/dt + \alpha)G(t, \tau) = \delta(t - \tau)$$

If we write $G = G_0 + G_1 + \cdots$ we immediately have [using $l = 1$, $L_2 = \alpha$, $y = G$, and $x = \delta(t - \tau)$]

$$G_0 = \int_\tau^t \delta(t - \tau)\, d\tau = 1, \qquad (t > \tau)$$

Remembering that $k(t, \tau) = l(t - \tau)\alpha = \alpha$,

$$G_1 = \alpha \int_\tau^t d\tau = \alpha(t - \tau)$$

$$G_2 = \int_0^t d\tau \int_0^\tau d\gamma \, \alpha^2 = \alpha^2(t - \tau)/2 \qquad (4.4.16)$$

$$\vdots$$

Consequently

$$G = 1 + \alpha(t - \tau) + \alpha^2(t - \tau)/2 + \cdots \qquad (4.4.17)$$

an approximation to

$$G = e^{-\alpha(t - \tau)} \qquad (4.4.18)$$

Physically this equation could model a particle of mass m moving as a result of a force $f(t)$ in a resisting medium

$$m \frac{dv}{dt} + Rv = f(t)$$

or

$$(L + \alpha)v = f(t)/m$$

where $L = d/dt$ and $\alpha = R/m$. We have

$$(L + \alpha)G(t, \tau) = \delta(t - \tau)/m$$

Now $G_0 = L_1^{-1}[\delta(t - \tau)/m] = 1/m$, $G_1 = -(\alpha/m) \int_0^t \int_0^\tau \delta(\gamma - \tau) \, d\gamma \, d\tau = -(\alpha/m)(t - \tau)$, ... Thus,

$$G = \frac{1}{m}\left(1 - \frac{R}{m}(t - \tau) + \cdots\right) \simeq \frac{1}{m} e^{-R(t - \tau)/m}, \qquad t > \tau$$

Thus, we use L_1^{-1} as a first approximation and find the total response function G as a series in which L_2 *need not be a perturbation on* L_1.

For an example of a second-order differential equation, let $L_1 = d^2/dt^2$ and $L_2 = \alpha d/dt + \beta(t)$. Then,

$$y = L_1^{-1}x - L_1^{-1}L_2L_1^{-1}x + L_1^{-1}L_2L_1^{-1}L_2L_1^{-1}x - \cdots;$$

hence, $G(t, \tau)$ satisfies

$$[(d^2/dt^2) + \alpha(d/dt) + \beta]G(t, \tau) = \delta(t - \tau)$$

The Green's function $l(t, \tau)$ for $L = d^2/dt^2$ is now $(t - \tau)$, where $t > \tau$, and $G(t, \tau)$ is again determinable as a series as before. If $G(0, \tau) = G'(0, \tau) = 0$, then $G(t, \tau)$ is easily found by decomposition $G(t, \tau) = L_1^{-1}\delta(t - \tau) - L_1^{-1}L_2G(t, \tau)$, since $G_0 = L_1^{-1}\delta(t - \tau)$ and $G(t, \tau) = G_0(t, \tau) + G_1(t, \tau) + \cdots$.

Initial Conditions: If initial conditions are not zero and the equation is second order, the first term for y is not simply $y_0 = L_1^{-1}x$ but $y(0) + ty'(0) + L_1^{-1}x$. This is best seen by writing $L_1 y + L_2 y = x$ as $L_1 y = x - L_2 y$ and operating with L_1^{-1} from the left to write $L_1^{-1}L_1 y = L_1^{-1}x - L_1^{-1}L_2 y$. The left-hand side involves a double integration of a second derivative resulting in $y(t) - y(0) - ty'(0)$. For nth-order equations

$$y_0 = L^{-1}x + \sum_{v=0}^{n-1} \frac{t^v}{v!} y^{(v)}(0)$$

Consider now the linear stochastic differential equation in the form $\mathscr{L}y = x$; where x is a stochastic process on $T \times \Omega$, where (Ω, F, μ) is a probability space and $\mathscr{L}$ a stochastic operator, in this case, a linear ordinary differential stochastic operator. Since it is assumed that stochasticity can occur in all coefficients except the highest-ordered derivative, we will write

$$\mathscr{L}(t, \omega) = \frac{d^n}{dt^n} + \sum_{v=0}^{n-1} a_v(t, \omega) \frac{d^v}{dt^v}$$

we can then take $L = d^n/dt^n$ rather than $L = \langle \mathscr{L} \rangle$ since a simple Green's function is desirable. We are still decomposing $\mathscr{L}$ into deterministic and random parts (but into $L + R + \mathscr{R}$) and solving for Ly as before. R now is given by $\sum_{v=0}^{n-1} \langle a_v(t, \omega) \rangle d^v/dt^v$, and $\mathscr{R}$ is given by $\sum_{v=0}^{n-1} \alpha_v(t, \omega) d^v/dt^v$, where $a_v = \langle a_v \rangle + \alpha_v(t, \omega)$ for $v = 0, 1, \ldots, n - 1$, so that $\mathscr{R}$ is zero-mean. Now

$$Ly = x - Ry - \mathscr{R}y$$

$$y = L^{-1}x - L^{-1}Ry - L^{-1}\mathscr{R}y$$

or simply

$$y = L^{-1}x - L^{-1}\mathscr{R}y \qquad (4.4.19)$$

if we allow $\mathscr{R}$ to have a mean value and identify it as $\sum_{v=0}^{n-1} a_v(t, \omega) d^v/dt^v$. Letting $L = \langle \mathscr{L} \rangle$ was a convenience if L^{-1} was easily determinable, but it is not a restriction.

Here L^{-1} is, of course, an n-fold integral, hence

$$L^{-1}Ly = \int_0^t \cdots \int_0^t Ly = L^{-1}x - L^{-1}\mathscr{R}y \qquad (4.4.20)$$

The left-hand side of (4.4.20) is

$$y(t) - \sum_{v=0}^{n-1} \frac{t^v}{v!} y^{(v)}(0). \qquad (4.4.21)$$

For example, if $L = d^2/dy^2$, we have $\int_0^t \int_0^t d^2y/dt^2$. The first integral yields $y'|_0^t = y'(t) - y'(0)$. The second yields $y(t) - y(0) - ty'(0)$. Hence (4.4.20) becomes

$$y(t) = \sum_{v=0}^{n-1} \frac{t^v}{v!} y^{(v)}(0) + L^{-1}x - L^{-1}\mathscr{R}y. \tag{4.4.22}$$

If the initial conditions are zero, the first term of our solution for y by decomposition into $\sum_{i=0}^{\infty} y_i$ is $y_0 = L^{-1}x$. If not, then

$$y_0 = L^{-1}x + \sum_{v=0}^{n-1} y^{(v)}(0)\left[\frac{t^v}{v!}\right] \tag{4.4.23}$$

Additional terms may also appear from the stochastic bilinear concomitant term of the Adomian–Sibul theorem [1] when an operator $\mathscr{R}$ involving derivatives is replaced by its adjoint $\mathscr{R}^\dagger$.

Since nonlinear equations only change the integral equation (4.4.19) to

$$y = L^{-1}x - L^{-1}\mathscr{R}y - L^{-1}\mathcal{N}y \tag{4.4.24}$$

the same result holds for nonlinear equations.

4.5 POLYNOMIAL NONLINEARITIES

Derivation of the A_n for polynomial nonlinearities makes it easy to write solutions for nonlinear stochastic, or in the limiting case, deterministic differential equations involving such nonlinearities. Let us consider equations of the form $Ly + Ny = x(t)$, where the nonlinear term $Ny = y^m$ for positive integers m. Since we have

$$Ly = x - Ny$$
$$L^{-1}Ly = L^{-1}x - L^{-1}Ny$$

or

$$y = y_0 - L^{-1}Ny$$

where y_0 includes $L^{-1}x$ and appropriate terms depending on the order of L and specified conditions such as $y(0) + ty'(0) + L^{-1}x$ for a second-order operator and given initial conditions. Now Ny is replaced by the A_n; consequently

$$y = y_0 - L^{-1}\sum_{n=0}^{\infty} A_n$$

so that decomposition of y into $\sum_{n=0}^{\infty} y_n$ yields

$$y_0 = y_0$$
$$y_1 = -L^{-1}A_0$$
$$y_2 = -L^{-1}A_1$$
$$\vdots$$

and y is determined once the A_n are known. Referring to Chapter 3, for $Ny = y^5$, the A_n (or $A_n(y^5)$ to specify it more completely) are substituted into the above expressions to obtain the solution. For convenience some A_n are listed for powers of y.

Case 1: $Ny = y^5$. The A_n are given by

$$A_0 = y_0^5$$
$$A_1 = 5y_0^4 y_1$$
$$A_2 = 5y_0^4 y_2 + 10y_0^3 y_1^2$$
$$A_3 = 5y_0^4 y_3 + 20y_0^3 y_1 y_2 + 10y_0^2 y_1^3$$
$$A_4 = 5y_0^4 y_4 + 5y_1^4 y_0 + 10y_0^3 y_2^2 + 20y_0^3 y_1 y_3 + 30y_0^2 y_1^2 y_2$$

Notice that for y^m each individual term is the product of m factors. Each term of A_n has five factors—the sum of superscripts is m (or 5 in this case).

The sum of subscripts is n. The second term of A_4, as an example, is $5y_1 y_1 y_1 y_1 y_0$ and the sum of subscripts is 4.

A very convenient check on the numerical coefficients in each term is the following. Each coefficient is $m!$ divided by the product of factorials of the superscripts for a given term. Thus, the second term of $A_3(y^5)$ has the coefficient $5!/(3!)(1!)(1!) = 20$. The last term of A_4 has the coefficient $5!/(2!)(2!)(1!) = 30$. This makes a nice final check on our generation of the A_n. Continuing with the A_n, we have

$$A_5 = y_1^5 + 5y_0^4 y_5 + 20y_0^3 y_1 y_4 + 20y_0^3 y_2 y_3 + 20y_1^3 y_0 y_2$$
$$+ 30y_0^2 y_2^2 y_1 + 30y_0^2 y_1^2 y_3$$

$$A_6 = 5y_0^4 y_6 + 5y_1^4 y_2 + 10y_0^3 y_3^2 + 10y_0^3 y_2^2 + 20y_0^3 y_1 y_5 + 20y_0^3 y_2 y_4$$
$$+ 20y_1^3 y_0 y_3 + 30y_0^2 y_1^2 y_4 + 30y_1^2 y_2^2 y_0 + 60y_0^3 y_1 y_2 y_3$$

$$A_7 = 5y_0^4 y_7 + 5y_1^4 y_3 + 10y_1^3 y_2^2 + 20y_0^3 y_1 y_6 + 20y_0^3 y_2 y_5 + 20y_0^3 y_3 y_4$$
$$+ 20y_2^3 y_1 y_0 + 20y_1^3 y_0 y_4 + 30y_0^2 y_2^2 y_3 + 30y_0^2 y_3^2 y_1 + 30y_0^2 y_1^2 y_5$$
$$+ 60y_0^2 y_1 y_2 y_4 + 60y_1^2 y_0 y_2 y_3$$

$$A_8 = 5y_0^4 y_8 + 5y_2^4 y_0 + 5y_1^4 y_4 + 10y_0^3 y_4^2 + 10y_1^3 y_2^3 + 20y_0^3 y_3 y_5 + 20y_0^3 y_2 y_6$$
$$+ 20y_0^3 y_1 y_7 + 20y_1^3 y_5 y_0 + 20y_1^3 y_2 y_3 + 30y_0^2 y_2 y_3^2 + 30y_0^2 y_2^2 y_4$$
$$+ 30y_0^2 y_1^2 y_6 + 30y_1^2 y_3^2 y_0 + 60y_1^2 y_2 y_4 y_0 + 60y_1 y_2^2 y_3 y_0 + 60y_0^2 y_1 y_3 y_4$$
$$+ 60y_0^2 y_1 y_2 y_5$$

$$A_9 = 5y_0^4 y_9 + 5y_1^4 y_5 + 5y_2^4 y_1 + 10y_0^2 y_3^3 + 10y_1^3 y_3^2 + 20y_0^3 y_4 y_5 + 20y_0^3 y_3 y_6$$
$$+ 20y_0^3 y_2 y_7 + 20y_0^3 y_1 y_8 + 20y_0 y_2^3 y_3 + 20y_0 y_1^3 y_6 + 20y_1^3 y_2 y_4$$
$$+ 30y_2^3 y_5 y_0^2 + 30y_4^3 y_1 y_0^2 + 30y_1^2 y_7 y_0^2 + 30y_1^2 y_2^2 y_3 + 60y_0^2 y_2 y_3 y_4$$
$$+ 60y_0^2 y_1 y_3 y_5 + 60y_0^2 y_1 y_2 y_6 + 60y_0 y_1 y_2 y_3^2 + 60y_0 y_1 y_2^2 y_4$$
$$+ 60y_0 y_1^2 y_3 y_4 + 60y_1^2 y_0 y_2 y_5$$

$$A_{10} = y_2^5 + 5y_0^4 y_{10} + 5y_1^4 y_6 + 10y_0^3 y_5^2 + 20y_1 y_2^3 y_3 + 20y_1^3 y_3 y_4$$
$$+ 20y_1^3 y_0 y_7 + 20y_1^3 y_2 y_5 + 20y_0^3 y_4 y_6 + 20y_0^3 y_3 y_7 + 20y_0^3 y_2 y_8$$
$$+ 20y_0^3 y_1 y_9 + 20y_0 y_3^3 y_4 + 20y_0 y_1 y_3^3 + 30y_0^2 y_3^3 y_4 + 30y_0^2 y_2 y_4^2$$
$$+ 30y_0^2 y_2^2 y_6 + 30y_0^2 y_1^2 y_8 + 30y_0 y_2^2 y_3^2 + 30y_1^2 y_4^2 y_0 + 30y_1^2 y_3 y_2$$
$$+ 30y_1^2 y_2^2 y_4 + 60y_0^2 y_2 y_3 y_5 + 60y_0^2 y_1 y_4 y_5 + 60y_0^2 y_1 y_3 y_6$$
$$+ 60y_0^2 y_1 y_2 y_7 + 60y_0 y_1 y_2^2 y_5 + 60y_1^2 y_0 y_3 y_5 + 60y_0 y_1^2 y_2 y_6$$
$$+ 120y_0 y_1 y_2 y_3 y_4$$

Case 2: $Ny = y^4$. (Now all terms have 4 factors; for y^m, all terms have m factors.)

$$A_0 = y_0^4$$

$$A_1 = 4y_0^3 y_1$$

$$A_2 = 4y_0^3 y_2 + 6y_0^2 y_1^2$$

$$A_3 = 4y_0^3 y_3 + 4y_1^3 y_0 + 12y_0^2 y_1 y_2$$

$$A_4 = y_1^4 + 4y_0^3 y_4 + 6y_0^2 y_2^2 + 12y_0^2 y_1 y_3 + 12y_1^2 y_0 y_2$$

$$A_5 = 4y_0^3 y_5 + 4y_1^3 y_2 + 12y_0^2 y_1 y_4 + 12y_0^2 y_2 y_3 + 12y_1^2 y_0 y_3 + 12y_2^2 y_0 y_1$$

$$A_6 = 4y_0^3 y_6 + 4y_1^3 y_3 + 4y_2^3 y_0 + 6y_0^2 y_3^2 + 6y_1^2 y_2^2 + 12y_0^2 y_1 y_5 + 12y_0^2 y_2 y_4$$
$$+ 12y_1^2 y_0 y_4 + 24y_0 y_1 y_2 y_3$$

$$A_7 = 4y_0^3 y_7 + 4y_1^3 y_4 + 4y_2^3 y_1 + 12y_0^2 y_1 y_6 + 12y_0^2 y_2 y_5 + 12y_0^2 y_3 y_4$$
$$+ 12y_1^2 y_0 y_5 + 12y_1^2 y_2 y_3 + 12y_2^2 y_0 y_3 + 12y_3^2 y_0 y_1 + 24y_0 y_1 y_2 y_4$$

$$A_8 = y_2^4 + 4y_0^3 y_8 + 4y_1^3 y_5 + 6y_0^2 y_4^2 + 6y_1^2 y_3^2 + 12y_0^2 y_1 y_7 + 12y_0^2 y_2 y_6$$
$$+ 12y_0^2 y_3 y_5 + 12y_1^2 y_6 y_0 + 12y_2^2 y_4 y_0 + 12y_3^2 y_2 y_0 + 12y_1^2 y_2 y_4$$
$$+ 12y_2^2 y_1 y_3 + 24y_0 y_1 y_2 y_5 + 24y_0 y_1 y_3 y_4$$

$$A_9 = 4y_0^3 y_9 + 4y_1^3 y_6 + 4y_2^3 y_3 + 4y_3^3 y_0 + 12y_0^2 y_1 y_8 + 12y_0^2 y_2 y_7$$
$$+ 12y_0^2 y_3 y_6 + 12y_0^2 y_4 y_5 + 12y_1^2 y_7 y_0 + 12y_2^2 y_5 y_0 + 12y_3^2 y_1 y_2$$
$$+ 12y_1^2 y_2 y_5 + 12y_2^2 y_1 y_4 + 12y_4^2 y_1 y_0 + 12y_1^2 y_3 y_4 + 24y_0 y_2 y_3 y_4$$
$$+ 24y_0 y_1 y_2 y_6 + 24y_0 y_1 y_3 y_5$$

$$A_{10} = 4y_0^3 y_{10} + 4y_1^3 y_7 + 4y_2^3 y_4 + 4y_3^3 y_1 + 6y_0^2 y_5^2 + 6y_1^2 y_4^2 + 6y_2^2 y_3^2$$
$$+ 12y_0^2 y_1 y_9 + 12y_0^2 y_2 y_8 + 12y_0^2 y_3 y_7 + 12y_0^2 y_4 y_6 + 12y_1^2 y_0 y_8$$
$$+ 12y_2^2 y_0 y_6 + 12y_3^2 y_0 y_4 + 12y_4^2 y_2 y_0 + 12y_2^2 y_1 y_5 + 12y_1^2 y_3 y_5$$
$$+ 12y_1^2 y_2 y_6 + 24y_0 y_2 y_3 y_5 + 24y_1 y_2 y_3 y_4 + 24y_0 y_1 y_4 y_5$$
$$+ 24y_0 y_1 y_3 y_6 + 24y_0 y_1 y_2 y_7$$

Case 3: $Ny = y^3$.

$$A_0 = y_0^3$$

$$A_1 = 3y_0^2 y_1$$

$$A_2 = 3y_0^2 y_2 + 3y_1^2 y_0$$

$$A_3 = y_1^3 + 3y_0^2 y_3 + 6y_0 y_1 y_2$$

$$A_4 = 3y_0^2 y_4 + 3y_1^2 y_2 + 3y_2^2 y_0 + 6y_0 y_1 y_3$$

$$A_5 = 3y_0^2 y_5 + 3y_1^2 y_3 + 3y_2^2 y_1 + 6y_0 y_1 y_4 + 6y_0 y_2 y_3$$

$$A_6 = y_2^3 + 3y_0^2 y_6 + 3y_1^2 y_4 + 3y_3^2 y_0 + 6y_0 y_1 y_5 + 6y_0 y_2 y_4 + 6y_1 y_2 y_3$$

$$A_7 = 3y_0^2 y_7 + 3y_1^2 y_5 + 3y_2^2 y_3 + 3y_3^2 y_1 + 6y_0 y_1 y_6 + 6y_0 y_2 y_5 + 6y_0 y_3 y_4$$
$$+ 6y_1 y_2 y_4$$

$$A_8 = 3y_0^2 y_8 + 3y_1^2 y_6 + 3y_2^2 y_4 + 3y_3^2 y_2 + 3y_4^2 y_0 + 6y_0 y_1 y_7 + 6y_0 y_2 y_6$$
$$+ 6y_0 y_3 y_5 + 6y_1 y_2 y_5 + 6y_1 y_3 y_4$$

$$A_9 = y_3^3 + 3y_0^2 y_9 + 3y_1^2 y_7 + 3y_2^2 y_5 + 3y_4^2 y_1 + 6y_0 y_1 y_8 + 6y_0 y_2 y_7$$
$$+ 6y_0 y_3 y_6 + 6y_0 y_4 y_5 + 6y_1 y_2 y_6 + 6y_1 y_3 y_5 + 6y_2 y_3 y_4$$

$$A_{10} = 3y_0^2 y_{10} + 3y_1^2 y_8 + 3y_2^2 y_6 + 3y_3^2 y_4 + 3y_4^2 y_2 + 3y_5^2 y_0 + 6y_0 y_1 y_9$$
$$+ 6y_0 y_2 y_8 + 6y_0 y_3 y_7 + 6y_0 y_4 y_6 + 6y_1 y_2 y_7 + 6y_1 y_3 y_6$$
$$+ 6y_1 y_4 y_5 + 6y_2 y_3 y_5$$

Case 4: $Ny = y^2$

$$A_0 = y_0^2$$

$$A_1 = 2y_0 y_1$$

$$A_2 = y_1^2 + 2y_0 y_2$$

$$A_3 = 2y_1 y_2 + 2y_0 y_3$$

$$A_4 = y_2^2 + 2y_1 y_3 + 2y_0 y_4$$

$$A_5 = 2y_2 y_3 + 2y_1 y_4 + 2y_0 y_5$$

$$A_6 = y_3^2 + 2y_2y_4 + 2y_1y_5 + 2y_0y_6$$

$$A_7 = 2y_3y_4 + 2y_2y_5 + 2y_1y_6 + 2y_0y_7$$

$$A_8 = y_4^2 + 2y_3y_5 + 2y_2y_6 + 2y_1y_7 + 2y_0y_8$$

$$A_9 = 2y_4y_5 + 2y_3y_6 + 2y_2y_7 + 2y_1y_8 + 2y_0y_9$$

$$A_{10} = y_5^2 + 2y_4y_6 + 2y_3y_7 + 2y_2y_8 + 2y_1y_9 + 2y_0y_{10}$$

With the above substitutions and application of the decomposition method, solutions to nonlinear differential equations with polynomial nonlinearities can be made *without linearization procedures.*

As elementary examples consider the following equations:

(1) $\dot{y} + y^2 = -1$ with $y(0) = 0$, which we write as $Ly + y^2 = -1$ with $L = d/dt$ and $L^{-1} = \int_0^t [\cdot] \, dt$ and $y(0) = 1$. Then

$$Ly = -1 - y^2$$

$$y = y_0 - \sum_{n=0}^{\infty} L^{-1} \sum_{n=0}^{\infty} A_n$$

with $y_0 = y(0) + L^{-1}(-1) = -t$

$$y_1 = -L^{-1}A_0 = -L^{-1}t^2 = \frac{-t^3}{3}$$

$$y_2 = -L^{-1}A_1 = -\frac{2t^5}{15}$$

$$\vdots$$

$$y = -\left[t + \frac{t^3}{3} + \frac{2t^5}{15} + \cdots \right]$$

or the series for $-\tan t$ as expected.

(2) A Riccati type equation, e.g.,

$$\dot{u}(t) + f(t)u(t) + u^2(t) = -g(t)$$

is written in the form

$$\sum_{n=0}^{\infty} u_n = u = -L^{-1}g - L^{-1}f \sum_{n=0}^{\infty} u_n - L^{-1} \sum_{n=0}^{\infty} A_n$$

where $u_0 = u(0) - L^{-1}g$

$$u_1 = -L^{-1}fu_0 - L^{-1}A_0$$
$$u_2 = -L^{-1}fu_1 - L^{-1}A_1$$
$$\vdots$$

and is solvable even with stochastic f and/or g.

EXAMPLE: $y' = y^2 - y$, which is written in the form

$$Ly = -y + \sum_{n=0}^{\infty} A_n(y^2)$$

or

$$y = y(0) - L^{-1}y + L^{-1} \sum A_n$$

$$y_0 = y(0)$$

$$y_1 = -L^{-1}y_0 + L^{-1}A_0 = -L^{-1}y_0 + L^{-1}y_0^2$$

$$y_2 = -L^{-1}y_1 + L^{-1}A_1 = -L^{-1}y_1 + L^{-1}(2y_0y_1)$$

$$y_3 = -L^{-1}y_2 + L^{-1}A_2 = -L^{-1}y_2 + L^{-1}(y_1^2 + 2y_0y_2)$$

$$y_4 = -L^{-1}y_3 + L^{-1}A_3 = -L^{-1}y_3 + L^{-1}(2y_1y_2 + 2y_0y_3)$$
$$\vdots$$

Suppose $y(0) = 2$. Then

$$y = 2 + 2t + 3t^2 + \frac{13t^3}{3} + \frac{75t^4}{12} + \cdots$$

which by the ratio test we know to be correct for $t < 0.693$ or $\ln 2$.

EXAMPLE: Consider the nonlinear differential equation $dy/dt - t(a^2 + t^2)^{-3/2}y^2 = 0$ with $y(0) = a$. We write

$$Ly = t(a^2 + t^2)^{-3/2}y^2$$

$$y = y(0) + L^{-1}t(a^2 + t^2)^{-3/2}y^2$$

$$\sum_{n=0}^{\infty} y_n = y(0) + L^{-1}t(a^2 + t^2)^{-3/2} \sum_{n=0}^{\infty} A_n$$

$$y_0 = y(0) = a$$

$$y_1 = L^{-1}t(a^2 + t^2)^{-3/2}A_0$$

$$y_2 = L^{-1}t(a^2 + t^2)^{-3/2}A_1$$
$$\vdots$$

After substitution of $A_0 = y_0^2$, $A_1 = 2y_0 y_1, \ldots$ and elementary integrations, the reader can easily verify that we get a series which converges to $(a^2 + t^2)^{1/2}$.

As a check, let $a = t = 1$ so $y = \sqrt{2}$ then $\phi_1 = y_0 = 1$, $\phi_2 = y_0 + y_1 = 1.29289$, $\phi_3 = y_0 + y_1 + y_2 = 1.37867, \ldots$. Thus, the error is already down to 2.5% by ϕ_3.

EXAMPLE:

$$d^2 y/dx^2 + x^2 e^y = 0, \qquad x > 0$$

$$y(0) = 1, \qquad y'(0) = 0$$

Write $Ly = -x^2 \sum_{n=0}^{\infty} A_n$ or $y = y_0 - L^{-1} x^2 \sum_{n=0}^{\infty} A_n$. Then

$$y_0 = 1$$

$$y_1 = -L^{-1} x^2 A_0 = -L^{-1} x^2 e^{y_0} = -ex^4/12$$

$$y_2 = -L^{-1} x^2 A_1 = -L^{-1} x^2 y_1 e^{y_0} = (e^2/12) L^{-1} x^6 = \frac{e^2 x^8}{12 \cdot 7 \cdot 8}$$

$$y = 1 - \frac{ex^4}{12} + \frac{e^2 x^8}{12 \cdot 7 \cdot 8} - \cdots$$

EXAMPLE:　Consider the equation

$$y' + y^2 = t^2 + 1, \qquad y(0) = 0$$

i.e., $x(t) = t^2 + 1$, $L = d/dt$, and $Ny = y^2$

$$y = L^{-1} x - L^{-1} \sum_{n=0}^{\infty} A_n$$

$$y_0 = L^{-1} x(t) = \int_0^t (\tau^2 + 1) \, d\tau = t + (t^3/3)$$

$$y_1 = -L^{-1} A_0 = -\int_0^t y_0^2(\tau) \, d\tau$$

$$= -\int_0^t \left(\frac{\tau^6}{9} + \tau^2 + \frac{2\tau^4}{3} \right) d\tau$$

$$= -\frac{t^3}{3} - \frac{2t^5}{15} - \frac{t^7}{63}.$$

A *two-term* approximation $\phi_2 = y_0 + y_1$ is therefore given by

$$\phi_2 = \left(t + \frac{t^3}{3}\right) - \left(\frac{t^3}{3} + 2\frac{t^5}{15} + \frac{t^7}{63}\right).$$

Consequently

$$y' \simeq t^2 + 1 - \frac{t^6}{9} - \frac{2t^4}{3} - t^2$$

$$y' + y^2 = 1 - \frac{t^6}{9} - \frac{2t^4}{3} + \left(\frac{t^3}{3} + t\right)^2 + \cdots$$

$$= t^2 + 1$$

thus verifying the solution.

It is worthwhile to remark further concerning these verifications. For an n-term approximation ϕ_n we have

$$L\phi_{m+1} + \sum_{i=0}^{m-1} A_i = x(t), \qquad (m + 1 = n)$$

i.e., in substituting for y^2 we use only y_0, not $y_0 + y_1$ as in the y' term. In approximating the derivative term up to y_1, the $\sum_{n=0}^{\infty} A^n$ should include only A_0 since y_1 depends on A_0. We will see that the nonlinear terms expanded in the A_n polynomials approach zero for high n so that we get an accurate solution and, as we will see, generally only a few terms are sufficient for most purposes.

4.6. NEGATIVE POWER NONLINEARITIES

Here, we will show that extension to cases such as

$$\frac{dy}{dt} - y^{-m} = 0, \qquad m > 0 \qquad \text{and} \qquad y(0) = k \qquad (4.6.1)$$

(where m is an integer) are now simple generalizations. Equation (4.6.1) is in our standard form $Fy = Ly + Ny = x$, where $x = 0$, $Ny = -y^{-m}$, and $L = d/dt$. Hence $L^{-1}(\cdot) = \int_0^t (\cdot) \, dt$. We can, of course, solve the problem as easily for nth order differential operators. The only differences are in the y_0 term and in having a multiple integration for L^{-1}. A simple operator is used for clarity. Also, a nonzero forcing function $x(t)$ only means adding an $L^{-1}x$

term to y_0. (We might mention also that equations such as $y' + y^2 = 0$ can be solved by separation of variables, and similarly some examples we give are solvable by other techniques, which is of no concern. We are illustrating a methodology, and simple examples easily checked by other methods are most useful.) Now

$$Ly = -Ny$$

$$L^{-1}Ly = -L^{-1}Ny$$

$$y - y(0) = -L^{-1}Ny$$

$$y = k - L^{-1}Ny$$

We write $y = \sum_{n=0}^{\infty} y_n$ and $Ny = \sum_{n=0}^{\infty} A_n$, where the A_n are the previously defined polynomials. Then

$$\sum_{n=0}^{\infty} y_n = k + L^{-1} \sum_{n=0}^{\infty} A_n \,^4$$

We obtain immediately

$$y_0 = k$$

$$y_1 = L^{-1}A_0$$

$$y_2 = L^{-1}A_1$$

$$y_3 = L^{-1}A_2$$

$$y_4 = L^{-1}A_3$$

$$\vdots$$

The A_n are given by

$$A_0 = y_0^{-m}$$

$$A_1 = -my_0^{-(m+1)}y_1$$

$$A_2 = \tfrac{1}{2}m(m+1)y_0^{-(m+2)}y_1^2 - my_0^{-(m+1)}y_2$$

$$A_3 = -\tfrac{1}{6}m(m+1)(m+2)y_0^{-(m+3)}y_1^3 + m(m+1)y_0^{-(m+2)}y_1y_2 - my_0^{-(m+1)}y_3$$

$$\vdots$$

---

[4] Rather than $y = k - L^{-1}\sum_{n=0}^{\infty} A_n$, where A_n are the polynomials for $-y^{-m}$, which we can write as $A_n(-y^{-m})$, we have used $A_n(y^{-m})$.

Consequently,

$$y_0 = k$$

$$y_1 = L^{-1}A_0 = L^{-1}(k^{-m}) = (k^{-m})t$$

$$y_2 = L^{-1}A_1 = -mk^{-(2m+1)}t^2/2!$$

$$y_3 = L^{-1}A_2 = m(2m+1)k^{-(3m+2)}t^3/3!$$

$$y_4 = L^{-1}A_3 = -m(2m+1)(3m+2)k^{-(4m+3)}t^4/4!$$

$$\vdots$$

$$y_n = (-1)^n \prod_{v=0}^{n-1} [vm + v - 1]k^{-(nm+n-1)}t^n/n!$$

so that

$$y(t) = \sum_{n=0}^{\infty} (-1)^n \prod_{v=0}^{n-1} [vm + v - 1]k^{-(nm+n-1)}t^n/n!$$

a convergent series whose sum is $[(m + 1)t + k^{m+1}]^{1/(m+1)}$.

The case $m = 3$ or the equation $dy/dt - y^{-3} = 0$ with $y(0) = k = 1$ immediately yields the solution

$$y = 1 + t - 3\frac{t^2}{2!} + (3)(7)\frac{t^3}{3!} - (3)(7)(11)\frac{t^4}{4!} + \cdots$$

$$= (1 + 4t)^{1/4}$$

where convergence is assured for $k \geq 1$.

EXERCISE

Verify the solution given.

Let us consider now the equation $dy/dt = t + y^{-1}$. We now have $L = d/dt$, $Ny = -y^{-1}$, $x(t) = t$. Assume $y(0) = k$ is an integer. Then

$$L^{-1}Ly = L^{-1}x - L^{-1}Ny$$

$$y - y(0) = L^{-1}t + L^{-1} \sum_{n=0}^{\infty} A_n$$

where the $A_n = A_n(y^{-1})$.

$$y = y(0) + L^{-1} \sum_{n=0}^{\infty} A_n$$

$$y_0 = k + t^2/2$$

Table 1

t	Decomposition method ϕ_2	Numerical integration y	$\Delta = \phi_2 - y$	% Error
0	4.0	4.0	0	0
0.5	4.25	4.25	0	0
1.0	4.74	4.73	0.01	0.21
1.5	5.47	5.46	0.01	0.18
2.0	6.44	6.42	0.02	0.31
2.5	7.64	7.61	0.03	0.39
3.0	9.08	9.05	0.03	0.33
4.0	12.68	12.64	0.04	0.32
5.0	17.25	17.21	0.04	0.23
10.0	54.92	54.88	0.04	0.07
20.0	205.01	204.97	0.04	0.02

and since $A_0 = y_0^{-1}$, $A_1 = -y_0^{-2}y_1$, $A_2 = -y_0^{-2}y_2 + y_0^{-3}y_1^2, \ldots,$

$$y_1 = \int_0^t y_0^{-1}\, dt = \int_0^t (k + t^2/2)^{-1}\, dt$$

$$y_1 = (2/k)^{1/2} \tan^{-1}[t/(2k)^{1/2}]$$
$$\vdots$$

Let us consider a *two-term* approximation $\phi_2 = y_0 + y_1$. (The complete solution, of course, is $\sum_{n=0}^{\infty} y_n$.) Then

$$\phi_2 = k + t^2/2 + (2/k)^{1/2} \tan^{-1}[t/(2k)^{1/2}]$$

Table 1 compares this approximation with results of a numerical integration using $k = 4$. With only a little more effort we could go to a higher ϕ_n (ϕ_5, for example) for a better approximation, which is unnecessary since the percentage error is already extremely small. The worst case is less than 0.4%. However, if we go to ϕ_3 we find the worst case has an error less than 0.02%—this for only a three term approximation! Thus, we have very rapid convergence.

4.7. DECIMAL POWER NONLINEARITIES

We now consider differential equations in the standard form with $Nu = u^\gamma$, where γ is a decimal number. For convenience, we will assume a zero right-hand side and will assume the linear differential operator L to be first order.

Thus, we will consider

$$\dot{u} + u^\gamma = 0, \qquad u(0) = k$$

where k is a given constant and γ a decimal number.

We calculate solutions in a range from $\gamma = 0$ to 2.0 in increments of 0.1. We have as usual $u = \sum_{n=0}^{\infty} u_n(t)$ and $Nu = u^\gamma = \sum_{n=0}^{\infty} A_n$, where the A_n are generated for this nonlinearity. Thus, $Lu = -u^\gamma$, $L^{-1}Lu = -L^{-1}u^\gamma$, then $u = u(0) - L^{-1}u^\gamma$, consequently $u_0 = u(0) = k$ and $u_1 = -L^{-1}A_0(u^\gamma), \ldots$

$$A_0 = u_0^\gamma$$

$$A_1 = \gamma u_0^{\gamma-1} u_1$$

$$A_2 = \gamma u_0^{\gamma-1} u_2 + \tfrac{1}{2}\gamma(\gamma - 1)u_0^{\gamma-2}u_1^2$$

$$A_3 = \gamma u_0^{\gamma-1} u_3 + \gamma(\gamma - 1)u_0^{\gamma-2}u_1 u_2 + \tfrac{1}{6}\gamma(\gamma - 1)(\gamma - 2)u_0^{\gamma-3}u_1^3$$

$$A_4 = \gamma u_0^{\gamma-1} u_4 + \gamma(\gamma - 1)u_0^{\gamma-2}(\tfrac{1}{2}u_2^2 + u_1 u_3) + \tfrac{1}{2}\gamma(\gamma - 1)(\gamma - 2)u_0^{\gamma-3}u_1^2 u_2$$
$$+ \tfrac{1}{24}\gamma(\gamma - 1)(\gamma - 2)(\gamma - 3)u_0^{\gamma-4}u_1^4$$
$$\vdots$$

Hence,

$$u_0 = k$$

$$u_1 = -k^\gamma t$$

$$u_2 = \gamma k^{2\gamma-1} \frac{t^2}{2!}$$

$$u_3 = -\gamma(2\gamma - 1)k^{3\gamma-2} \frac{t^3}{3!}$$

$$u_4 = \gamma(2\gamma - 1)(3\gamma - 2)k^{4\gamma-3} \frac{t^4}{4!}$$
$$\vdots$$

$$u_m = (-1)^m \left\{ \prod_{\mu=0}^{m-1} [\mu\gamma - (\mu - 1)] \right\} k^{m\gamma-(m-1)} \frac{t^m}{m!}$$

Consequently,

$$u(t) = \sum_{m=0}^{\infty} (-1)^m \left\{ \prod_{\mu=0}^{m-1} [\mu\gamma - (\mu - 1)] \right\} k^{m\gamma-(m-1)} \frac{t^m}{m!}$$

Taking $u(0) = k = \frac{1}{2}$, we plot u_γ, i.e., u for various values of γ. Some examples are

$$u_{1.0}(t) = 0.5000 - 0.5000t + 0.5000t^2/2 - 0.5000t^3/6$$
$$+ 0.5000t^4/24 - 0.5000t^5/120 + \cdots$$

$$u_{1.5}(t) = 0.5000 - 0.3536t + 0.3750t^2/2 - 0.5303t^3/6$$
$$+ 0.9375t^4/24 - 1.9887t^5/120 + \cdots$$

$$u_{2.0}(t) = 0.5000 - 0.2500t + 0.2500t^2/2 - 0.3750t^3/6$$
$$+ 0.7500t^4/24 - 1.8750t^5/120 + \cdots$$

Results are given in Table 2 and Fig. 1. The case $\gamma = 0$ provides a linear solution. The case $\gamma = 1$ is a linear equation, and as γ departs from 1.0 we can see the departure from linearity. The results are given in the table for 12 terms of the series, i.e., for $u(t) \simeq \phi_{12}$ for values of γ for the equation $u' + u^\gamma = 0$ with $u(0) = \frac{1}{2}$. Accurate approximations are obtained for any desired value of γ. The solutions for $\gamma = 0$, 0.5, 0.8, and 0.9 are finite series, so the exact solution is obtained.

EXERCISES

1. Show that in the equation $Ly + y^\gamma = 0$ with $y(0) = k$ and $y'(0) = y''(0) = \cdots = y^{(m-1)}(0) = 0$, the solution converges faster for $L = d^m/dt^m$ for m a positive integer greater than 1 than it does for $m = 1$.

2. Solve $y' + y^\gamma = 0$ with $y(0) = k$ and $\gamma = 0.1$ and compare with the solution for $\gamma = 0$.

3. Solve $y' + y^\gamma = 0$ with $y(0) = k$ and $\gamma = \pi$.

4. Show that if $\gamma = 1 - (1/m)$, where m is a positive integer, we get a terminating series and therefore an exact solution rather than an infinite, albeit very rapidly converging series.

4.8. PRODUCT NONLINEARITIES

Suppose $\mathscr{F}y$ is decomposable into $\mathscr{L}y + \mathscr{N}(y, y', \ldots) = x$, where $\mathscr{L}$ is a linear operator itself decomposable into $L + \mathscr{R}$ with $L = \langle \mathscr{L} \rangle$ and $\mathscr{R} = \mathscr{L} - L$. The fact that L must be invertible is not a strong assumption, since L is only the linear deterministic part of $\mathscr{F}$. We can consider terms such as

$$\mathscr{N}(y, y', \ldots) = \sum_{\mu=0}^{M_\mu} b_\mu(t, \omega)(y^{(\mu)})^{m_\mu}$$

or even

$$\sum_{\mu=0}^{M_\mu} \sum_{\nu=0}^{M_\nu} b_{\mu\nu}(t, \omega)(y^{(\mu)})^{m_\mu}(y^{(\nu)})^{m_\nu}$$

TABLE 2

t	$\gamma = 0$	$\gamma = 0.1$	$\gamma = 0.2$	$\gamma = 0.3$	$\gamma = 0.4$	$\gamma = 0.5$	$\gamma = 0.6$
0.0	0.50000000	0.50000000	0.50000000	0.50000000	0.50000000	0.50000000	0.50000000
0.1	0.40000000	0.40761438	0.41451693	0.42079893	0.42653545	0.43178932	0.43661313
0.2	0.30000000	0.31729085	0.33243604	0.34584433	0.35781543	0.36857864	0.37830952
0.3	0.20000000	0.22949529	0.25424375	0.27548465	0.29400964	0.31036797	0.32494548
0.4	0.10000000	0.14499410	0.18062828	0.21016058	0.23531520	0.25715729	0.27637301
0.5	0.00000000	0.06523552	0.11264439	0.15045283	0.18196546	0.20894661	0.23243938
0.6			0.05207376	0.09716823	0.13424335	0.16573593	0.19298667
0.7				0.05150073	0.09250234	0.12752525	0.15785117
0.8					0.0572001132	0.09431457	0.12686270
0.9						0.06610390	0.09984381
1.0						0.04289322	0.07660873

t	$\gamma = 0.7$	$\gamma = 0.8$	$\gamma = 0.9$	$\gamma = 1.0$	$\gamma = 1.1$	$\gamma = 1.2$	$\gamma = 1.3$
0.0	0.50000000	0.50000000	0.50000000	0.50000000	0.50000000	0.50000000	0.50000000
0.1	0.44105188	0.44514416	0.44892340	0.45241871	0.45565566	0.45865680	0.46144215
0.2	0.38714941	0.39521224	0.40259160	0.40936538	0.41559916	0.42134873	0.42666197
0.3	0.33803627	0.34986505	0.36060866	0.37040911	0.37938217	0.38762372	0.39521403
0.4	0.29345953	0.30877936	0.32260778	0.33516002	0.34660671	0.35708665	0.36671395
0.5	0.25316974	0.27164750	0.28824930	0.30326533	0.31691907	0.32939143	0.34082886

t	$\gamma = 1.4$	$\gamma = 1.5$	$\gamma = 1.6$	$\gamma = 1.7$	$\gamma = 1.8$	$\gamma = 1.9$	$\gamma = 2.0$
0.6	0.21692101	0.23817697	0.25721863	0.27440582	0.29000463	0.30423426	0.31726960
0.7	0.18447115	0.20809009	0.22922411	0.24829265	0.26558317	0.28134786	0.29578417
0.8	0.15558178	0.18112356	0.20399481	0.22466448	0.24340489	0.26049665	0.27615230
0.9	0.13001843	0.15702811	0.18127804	0.20328483	0.22324690	0.24147252	0.25818069
1.0	0.10755072	0.13556814	0.16083672	0.18393972	0.20491006	0.22409117	0.24169885

t	$\gamma = 1.4$	$\gamma = 1.5$	$\gamma = 1.6$	$\gamma = 1.7$	$\gamma = 1.8$	$\gamma = 1.9$	$\gamma = 2.0$
0.0	0.50000000	0.50000000	0.50000000	0.50000000	0.50000000	0.50000000	0.50000000
0.1	0.46402957	0.46643502	0.46867289	0.47075615	0.47269654	0.47450474	0.47619048
0.2	0.43158029	0.43613982	0.44037222	0.44430546	0.44796437	0.45137109	0.45454545
0.3	0.40222111	0.40870308	0.41471005	0.42028559	0.42546780	0.43029023	0.43478261
0.4	0.37558373	0.38377618	0.39135960	0.39839266	0.40492620	0.41100455	0.41666666
0.5	0.35135213	0.36106208	0.37004388	0.37837014	0.38610329	0.39329748	0.39999998
0.6	0.32925397	0.34030638	0.35052679	0.36000002	0.36879872	0.37698558	0.38461518
0.7	0.30905363	0.32129008	0.33260575	0.34309569	0.35284112	0.36191199	0.37036912
0.8	0.29054628	0.30382347	0.31610549	0.32749553	0.33808180	0.34794019	0.35713687
0.9	0.27355277	0.28774037	0.30087166	0.31305595	0.32438718	0.33494614	0.34480381
1.0	0.25791454	0.27289191	0.28676279	0.29964142	0.31162708	0.32280514	0.33325195

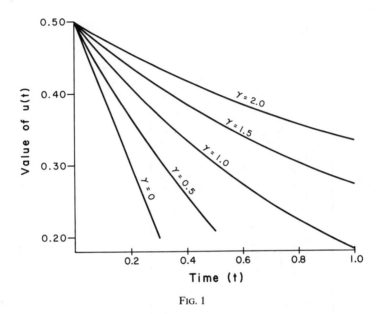

FIG. 1

Consider, for example, a product nonlinearity such as y^2y'. An example of such a product nonlinearity arises, for example, in the Van der Pol equation $y'' + \xi(y^2 - 1)y' + y = x$, which we can write as $\mathscr{L}y + \xi g(y, y') = x$, where $g(y, y')$ is a nonlinear term of the form $y^2y' - y'$. Returning to the form y^2y' which is sufficient to demonstrate the method, with $\mathscr{L}$ a linear (and possibly stochastic) operator, we have

$$y = L^{-1}x - L^{-1}\mathscr{R}y - L^{-1}\mathscr{N}(y, y', \ldots)$$
$$= L^{-1}x - L^{-1}\mathscr{R}y - L^{-1}y^2y'$$

Assume a decomposition for y in the form[5] $\sum_{i=0}^{\infty} \lambda^i y_i$ and parametrize the above equation as

$$y = L^{-1}x - \lambda L^{-1}\mathscr{R}y - \lambda L^{-1}y^2y'$$

Thus

$$y = L^{-1}x - \lambda L^{-1}\mathscr{R}\sum_{i=0}^{\infty} \lambda^i y_i - \lambda L^{-1}\left(\sum_{i=0}^{\infty} \lambda^i y_i\right)^2 \sum_{i=0}^{\infty} \lambda^i y_i'$$

[5] It must be emphasized that λ is *not* a perturbation parameter; it is *not* small. Comparison with perturbation theory is discussed by Adomian [2] and also in the work of Professor N. Bellomo [4].

Let $y_0 = L^{-1}x$ (with inclusion of appropriate terms if initial conditions are nonzero or random). We have by examining powers of λ,

$$
\begin{aligned}
y &= y_0 - \lambda(L^{-1}\mathscr{R})(y_0 + \lambda y_1 + \lambda^2 y_2 + \cdots) \\
&\quad - \lambda L^{-1}(y_0 + \lambda y_1 + \lambda^2 y_2 + \cdots)^2(y_0 + \lambda y_1 + \lambda^2 y_2 + \cdots)' \\
&= y_0 - \lambda(L^{-1}\mathscr{R})(y_0 + \lambda y_1 + \lambda^2 y_2 + \cdots) \\
&\quad - \lambda L^{-1}(y_0^2 y_0' + \lambda^2 y_1^2 y_0' + 2\lambda y_0 y_1 y_0' \\
&\quad + \lambda y_0^2 y_1' + \lambda^3 y_1^2 y_1' + 2\lambda^2 y_0 y_1 y_1' \\
&\quad + 2\lambda^2 y_0 y_2 y_0' + 2\lambda^3 y_0 y_2 y_1' + \cdots)
\end{aligned}
$$

We obtain

$$
y_0 = L^{-1}x
$$

$$
y_1 = -(L^{-1}\mathscr{R})y_0 - L^{-1}(y_0^2 y_0')
$$

$$
y_2 = -(L^{-1}\mathscr{R})y_1 - L^{-1}(2y_0 y_1 y_0' + y_0^2 y_1')
$$

$$
y_3 = -(L^{-1}\mathscr{R})y_2 - L^{-1}(y_1^2 y_0' + 2y_0 y_1 y_1' + 2y_0 y_2 y_0')
$$

The results for y_i are not unique, of course. An acceptable grouping of terms can be obtained also by omitting the parametrization, writing $y = y_0 + y_1 + \cdots$, identifying $y_0 = L^{-1}x$, and identifying for each y_i only those terms in which i has a lower value. The final results are the same. Only what we identify as y_i is different. With the parametrization, but after λ is set equal to 1, $y = \sum_{i=0}^{\infty} y_i$. Then each y_i is clearly determinable from preceding terms, and no statistical separability problem requiring closure approximations exists. Since

$$
y_0 = L^{-1}x = \int_0^t l(t - \tau)x(\tau)\,d\tau,
$$

$$
y_0' = \frac{d}{dt}\int_0^t l(t - \tau)x(\tau)\,d\tau
$$

$$
= \int_0^t l'(t - \tau)x(\tau)\,d\tau + l(0)x(t) = \int_0^t l'(t - \tau)x(\tau)\,d\tau
$$

since the system is initially passive, and $l(0)$ is therefore zero.

The nonlinear term need not be a weak nonlinearity. It can be deterministic or involve stochastic coefficients and be of the form $\mathscr{N}(y, \dot{y}, \ldots)$.

Products of Nonlinear Functions: Examples—whether algebraic or differential equations—which involve complicated nonlinearities sometimes are more easily calculable by considering the nonlinearity to be composed of simpler nonlinearities. Let us consider a simple example:

$$
x = k + e^{-x}\sin(x/2) \tag{4.8.1}
$$

which is in our usual general form [1] with the nonlinear function $N(x) =$ $e^{-x} \sin(x/2)$. We will consider $N(x)$ to be the product of $N_1(x)N_2(x)$, where $N_1(x) = e^{-x}$ and $N_2(x) = \sin(x/2)$. We expand $N_1(x)$ in the A_n polynomials and similarly expand $N_2(x)$ by using B_n for the second set simply to distinguish the two. With the usual decomposition, (4.8.1) becomes

$$\sum_{n=0}^{\infty} x_n = k + \left(\sum_{n=0}^{\infty} A_n \right) \left(\sum_{n=0}^{\infty} B_n \right) \qquad (4.8.2)$$

We will solve (4.8.2) for $k = 1$ in more detail than necessary to learn as much as possible about its behavior. To the nearest 1×10^{-10} the solution is $x = 1.1713285129$. (The last digit can be verified by writing $x = A + B$, where $A = 1$ and $B = 0.1713285129$. Then $e^{-A-B} = e^{-A}e^{-B}$ and

$$\sin(\tfrac{1}{2}A + \tfrac{1}{2}B) = \sin \tfrac{1}{2}A \cos \tfrac{1}{2}B + \cos \tfrac{1}{2}A \sin \tfrac{1}{2}B$$

and the right-hand side of (4.7.2) is given by

$$\tilde{x} = 1 + e^{-A}e^{-B}[\sin \tfrac{1}{2}A \cos \tfrac{1}{2}B + \cos \tfrac{1}{2}A \sin \tfrac{1}{2}B]$$

which yields $\tilde{x} = x$.)

First, let us examine the results of computation by the decomposition method before considering the detailed calculation. Our approximate solution is $\phi_n = \sum_{i=0}^{n-1} x_i$. The percentage error $\Psi_n = 100(x - \phi_n)/x$. (See Table 3.) Note that by ϕ_7, the error is less than 0.0004% and is less than 0.5% with ϕ_2 which required computing only the *single* term x_1. If we did not know the correct solution, we could stop the calculation as the results had clearly stabilized to the desired accuracy. If accuracy to 10^{-2} is sufficient we would stop at ϕ_3, which requires computing only x_1 and x_2, and verify the solution by substitution. The procedure is so easy, it is not much trouble to go further as desired. Now let us look at the calculation.

TABLE 3

n	x_n	ϕ_n	Ψ_n
0	1.000...	—	—
1	0.1763707992	1.000...	14.63%
2	−0.0026364803	1.1763707992	−0.43%
3	−0.0029245319	1.1737344319	−0.21%
4	0.0004979183	1.170809787	0.044%
5	0.0000511587	1.171307705	0.0018%
6	−0.0000345495	1.171358864	−0.00259%
7	—	1.171324315	0.00036%

We can see quickly how the computation is done for a few terms (which are usually quite sufficient) after which we will take a deeper look. Since $e^{-x} = \sum_{n=0}^{\infty} A_n$ and $\sin(x/2) = \sum_{n=0}^{\infty} B_n$ we calculate the A_n and B_n (see Chapter 3). A preferred notation henceforth for the A_n and B_n here would be $A_n(e^{-x})$ and $A_n(\sin \frac{1}{2}x)$ i.e., we always write $A_n(Ny)$

$$A_0 = e^{-x_0}$$
$$A_1 = e^{-x_0}(-x_1)$$
$$A_2 = e^{-x_0}(-x_2 + \tfrac{1}{2}x_1^2)$$
$$\vdots$$
$$B_0 = \sin \frac{x_0}{2}$$
$$B_1 = \frac{x_1}{2} \cos \frac{x_0}{2}$$
$$B_2 = \frac{x_2}{2} \cos \frac{x_0}{2} - \frac{x_1^2}{8} \sin \frac{x_0}{2}$$
$$\vdots$$

We have now $x = 1 + (A_0 + A_1 + \cdots)(B_0 + B_1 + \cdots) = 1 + A_0 B_0 + \cdots$, where we employ our simple rule that each x_i involves terms of lower index; thus $x_0 = 1$ and

$$x_1 = A_0 B_0$$
$$x_2 = A_0 B_1 + A_1 B_0$$
$$x_3 = A_1 B_1 + A_0 B_2 + A_2 B_0$$
$$\vdots$$
$$x_n = \sum_{i+j=n-1} A_i B_j$$

and using the above A_i and B_i.

$$x_1 = e^{-1} \sin \tfrac{1}{2} = 0.1763708$$
$$x_2 = -0.00263648$$
$$x_3 = -0.0029245319$$
$$x_4 = 0.0004979183$$
$$x_5 = 0.0000511587$$
$$x_6 = -0.0000345495$$

and ϕ_n, our approximation to n terms is given by $\phi_n = \sum_{i=0}^{n-1} x_i$. Here ϕ_1, of course, is 1.0, and ϕ_2 which required computing only x_1 is equal to 1.176

which is already a good approximation (under 0.5%). Increasing n yields better and better approximations ϕ_n. The correct solution satisfying the equation is $x = 1.713285129$. If we calculate $\Psi_n = [(x - \phi_n)/x](100)$ to determine percentage error, Ψ_2 is already less than 0.4%, Ψ_4 is less than 0.04%, and by Ψ_7 the error is less than 0.0004%. If the correct solution is not available for comparison, how do we know where to stop the computation?

By the time we get to ϕ_4 or ϕ_5 it is clear the solution has stabilized to a certain number of decimals and we need go on only if we require a more exact solution. We can also calculate the right-hand side with a given ϕ_n i.e., $1 + e^{-\phi_n} \sin(\phi_n/2)$ (call this $\tilde{\phi}_n$) and see how closely $\tilde{\phi}_n$ approaches ϕ_n, since ϕ_n is the approximation to x on the left-hand side. Thus, $\tilde{\phi}_2 - \phi_2 = -0.00525661$. We see that $\lim_{m \to \infty} \tilde{\phi}_m - \phi_m \to 0$.

Detailed Computation: From Chapter 3, we have seen that a nonlinear function $Ny = f(y) = \sum_{n=0}^{\infty} A_n = \sum_{n=0}^{\infty} C(v, n)h_n(y_0)$. In this problem the nonlinearity is $Nx = e^{-x} \sin(x/2)$ and we will consider it to be the product $N_1(x)N_2(x)$, where $N_1(x) = e^{-x}$ and $N_2(x) = \sin(x/2)$.

Evaluating the $N_1(x)$ term, we have

$$f(x) = e^{-x} \quad \text{and} \quad h_n(x_0) = (d^n/dx^n)f(x)|_{\lambda=0}$$

thus

$$h_n(x_0) = (-1)^n e^{-x_0} = (-1)^n e^{-1} = (-1)^n[0.3678794412].$$

Evaluating $N_2(x)$, $f(x) = \sin(x/2)$ we have (since $x_0 = 1$, $\sin \frac{1}{2} = 0.4794255386$, and $\cos \frac{1}{2} = 0.8775825619$)

$$h_0(x_0) = \sin(x_0/2) = 0.4794255386$$

$$h_1(x_0) = \tfrac{1}{2} \cos(x_0/2) = 0.4387912809$$

$$h_2(x_0) = -\tfrac{1}{4} \sin(x_0/2) = -0.1198563847$$

$$h_3(x_0) = -\tfrac{1}{8} \cos(x_0/2) = -0.1096978202$$

$$h_4(x_0) = \tfrac{1}{16} \sin(x_0/2) = 0.0299640962$$

$$h_5(x_0) = \tfrac{1}{32} \cos(x_0/2) = 0.0274244551$$

Since we see that the h_n are cyclic with a period of four terms, we can write for $n \geq 0$

$$h_{4n}(x_0) = (\tfrac{1}{2})^{4n} \sin(x_0/2)$$

$$h_{4n+1}(x_0) = (\tfrac{1}{2})^{4n+1} \cos(x_0/2)$$

$$h_{4n+2}(x_0) = (\tfrac{1}{2})^{4n+2}(-1) \sin(x_0/2)$$

$$h_{4n+3}(x_0) = (\tfrac{1}{2})^{4n+3}(-1) \cos(x_0/2)$$

Product nonlinearities are discussed again in Chapter 10 (Section 10.12). Composite nonlinearities are discussed in Section 10.14 with remarks on differential equations with composite nonlinear terms at the end of that section.

4.9. ANHARMONIC OSCILLATOR SYSTEMS

When fluctuations of dynamical variables occur in nonlinear oscillating systems, usual methods involve replacing the actual nonlinear system with a so-called "equivalent" linear system and averagings which are only valid within the limits of perturbation theory or the assumption of white noise processes for reasons of mathematical tractability. The anharmonic oscillator, the Duffing oscillator, the Van der Pol oscillator, and others can be dealt with more generally (see [5]).

The Duffing oscillator in a random force field modeled by $y'' + \alpha y' + \beta y + \gamma y^3 = x(t)$, can similarly be analyzed without limiting the force $x(t)$ to a white noise and allowing α, β, or γ to be stochastic as well. Still another application is the Van der Pol oscillator modeled by $y'' + \xi y^2 y' - \xi y' + y = x(t)$, which involves a product-type nonlinearity.

This section will deal with the anharmonic oscillator for the deterministic case to stress the point that the methods developed for nonlinear stochastic systems are valid in the linear or deterministic limiting cases as well and can be compared with known results there.

The anharmonic oscillator is described by

$$d^2\theta/dt^2 + k^2 \sin \theta = 0 \qquad (4.9.1)$$

with $k^2 = (g/l)$ for large-amplitude motion. Let $L = d^2/dt^2$ and $N(\theta) = k^2 \sin \theta$ and write

$$L\theta + N(\theta) = 0 \qquad (4.9.2)$$

a nonlinear deterministic homogeneous differential equation. Assume initial conditions $\theta(0) = \gamma = $ constant and $\theta'(0) = \omega = 0$. We can do it as well for $\gamma = 0$ and $\omega \neq 0$ or $\gamma \neq 0$ and $\omega \neq 0$. Since $x = 0$ and $\theta'(0) = 0$, we write immediately $\theta = \theta(0) - L^{-1}N(\theta)$. The $N(\theta)$ term becomes $\sum_{n=0}^{\infty} A_n$, where the A_n are obtainable by implicit differentiation. For $N(\theta) = \sin \theta$, the A_n have been given as

$$A_0 = \sin \theta_0$$
$$A_1 = \theta_1 \cos \theta_0$$
$$A_2 = -(\theta_1^2/2) \sin \theta_0 + \theta_2 \cos \theta_0 \qquad (4.9.3)$$
$$A_3 = -(\theta_1^3/6) \cos \theta_0 - \theta_1\theta_2 \sin \theta_0 + \theta_3 \cos \theta_0$$
$$\vdots$$

We have, therefore, the result $\theta = \gamma - L^{-1}[A_0 + A_1 + \cdots] = \theta_0 + \theta_1 + \theta_2 + \cdots$, where

$$\theta_0 = \gamma$$
$$\theta_1 = -L^{-1}A_0 \qquad\qquad (4.9.4)$$
$$\theta_2 = -L^{-1}A_1$$
$$\vdots$$

Since we know $L^{-1} = \int_0^t dt \int_0^t dt$,

$$\theta_1 = -\int dt \int dt \, k^2 \sin\theta_0$$

$$= -\int dt \int dt \, k^2 \sin\gamma$$

$$= -(\sin\gamma)\left(\frac{k^2 t^2}{2!}\right)$$

$$\theta_2 = -\int dt \int dt \, k^2(\theta_1 \cos\theta_0)$$

$$= -\int dt \int dt \, k^2\left[-\left(\frac{k^2 t^2}{2!}\right)\sin\gamma\right]\cos\gamma$$

$$= \left(\frac{k^4 t^4}{4!}\right)\sin\gamma\cos\gamma$$

$$\theta_3 = -\int dt \int dt \, k^2[-(\theta_1^2/2)\sin\theta_0 + \theta_2\cos\theta_0]$$

$$= -\int dt \int dt \, k^2(-\tfrac{1}{2})[-(k^2 t^2/2)\sin\gamma]^2 \sin\gamma$$

$$\qquad + \{(k^4 t^4/4!)\sin\gamma\cos\gamma\}\cos\gamma]$$

$$= -\int dt \int dt \, k^2[-(4!\sin^3\gamma)/8 + (\sin\gamma\cos^2\gamma)]\cdot[k^4 t^4/4!]$$

$$= -\int dt \int dt \, k^2[-3\sin^3\gamma + \sin\gamma\cos^2\gamma]\cdot[k^4 t^4/4!]$$

$$= -(k^6 t^6/6!)\cdot[\sin\gamma\cos^2\gamma - 3\sin^3\gamma]$$

$$\theta_4 = -L^{-1}A_3$$

$$= -\int dt \int dt\, k^2 [-(\theta_1^3/6)\cos\theta_0 - \theta_1\theta_2\sin\theta_0 + \theta_3\cos\theta_0]$$

$$= -\int dt \int dt\, k^2 [-(\tfrac{1}{6})\{-(\sin\gamma)(k^2t^2/2)\}^3\cos\gamma$$

$$-\{-(\sin\gamma)(k^2t^2/2)\}\cdot\{(k^4t^4/4!)\sin\gamma\cos\gamma\}\sin\gamma$$

$$+\{-(k^6t^6/6!)(\sin\gamma\cos^2\gamma - 3\sin^3\gamma)\}\cos\gamma]$$

$$= (k^8t^8/8!)(-33\sin^3\gamma\cos\gamma + \sin\gamma\cos^3\gamma)$$

$$\vdots$$

Thus,

$$\begin{aligned}
\theta(t) = \gamma &- [(kt)^2/2!]\sin\gamma + [(kt)^4/4!]\sin\gamma\cos\gamma \\
&- [(kt)^6/6!][\sin\gamma\cos^2\gamma - 3\sin^3\gamma] \\
&+ [(kt)^8/8!][-33\sin^3\gamma\cos\gamma + \sin\gamma\cos^3\gamma] \\
&- \cdots
\end{aligned} \tag{4.9.5}$$

As a check we can let γ be sufficiently small so that small amplitude motion is being considered. Then

$$\theta(t) = \gamma[1 - (k^2t^2/2!) + ((kt)^4/4!) - \cdots]$$

which is, of course, the result for the linear harmonic oscillator with the given initial condition.

Finally, we can take a few terms of the series for $\theta(t)$ and substitute back into the original differential equation (4.9.1). Let us try two terms of (4.9.5) thus,

$$\theta \simeq \gamma - [(kt)^2/2!]\sin\gamma.$$

Using the well-known identity for the sine of a sum of two angles,

$$\sin\theta \simeq \sin\gamma\cos[(k^2t^2/2)\sin\gamma] + \cos\gamma\sin[(k^2t^2/2)\sin\gamma]$$

and

$$d\theta/dt = d/dt(\gamma - (k^2t^2/2)\sin\gamma) = -k^2t\sin\gamma$$

Consequently,

$$d^2\theta/dt^2 = -k^2\sin\gamma$$

Substituting into (4.8.1)

$$\begin{aligned}
-k^2\sin\gamma &+ k^2\sin\gamma\{\cos[(k^2t^2/2)\sin\gamma]\} \\
&+ k^2\cos\gamma\{\sin[(k^2t^2/2)\sin\gamma]\} \simeq 0
\end{aligned}$$

For small γ we are approaching the harmonic oscillator case so an identity is to be expected. For the anharmonic case noticing the terms get smaller by virtue of the $n!$, consider small kt. Since the first of the two expressions enclosed in the curly brackets is nearly unity and the second is nearly zero, we can see even from only a two-term series that our solution will satisfy the original equation at least when kt is small.

4.10. LIMITING CASE: THE HARMONIC OSCILLATOR

Consider the equation $d^2\theta/dt^2 + k^2\theta = 0$ and assume the decomposition $\theta(t) = \sum_{n=0}^{\infty} \theta_n(t)$ with $\theta_0 = \theta(0) + t\theta'(0)$, where $\theta(0)$ and $\theta'(0)$ are the initial conditions. We take $L = d^2/dt^2$ and let $k^2 = R$. There is, of course, no $L^{-1}x$ term here since there is no forcing term $x(t)$.

Case 1: Suppose we choose initial conditions $\theta(0) = \gamma$ and $\theta'(0) = 0$. Then, $\theta = \theta(0) - L^{-1}R(\theta_0 + \theta_1 + \cdots)$. We get

$$\theta_1 = -L^{-1}R\theta_0 = -\int dt \int dt\, k^2\gamma = -\gamma k^2 t^2/2!,$$

$$\theta_2 = -L^{-1}R\theta_1 = -\int dt \int dt\, k^2[-\gamma k^2 t^2/2!] = \gamma k^4 t^4/4!,$$

$$\theta_3 = -L^{-1}R\theta_2 = -\int dt \int dt\, k^2[\gamma k^4 t^4/4!] = -\gamma k^6 t^6/6!, \text{ etc.,}$$

to

$$\theta_n = (-1)^{n-1}\gamma(kt)^{2n-2}/(2n-2)!.$$

Hence

$$\theta(t) = \gamma\{1 - [(kt)/2!] + [(kt)^4/4!] - [(kt)^6/6!] + \cdots\}$$

$$= \gamma \sum_{n=1}^{\infty} (-1)^{n-1}[(kt)^{2n-2}/(2n-2)!]$$

or $\theta(t) = \gamma \cos kt$.

Case 2: Consider the same problem with $\theta(0) = 0$ and $\theta'(0) = \omega$, where ω is the initial angular velocity. We now have $\theta_0 = t\theta'(0) = \omega$ and

$$\theta = \theta_0 - L^{-1}R(\theta_0 + \theta_1 + \cdots),$$

where

$$\theta_1 = -L^{-1}R\theta_0 = -\int dt \int dt\, k^2\omega kt/k = -(\omega/k)k^3 t^3/3!,$$

$$\theta_2 = -L^{-1}R\theta_1 = -\int dt \int dt\, k^2(-\omega/k)k^3 t^3/3! = (\omega/k)k^5 t^5/5!,$$

$$\theta_3 = -L^{-1}R\theta_2 = -\int dt \int dt\, k^2(\omega/k)k^5 t^5/5!$$

$$= -(\omega/k)k^7 t^7/7!, \text{ etc.,}$$

i.e.,

$$\theta_n = (-1)^{n-1}(\omega/k)(kt)^{2n-1}/(2n-1)!.$$

Thus,

$$\theta(t) = (\omega/k)[(kt) - (kt)^3/3! + (kt)^5/5! - \cdots]$$

$$= (\omega/k) \sum_{n=1}^{\infty} (-1)^{n-1}(kt)^{2n-1}/(2n-1)!$$

or

$$\theta(t) = (\omega/k) \sin kt.$$

Case 3:   Finally, let $\theta(0) = \gamma$ and $\theta'(0) = \omega$. Now

$$\theta_0 = \theta(0) + t\theta'(0) = \gamma + (\omega/k)kt$$

$$\theta_1 = -L^{-1}R\theta_0 = -L^{-1}R[\gamma + (\omega/k)kt]$$

$$= -L^{-1}R\gamma - L^{-1}R[(\omega/k)kt]$$

$$= -\int dt \int dt \, k^2\gamma - \int dt \int dt \, k^2(\omega/k)kt$$

$$= -\gamma(k^2t^2/2!) - (\omega/k)(k^3t^3/3!)$$

$$\vdots$$

Finally,

$$\theta_n = (-1)^{n-1}\gamma(kt)^{2n-2}/(2n-2)! + (\omega/k)(-1)^{n-1}(kt)^{2n-1}/(2n-1)!$$

or $\theta(t) = \gamma \cos kt + (\omega/k)\sin kt$, the general solution of the harmonic oscillator, which we find quickly and elegantly.

4.11.   EXTENSIONS TO STOCHASTIC OSCILLATORS

The extension to forced oscillators, randomly forced oscillators, and stochastic oscillating systems with nonlinear effects is now straightforward. The Duffing oscillator–an anharmonic oscillator with forcing function and damping term–is described by

$$\ddot{y} + \alpha\dot{y} + \beta y + \gamma y^3 = x(t)$$

where $x(t) = b \sin 2\pi\omega t$ and the Van der Pol oscillator is described by

$$\ddot{y} + \xi y^2 \dot{y} - \xi\dot{y} + y = x(t)$$

which involves a product-type nonlinearity. Since we can write $(d/dt)(y^3/3) = y^2\dot{y}$, we can write

$$\ddot{y} + \alpha\dot{y} + \beta y + \gamma(d/dt)y^3 = x(t)$$

where $\alpha = -\xi$, $\beta = 1$, and $\gamma = \xi/3$. Hence, both equations are written as

$$Ly + Ny = x(t)$$

where $L = d^2/dt^2 + \alpha d/dt + \beta$ and Ny is a simple polynomial nonlinearity γy^3 for the Duffing oscillator and a differential nonlinearity $\gamma(d/dt)y^3$ for the Van der Pol equation. For both cases our y_0 term is

$$y_0 = L^{-1}x + c_1\phi_1(t) + c_2\phi_2(t)$$

where the second and third terms are the homogeneous solution. We have for both oscillators

$$y = y_0 - L^{-1}Ny$$

For the Duffing equation

$$y = y_0 - L^{-1}\gamma y^3$$

$$\sum_{n=0}^{\infty} y_n = y_0 - L^{-1}\gamma \sum_{n=0}^{\infty} A_n(y^3)$$

and for the Van der Pol equation

$$\sum_{n=0}^{\infty} y_n = y_0 - L^{-1}\gamma \frac{d}{dt} \sum_{n=0}^{\infty} A_n(y^3)$$

where the A_n have previously been computed in this chapter (and in Chapter 3).

We can, as previously suggested, get a simpler Green's function by using $L = d^2/dt^2$ and writing the rest of the linear operator as R and taking it to the right. This makes y_0 and the computations simpler, but convergence is less rapid. Much work can be done here in evaluating optimum procedures. We remark also that we have treated these two examples as deterministic but clearly our procedures allow stochastic process coefficients $\alpha(t, \omega)$, $\beta(t, \omega)$, $\gamma(t, \omega)$, a stochastic input process $x(t, \omega)$, and random initial or boundary conditions.

4.12.   ASYMPTOTIC SOLUTIONS

We now consider an interesting variation of the decomposition method suggested by the intuitive idea that if $x(t)$ is a polynomial, we would expect to get a terminating series when Ly is on the right-hand side of the equation. We will still use the basic decomposition of y into $\sum_{n=0}^{\infty} y_n$ (or possibly $\sum_{n=0}^{\infty} \lambda^n y_n$) and the $Ny = \sum_{n=0}^{\infty} A_n$ as before but rather than solve for Ly as before, we solve now for Ny. Suppose, for example, we have $Ly + Ny = x(t)$ with $x(t) = t^2$, $L = d/dt$, $Ny = y^2$. We then write

$$y^2 = x(t) - (d/dt)y$$

$$\sum_{n=0}^{\infty} A_n = x(t) - \frac{d}{dt} \sum_{n=0}^{\infty} y_n$$

$$A_0 = y_0^2 = x(t)$$

consequently $y_0 = \sqrt{x(t)} = t$ and

$$A_1 = 2y_0 y_1 = -(d/dt)t = -1$$
$$y_1 = -1/2t$$
$$y_2 = 0$$

or $y = t - 1/2t$. For large t, y behaves as t. It is interesting to note that rather than integrations we now have differentiations which can lead to rapidly terminating series if $x(t)$ is a polynomial. Consider the equation

$$y' + y = 2t + t^2$$

Here $L = d/dt$ and Ny is simply y. We solve for the Ny or, in this case, y term

$$y = (2t + t^2) - \frac{d}{dt} \sum_{n=0}^{\infty} y_n$$

We now have $y_0 = x(t) = 2t + t^2$ and

$$y_1 = -Ly_0 = -2 - 2t$$
$$y_2 = -Ly_1 = 2$$
$$y_{n \geq 3} = 0$$

or $y = t^2$, the correct solution (also obtainable by decomposition).

EXAMPLE: Consider the equation $y' + y^2 = t^2 + (t^6/9)$ or $Ly = t^2 + (t^6/9) - y^2$ first using decomposition. Supposing $y(0) = 0$ we get

$$y = L^{-1}t^2 + \frac{L^{-1}t^6}{9} - L^{-1}\sum A_n$$

$$y_0 = \frac{t^3}{3} + \frac{t^7}{63}$$

$$y_1 = -L^{-1}A_0 = -L^{-1}y_0^2 = \frac{-t^7}{63} + \cdots$$

$$\vdots$$

hence, $y = y_0 + y_1 + \cdots = t^3/3$. Calculation of a few more terms and/or substitution will verify that the solution is $y = t^3/3$.

By the asymptotic decomposition procedure now, we write $y^2 = t^2 + (t^6/9) - (d/dt)y$ or

$$\sum_{n=0}^{\infty} A_n = t^2 + \frac{t^6}{9} - \left(\frac{d}{dt}\right) \sum_{n=0}^{\infty} y_n$$

$$A_0 = y_0^2 = t^2 + \frac{t^6}{9}$$

$$y_0 = \left(t^2 + \frac{t^6}{9}\right)^{1/2}$$

$$\simeq \frac{t^3}{3} \qquad \text{for large } t$$

with following terms vanishing for large t.

EXAMPLE: Consider $Ly + Ny = x(t)$ with $x(t) = t$, $Ny = y^2$, and $L = d/dt$. Thus, the equation is $y' + y^2 = t$. By asymptotic decomposition, write $y^2 = t - (d/dt)y$ or

$$\sum_{n=0}^{\infty} A_n = t - \left(\frac{d}{dt}\right) \sum_{n=0}^{\infty} y_n$$

$$A_0 = t$$

$$A_1 = -\left(\frac{d}{dt}\right)y_0$$

$$A_2 = -\left(\frac{d}{dt}\right)y_1$$

$$\vdots$$

Since $A_0 = y_0^2$, we have $y_0 = \sqrt{t}$. Since $A_1 = 2y_0y_1$, we have $y_1 = -1/4t$. Since $A_2 = y_1^2 + 2y_0y_2 = \frac{1}{4}t^{-2}$, $y_2 = \frac{3}{16}t^2$, etc.; hence,

$$y = \sqrt{t} - \frac{1}{4t} + \frac{3}{16t^2} + \cdots$$

For large t, y behaves as $\sqrt{t}$.

EXAMPLE: Consider the equation $y' + y = x(t)$ with $y(0) = 1$ for $x(t)$ having the values 0, 1, and t both by decomposition and by asymptotic decomposition. By decomposition, we write $y = y(0) + L^{-1}x - L^{-1}y$ or

$$\sum_{n=0}^{\infty} y_n = y_0 - L^{-1} \sum_{n=0}^{\infty} y_n$$

where $y_0 = 1 + L^{-1}x(t)$.

By asymptotic decomposition, we write $y = x(t) - (d/dt)y$ or

$$\sum_{n=0}^{\infty} y_n = x(t) - \left(\frac{d}{dt}\right) \sum_{n=0}^{\infty} y_n$$

with $y_0 = x(t)$.

(a)   Suppose $x(t)$ is zero. Decomposition yields

$$y_0 = y(0) = 1$$
$$y_1 = -L^{-1}[1] = -t$$
$$y_2 = -L^{-1}[-t] = t^2/2$$
$$y_3 = -L^{-1}[t^2/2] = -t^3/3!$$
$$\vdots$$
$$y = 1 - t + t^2/2 - t^3/3! + \cdots = e^{-t}$$

Asymptotic decomposition simply gives zero, i.e., the asymptotic value of e^{-t} as $t \to \infty$.

(b)   Suppose $x(t) = 1$. Decomposition gives us $y_0 = 1 + t$, $y_1 = -L^{-1}[1 + t] = -t - (t^2/2)$, and $y_2 = L^{-1}[t + (t^2/2)] = t^2/2 + t^3/3!$; we soon see all terms after the 1 vanish. Consequently, the solution is $y = 1$. Asymptotic decomposition gives us $y = 1 - (d/dt) \sum_{n=0}^{\infty} y_n$ or $y_0 = 1$, and all other terms are zero, thus the solution is again $y = 1$.

(c)   Suppose $x(t) = t$. Decomposition leads to

$$y_0 = 1 + (t^2/2!)$$
$$y_1 = -t - (t^3/3!)$$
$$y_2 = (t^2/2!) + (t^4/4!)$$
$$y_3 = -(t^3/3!) - (t^5/5!)$$
$$\vdots$$
$$y = 1 - t + t^2 - 2t^3/3! + \cdots$$

Asymptotic decomposition leads to $y = t - (d/dt) \sum_{n=0}^{\infty} y_n$ or

$$y_0 = t$$
$$y_1 = -1$$
$$y_2 = 0$$
$$y_{n \geq 2} = 0$$

or

$$y = t - 1$$

For small t, of course, y is close to the initial condition. For large t, y behaves like t.

EXERCISES

1. Use asymptotic decomposition to show the solution of $y' + y = \alpha + \beta t$ is given exactly by $y = (\alpha - \beta) + \beta t$.

2. Use asymptotic decomposition to show the solution of $y' + y = \alpha + \beta t + \gamma t^2/2$ is given by $y = (\alpha - \beta + \gamma) + (\beta - \gamma)t + \gamma t^2/2$.

3. Use decomposition to show the solution of $y' + 2y = 0$ with $y(0) = 1$ is $y = e^{-2t}$ and then show by asymptotic decomposition that the value of y as $t \to 0$ is zero.

4. By decomposition show that the first two terms of the solution of $y' + y^2 = t^2 + 1$ with $y(0) = 0$ are given by $y_0 = t + (t^3/3)$ and $y_1 = -[(t^3/3) + (2t^5/15) + (t^7/63)]$. By asymptotic decomposition show that y behaves like $(t^2 + 1)^{1/2}$ or approximately t for $t^2 \gg 1$.

5. Show that $y' = xy$ with $y(0) = 1$ has the solution $y = e^{(1/2)x^2}$.

6. Use asymptotic decomposition for the equation $y' + y = x(t)$ with $x(t) = \sum_{n=0}^{m} \alpha_n t^n/n!$ to show that $y(t) = \sum_{n=0}^{m} (-1)^n \sum_{\mu=n}^{m} \alpha_\mu t^{\mu-n}/(\mu - n)!$.

EXAMPLE: Consider the nonlinear equation

$$\frac{d^2y}{dt^2} - y^2 = e^{-t} - e^{-2t}, \qquad y(0) = 1, \qquad y'(0) = -1$$

In our standard form this is $Ly + Ny = x(t)$ with $L = d^2/dt^2$, $Ny = -y^2$, and $x(t) = e^{-t} - e^{-2t}$. It is not necessary, of course, but we will approximate the exponentials with the first three terms of their expansions. Hence,

$$y'' - y^2 = 1 - t + (t^2/2) - 1 + 2t - 2t^2$$

or $x(t) = t - \frac{3}{2}t^2$. Then $L^{-1}x = (t^3/6) - (t^4/8)$. The y_0 term is, therefore,

$$y_0 = y(0) + ty'(0) + L^{-1}x$$
$$= 1 - t + (t^3/6) - t^4/8$$

$$y_1 = L^{-1}A_0 = L^{-1}y_0^2$$
$$= t^2/2 - t^3/6 + t^4/12$$

$$y = 1 - t + t^2/2 - t^3/6 - t^4/24 + \cdots$$

$$y = e^{-t}$$

If we use the asymptotic method we have $\sum_{n=0}^{\infty} A_n = (d^2/dt^2) \sum_{n=0}^{\infty} y_n$ and since there is no $x(t)$ term, $A_0 = 0$ hence $y_0 = 0$ and all $y_{n \geq 0}$ are zero, i.e., $y = 0$ is the limiting value for large t.

EXAMPLE: $d^2y/dt^2 - y(t) = 0$ with $y(0) = 1$ and $y'(0) = -1$. Then $Ly = y$ and

$$y_0 = y(0) + ty'(0) = 1 - t$$

since $x(t)$ is zero. Then

$$y_1 = L^{-1}y_0 = L^{-1}[1 - t] = t^2/2! - t^3/3!$$
$$y_2 = L^{-1}y_1 = t^4/4! - t^5/5!$$
$$\vdots$$
$$y = 1 - t + t^2/2! - t^3/3! + \cdots = e^{-t}$$

Asymptotic decomposition gives the limiting value as $t \to \infty$ or zero.

EXAMPLE: $y' - 10y = 0$ with $y(0) = 1$ or $Ly = 10y$. Then $y = 1 +$ $10L^{-1}\sum_{n=0}^{\infty} y_n$ yields $y = 1 + 10x + \cdots$. This problem is interesting because the exact solution is $y = 1/(1 - 10x)$, which has a vertical asymptote at $x = 0.1$. Decomposition gives us the solution for $x < 0.1$ (as we can see from ratio test). Asymptotic decomposition tells us $y \to 0$ as $x \to \infty$ so we see something of the behavior on the other side of the singularity.

EXERCISE

Show that the solution of $y' + 2y = 0$ with $y(0) = 1$ is $y = 1 - 2t + 2t^2 - \cdots = e^{-2t}$ and verify the asymptotic limit.

EXAMPLE: Consider the linear equation $y' + y = x(t)$ for $x(t) = t^2 + \alpha t + \beta$. Decomposition yields

$$Ly = t^2 + \alpha t + \beta - \sum_{n=0}^{\infty} y_n$$

$$y = y(0) + L^{-1}[t^2 + \alpha t + \beta] - L^{-1}\sum_{n=0}^{\infty} y_n.$$

Suppose $y(0) = \beta - \alpha + 2$. Now

$$y_0 = \beta - \alpha + 2 + t^3/3 + \alpha t^2/2 + \beta t$$
$$y_1 = -L^{-1}y_0 = -\beta t + \alpha t - 2t - t^4/12 - xt^3/6 - \beta t^2/2$$
$$y_2 = -L^{-1}y_1 = \beta t^2/2 - \alpha t^2/2 + t^2 + t^5/60 + \alpha t^4/24 + \beta t^3/6$$
$$\vdots$$
$$y = (\beta - \alpha + 2) - 2t + (1 + \alpha/2)t^2 - \cdots$$

If $\alpha = 0$ and $\beta = -2$, for example, then

$$y = t^2 - 2t$$

with other terms cancelling. By the asymptotic decomposition

$$y = x(t) - \left(\frac{d}{dt}\right) \sum_{n=0}^{\infty} y_n$$

$$y_0 = t^2 + \alpha t + \beta$$

$$y_1 = -\left(\frac{d}{dt}\right)(t^2 + \alpha t + \beta) = -2t - \alpha$$

$$y_2 = \left(\frac{d}{dt}\right)(2t + \alpha) = 2$$

$$y_3 = 0$$

$$\vdots$$

$$y = t^2 + (\alpha - 2)t + (\beta - \alpha + 2)$$

(a terminating series). For the same α and β as above

$$y = t^2 - 2t$$

Summarizing the two procedures, we have by decomposition

$$y = y_0 - L^{-1} \sum_{n=0}^{\infty} A_n \tag{4.11.1}$$

where $y_0 = L^{-1}x$ plus any initial condition terms $y(0) + ty'(0) + \cdots$ and by asymptotic decomposition

$$\sum_{n=0}^{\infty} A_n = x(t) - L \sum_{n=0}^{\infty} y_n \tag{4.11.2}$$

Thus (4.11.1) integrates the decomposition components and (4.11.2) differentiates the components of the asymptotic decomposition. (If we substitute $\sum_{n=0}^{\infty} y_n = y$ from (4.11.1) into (4.11.2) we get an identity.)

If we consider the equation $dy/dt + f(y) = x(t)$ we have $Ly = x(t) - f(y)$ or $y(t) = L^{-1}x(t) - L^{-1}f(y)$ or $f(y) = x(t) - (d/dt)y$. The first decomposition component $y_0 = L^{-1}x(t) = \int_0^t x(t) \, dt$. The first asymptotic decomposition component is $A_0 = x(t)$.

Thus, in solving a differential equation by either method we use the decomposition of y into $\sum_{n=0}^{\infty} y_n$ and use the $\sum_{n=0}^{\infty} A_n$ polynomials for a nonlinear term Ny. Decomposition requires integrations; asymptotic decomposition requires only differentiations. The latter procedure, however, requires more study as we shall discuss later in this chapter.

Since ordinarily we are solving for the appropriate A_n, when the Ny becomes y (i.e., in the linear limit) we simply solve for the y_n. Consider $Ly + Ny = x$ with $L = d/dt$ and $x(t) = at^2 + bt + c$. Then

$$\frac{d}{dt} y + Ny = at^2 + bt + c$$

$$Ny = at^2 + bt + c - \frac{d}{dt} y$$

$$\sum_{n=0}^{\infty} A_n = at^2 + bt + c - \frac{d}{dt} \sum_{n=0}^{\infty} y_n$$

Ordinarily then $A_0 = x(t)$. If Ny is y, we have

$$\sum_{n=0}^{\infty} y_n = at^2 + bt + c - \frac{d}{dt} \sum_{n=0}^{\infty} y_n$$

$$y_0 = x(t) = at^2 + bt + c$$

$$y_1 = -\frac{d}{dt} y_0 = -(2at + b)$$

$$y_2 = 2a$$

and $y_n = 0$ for $n \geq 3$, so we have a terminating series. Now

$$y = at^2 + bt + c - 2at - b + 2a$$

$$y = at^2 + (b - 2a)t + (c - b + 2a) = \alpha t^2 + \beta t + \gamma$$

which is the correct solution.

QUESTION: Why does asymptotic decomposition result in a solution for large t?

Consider an equation first which is linear in the general form $Ly + y = x(t)$. In decomposition we would write $Ly = x(t) - y$ and operate on both sides with L^{-1}, the definite integral operator, to get

$$y(t) = y_h + L^{-1}x(t) - L^{-1}y(t)$$

where y_h is the homogeneous solution for $Ly = 0$. We then write

$$\sum_{n=0}^{\infty} y_n = y_h + L^{-1}x - L^{-1} \sum_{n=0}^{\infty} y_n$$

with $y_0 = y_h + L^{-1}x$ and $y_n = -L^{-1}y_{n-1}$ for $n \geq 1$. If, for example, L is second order and $x(t) = t^3$, then $y_0 = y(0) + ty'(0) + t^4/4$ or $c_1 + c_2 t + t^4/4$, and the following terms are increasing powers of t.

If the equation is nonlinear in the form $Ly + Ny = x$ we have

$$\sum_{n=0}^{\infty} y_n = y_h + L^{-1}x - L^{-1}\sum_{n=0}^{\infty} A_n$$

using the A_n polynomials. In the linear case the A_n are simply the y_n and we have the previous result.

In the asymptotic decomposition with the linear case, $Ly + y = x(t)$ is written as

$$y(t) = x(t) - Ly(t)$$

$$\sum_{n=0}^{\infty} y_n = x(t) - L\sum_{n=0}^{\infty} y_n$$

with $y_0 = x(t)$ and $y_n = -Ly_{n-1}$ so the series starts with $x(t)$ and the following terms are differentiated by the differential operator L. Suppose $x(t) = t^3$ then $y_0 = t^3$, $y_1 = -3t^2$, $y_2 = -6t$, $y_3 = -6$ or $y = t^3 - 3t^2 - 6t - 6$ or decreasing powers of t in contrast to the corresponding linear case above.

For a nonlinear case, asymptotic decomposition leads to $Ny = x(t) - Ly$ or

$$\sum_{n=0}^{\infty} A_n = x(t) - Ly.$$

Now $A_0 = x(t)$. If $Ny = y^2$, for example, $y_0^2 = x(t)$ so $y_0 = x(t)^{1/2}$. For $x(t) = t^3$, $y_0 = t^{3/2}$. Then since A_1 for y^2 is $2y_0y_1$ we have $2y_0y_1 = -Ly_0 = \frac{3}{2}t^{1/2}$ so $y_1 = \frac{3}{2}t^{1/2}/2t^{3/2} = 3/4t$, etc., with powers of t rising in the denominator for following terms.

In decomposition we start with initial conditions and do integrations. In asymptotic decomposition we start with $x(t)$ and get terms of decreasing powers. If the solution is a polynomial or series in t, then Ly decreases the powers while Ny increases them. Thus, Ny dominates. In the solution for large t, the effect of initial conditions vanishes.

EXAMPLE: Consider the equation $y' + y^2 = t^2 + 1$ with $y(0) = 0$. In our standard form $Ly + Ny = x(t)$ we have $x(t) = t^2 + 1$, $L = d/dt$, and $Ny = y^2$. Write $y = L^{-1}x - L^{-1}\sum_{n=0}^{\infty} A_n$ then,

$$y_0 = L^{-1}x = \int_0^t (\tau^2 + 1)\,d\tau = t + \frac{t^3}{3}$$

$$y_1 = -L^{-1}A_0 = -\int_0^t y_0^2(\tau)\,d\tau = -\frac{t^3}{3} - \frac{2t^5}{15} - \frac{t^7}{63}$$

$$y_2 = -L^{-1}A_1 = \cdots$$

We see the term by term cancellations taking place and try $y = t$ as the solution which is immediately verifiable. If it were less obvious, we would simply calculate a few terms $\phi_n = \sum_{i=0}^{n-1} y_i$ and check whether it satisfies the equation. For an n-term approximation ϕ_n we have

$$L\phi_n + \sum_{i=0}^{n-1} A_i = x(t)$$

i.e., if we use only a two-term approximation ϕ_2, we must use only y_0 not $y_0 + y_1$ in the y' term. In approximating the derivative term up to y_1, the $\sum_{n=0}^{\infty} A_n$ can include only A_0 since y_1 depends on y_0. Now

$$\phi_2 = \left(t + \frac{t^3}{3}\right) - \left(\frac{t^3}{3} + 2\frac{t^5}{15} + \frac{t^7}{63}\right)$$

$$y' = t^2 + 1 - \frac{t^6}{9} - \frac{2t^4}{3} - t^2$$

$$y' + y^2 = 1 - \frac{t^6}{9} - \frac{2t^4}{3} + \left(\frac{t^3}{3} + t\right)^2$$

$$= t^2 + 1$$

thus verifying the solution.

Expanding the nonlinear terms farther in the A_n, we see that they approach zero for "high" n so we get accurate solutions and as we will see, generally, only a few terms are sufficient for most purposes and we can go farther with little effort.

Let us now reconsider this problem using our inverse or asymptotic decomposition. We write $y^2 = t^2 + 1 - y'$ or

$$\sum_{n=0}^{\infty} A_n = (t^2 + 1) - \frac{d}{dt}\sum_{n=0}^{\infty} y_n$$

$$A_0 = y_0^2 = t^2 + 1$$

$$y_0 = (t^2 + 1)^{1/2}$$

$$A_1 = 2y_0 y_1 = -\frac{d}{dt}(t^2 + 1)^{1/2} = -\frac{1}{2} \cdot 2t \cdot (t^2 + 1)^{-1/2}$$

$$y_1 = -\frac{t}{2(t^2 + 1)}$$

$$A_2 = y_1^2 + 2y_0 y_2 = \frac{d}{dt}\frac{t}{2(t^2 + 1)}$$

$$2y_0 y_2 = \frac{d}{dt} \frac{t}{2(t^2 + 1)} - \frac{t^2}{4(t^2 + 1)^2}$$

$$y_2 = \frac{2 - 3t^2}{8(t^2 + 1)^{5/2}}$$

$$\vdots$$

$$y = (t^2 + 1)^{1/2} - \frac{t}{2(t^2 + 1)} + \frac{2 - 3t^2}{8(t^2 + 1)^{5/2}} - \cdots$$

$$\approx (t^2 + 1)^{1/2} \simeq t \qquad \text{for large } t$$

Actually we needed only $A_0 = t^2 + 1$ so the behavior was immediately clear as soon as the A_0 for the particular Ny was written. [If $x(t)$ were t^3 and $Ny = y^3$, then $y = t$ as $t \to \infty$.] Since the solution behaves like t for large t and small t, it is reasonable to assume that the other terms of ϕ_n will all vanish and the solution will be t.

EXERCISE

Compute ϕ_3, ϕ_4, ϕ_5 and verify the above if true and explain if not.

Now for the second-order nonlinear differential equation

$$\frac{d^2\omega}{dt^2} + e^\omega = t^2 + \alpha t + \beta$$

by asymptotic decomposition, we write

$$e^\omega = (t^2 + \alpha t + \beta) - d^2\omega/dt^2$$

Replace e^ω by $\sum_{n=0}^\infty A_n$, where the A_n are evaluated for the nonlinearity $N\omega = e^\omega$ and replace ω by $\sum_{n=0}^\infty \omega_n$. The A_n's are given by

$$A_0 = e^{\omega_0}$$

$$A_1 = \omega_1 e^{\omega_0}$$

$$A_2 = (\omega_2 + \tfrac{1}{2}\omega_1^2)e^{\omega_0}$$

$$A_3 = (\omega_3 + \omega_1\omega_2 + \tfrac{1}{6}\omega_1^3)e^{\omega_0}$$

$$A_4 = (\omega_4 + \tfrac{1}{2}\omega_2^2 + \omega_1\omega_3 + \tfrac{1}{2}\omega_1^2\omega_2 + \tfrac{1}{24}\omega_1^4)e^{\omega_0}$$

$$A_5 = (\omega_5 + \omega_2\omega_3 + \omega_1\omega_4 + \tfrac{1}{2}\omega_1\omega_2^2$$
$$\qquad + \tfrac{1}{2}\omega_1^2\omega_3 + \tfrac{1}{6}\omega_1^3\omega_2 + \tfrac{1}{120}\omega_1^5)e^{\omega_0}$$

$$\vdots$$

Now

$$\sum_{n=0}^\infty A_n = (t^2 + \alpha t + \beta) - \frac{d^2}{dt^2} \sum_{n=0}^\infty \omega_n$$

yields

$$A_0 = e^{\omega_0} = t^2 + \alpha t + \beta$$

$$\omega_0 = \ln(t^2 + \alpha t + \beta)$$

$$A_1 = \omega_1 e^{\omega_0} = -\frac{d^2}{dt^2}\omega_0$$

$$= \frac{2t + \alpha}{(t^2 + \alpha t + \beta)^2} - \frac{2}{t^2 + \alpha t + \beta}$$

$$\omega_1 = \frac{2t + \alpha}{(t^2 + \alpha t + \beta)^3} - \frac{2(t^2 + \alpha t + \beta)}{(t^2 + \alpha t + \beta)^3}$$

$$= -\frac{[2t + 2(\alpha - 1)t + (2\beta - \alpha)]}{(t^2 + \alpha t + \beta)^3}$$

$$A_2 = (\omega_2 + \tfrac{1}{2}\omega_1^2)e^{\omega_0} = -\frac{d^2}{dt^2}\omega_1$$

$$= \frac{d^2}{dt^2}\left[\frac{2}{(t^2 + \alpha t + \beta)^2} - \frac{(2t + \alpha)}{(t^2 + \alpha t + \beta)^3}\right]$$

$$= \frac{-12(2t + \alpha)}{(t^2 + \alpha t + \beta)^5} + \frac{12}{(t^2 + \alpha t + \beta)^4} - \frac{2}{(t^2 + \alpha t + \beta)^3}$$

$$\omega_2 + \tfrac{1}{2}\omega_1^2 = \frac{-12(2t + \alpha)}{(t^2 + \alpha t + \beta)^6} + \frac{12}{(t^2 + \alpha t + \beta)^5} - \frac{2}{(t^2 + \alpha t + \beta)^4}$$

$$\omega_2 = \frac{-12(2t + \alpha)}{(t^2 + \alpha t + \beta)^6} + \frac{12}{(t^2 + \alpha t + \beta)^5} - \frac{2}{(t^2 + \alpha t + \beta)^4}$$

$$-\frac{1}{2}\left[\frac{2t + \alpha}{(t^2 + \alpha t + \beta)^3} - \frac{2}{(t^2 + \alpha t + \beta)^2}\right]^2$$

$$\vdots$$

$$\omega = \omega_0 + \omega_1 + \omega_2 + \cdots$$

Using decomposition, we have $L\omega + e^{\omega} = t^2 + \alpha t + \beta$ and $L\omega = (t^2 + \alpha t + \beta) - \sum_{n=0}^{\infty} A_n$ and finally

$$\sum_{n=0}^{\infty} \omega_n = \omega(0) + t\omega'(0) + L^{-1}(t^2 + \alpha t + \beta) - L^{-1}\sum_{n=0}^{\infty} A_n$$

Then

$$\omega_0 = \omega(0) + t\omega'(0) + L^{-1}(t^2 + \alpha t + \beta)$$

$$\omega_1 = -L^{-1}A_0$$

$$\omega_2 = -L^{-1}A_1$$

$$\vdots$$

Given the initial conditions, ω is determined.

EXAMPLE: Consider $dy/dt + ay = b$ with the normal (forward) decomposition and the inverse or asymptotic decomposition with $y(0) = 0$. We have $Ly + ay = b$, where $L = d/dt$ and L^{-1} is the definite integral from zero to t. Thus, $Ly = b - ay$ yields

$$y = y(0) + L^{-1}b - aL^{-1}\sum_{n=0}^{\infty} y_n$$

$$y_0 = L^{-1}b = bt$$

$$y_1 = -aL^{-1}y_0 = -\frac{abt^2}{2}$$

$$y_2 = -aL^{-1}y_1 = \frac{a^2bt^3}{3!}$$

$$\vdots$$

$$y = bt - \frac{abt^2}{2} + \frac{a^2bt^3}{6} - \cdots$$

$$y = \frac{b}{a}(1 - e^{-at})$$

which is easily verified. With asymptotic decomposition we have $ay = b - (d/dt)y$ or

$$y = \frac{b}{a} - \left(\frac{d}{dt}\right)\sum_{n=0}^{\infty} y_n$$

$$y_0 = \frac{b}{a}$$

$$y_{n\geq 1} = 0$$

Thus $y = b/a$ is the limit as $t \to \infty$ of the solution $y = (b/a)(1 - e^{-at})$ as is immediately verified.

Note that in the initial-value problem $Lu = 0$ when L is any second-order (linear deterministic differential) operator, we have

$$u = c_1\phi_1(t) + c_2\phi_2(t)$$

and if we specify $u(0) = b_1$, $u'(0) = b_2$ then

$$c_1\phi_1(0) + c_2\phi_2(0) = b_1$$
$$c_1\phi_1'(0) + c_2\phi_2'(0) = b_2$$

or

$$\begin{pmatrix} \phi_1(0) & \phi_2(0) \\ \phi_1'(0) & \phi_2'(0) \end{pmatrix} \cdot \begin{pmatrix} c_1 \\ c_2 \end{pmatrix} = \begin{pmatrix} b_1 \\ b_2 \end{pmatrix}$$

i.e., the product of the Wronskian matrix and the column vector of the c_1, c_2 is the column vector of the b_1, b_2.

$$\begin{pmatrix} c_1 \\ c_2 \end{pmatrix} = \begin{pmatrix} \phi_1(0) & \phi_2(0) \\ \phi_1'(0) & \phi_2'(0) \end{pmatrix}^{-1} \cdot \begin{pmatrix} b_1 \\ b_2 \end{pmatrix}$$

or

$$\begin{pmatrix} c_1 \\ c_2 \end{pmatrix} = \begin{pmatrix} \phi_2'(0)/W & -\phi_2(0)/W \\ -\phi_1'(0)/W & \phi_1(0)/W \end{pmatrix} \cdot \begin{pmatrix} b_1 \\ b_2 \end{pmatrix}$$

where W is the determinant of the Wronskian.

Why the Initial Condition Does Not Matter: Consider the standard solution by integrating the factor of the first-order equation

$$y' + P(x)y = Q(x)$$

$$y = e^{-\int P\,dx}\left[\int Q e^{\int P\,dx}\,dx + C\right] \tag{4.11.3}$$

Thus, two integrations are required here and the solution can be found if the integrations can be carried out. (In the decomposition method, we need only the integration denoted by L^{-1}.)

If P is a polynomial $P(x) = a_0 x^n + a_1 x^{n-1} + \cdots + a_n$ then $\int P\,dx = a_0 x^{n+1}/n+1 + \cdots$ and $a_0 > 0$ then as $x \to \infty$, whether n is even or odd,

$$\lim_{n \to +\infty} P(x) = +\infty, \qquad \lim_{n \to +\infty} \int P\,dx = +\infty$$

Consequently the last term of (4.11.3) vanishes, i.e.,

$$C/e^{\int P\,dx} \to 0$$

in the limit. Thus, if the leading coefficient of $P(x)$ is positive, the initial condition is of no importance as $x \to \infty$.

Now consider the nonlinear (Bernoulli equation) case

$$y' + P(x)y = Q(x)y^n$$

Multiply by y^{-n}

$$y^{-n}y' + Py^{1-n} = Q$$

Let $z = y^{1-n}$, then

$$dz/dx = (1 - n)y^{-n}\, dy/dx \quad \text{and} \quad y^{-n}\, dy/dx = 1/(1 - n)\, dz/dx.$$

Then

$$(dz/dx) + (1 - n)Pz = (1 - n)Q$$

and we define $\mathscr{P} = (1 - n)P$ and $\mathscr{Q} = (1 - n)Q$ to get

$$(dz/dx) + \mathscr{P}z = \mathscr{Q}$$

If a_0 is the leading coefficient in P, we now have

$$(1 - n)a_0 > 0$$

hence, if $a_0 > 0$, $n < 1$ and if $a_0 < 0$ then $n > 1$ are the conditions for which asymptotic decomposition works, and the initial condition disappears.

EXAMPLE: Consider $dy/dt + y = t + \alpha$. (It is interesting to note we have complete solution by either decomposition or asymptotic decomposition.) By asymptotic decomposition,

$$y = t + \alpha - \frac{dy}{dt}$$

$$\sum_{n=0}^{\infty} y_n = (t + \alpha) - \left(\frac{d}{dt}\right) \sum_{n=0}^{\infty} y_n$$

$$y_0 = t + \alpha$$

$$y_1 = -1$$

$$y_{n \geq 2} = 0$$

hence,

$$y = t + \alpha - 1$$

and we note $y(0) = \alpha - 1$.

By decomposition, if given $y(0) = \alpha - 1$ then

$Ly = (t + \alpha) - y$

$y = y(0) + L^{-1}(t + \alpha) - L^{-1}y$

$y_0 = (\alpha - 1) + \alpha t + (t^2/2)$

$y_1 = -(\alpha - 1)t - (\alpha t^2/2) - (t^3/3)$

$\vdots$

$y_n = (-1)^n\{[(\alpha - 1)t^n/n!] + [\alpha t^{n+1}/(n + 1)!] + [t^{n+2}/(n + 2)!] + \cdots\}$

$y = \sum_{n=0}^{\infty} y_n = t + \alpha - 1$

where the other terms in the series vanish. In this case, the asymptotic solution is faster—not requiring the verification of disappearance of the "noise" terms.

4.13.   THE QUESTION OF STABILITY

For nonlinear systems, a change of initial conditions can cause instability which presents us with a further research question since, in the asymptotic decomposition, A_0 depends only on $x(t)$. We speculate that we must transform $y(t)$ so that the resulting forcing function $X(t)$ will contain the initial conditions, yielding possible insight into system stability.

For example, let $L = d^2/dt^2$, $Ny = y^2$, $y(0) = k_1$, $y(0) = k_2$, and let $y = Y + ty(0) + y(0)$. Then $Ny = x(t) - Ly$ becomes $NY = X - LY - \alpha Y$ with $\alpha = 2[k_1 + k_2 t]$ and $X = x(t) - [k_2^2 t^2 + 2k_1 k_2 t + k_1^2]$. Then $A_0 + Y_0^2 = X(t)$ would yield the first term of the series, and we would proceed as before.

We then have $Y_0 = X^{1/2} = \{x(t) - [k_2^2 t^2 + 2k_1 k_2 t + k_1^2]\}^{1/2}$. Thus, if the initial conditions are zero, we have our earlier criterion for determining stability. Instability can also occur if $x(t)$ vanishes or is dominated by the bracketed term $[\cdot]$ above. Further investigation is in progress.

REFERENCES

1. G. Adomian and L. H. Sibul, Stochastic Green's formula and application to stochastic differential equations, *J. Math. Anal. Appl.* **60** (3), 743–746.
2. G. Adomian, "Stochastic Systems." Academic Press, New York, 1983.
3. A. G. Butkovskiy, "Green's Functions and Transfer Functions Handbook," Ellis Horwood Ltd, Chichester, England, 1982.
4. N. Bellomo and R. Monaco, A comparison between Adomian's decomposition methods and perturbation techniques for nonlinear random differential equations, *J. Math. Anal. Appl.*, **110**, 495–502, 1985.
5. G. Adomian, Decomposition solution for the Duffing and Van der Pol oscillators, to appear.
6. G. Adomian, Application of Nonlinear Stochastic Systems Theory to Physics, in press.

CHAPTER 5

Coupled Nonlinear Stochastic Differential Equations

5.1. DETERMINISTIC COUPLED DIFFERENTIAL EQUATIONS

Suppose we have two simple linear equations of the form $Lv + \alpha u = \xi$ and $Lu + \beta v = \eta$; L is a simple invertible differential operator with respect to time, i.e., $L = d^n/dt^n$, and ξ and η may be time dependent.

Solving for v using the first equation, we obtain $v = L^{-1}\xi - L^{-1}\alpha u$. Similarly solving the second equation for u, we have $u = L^{-1}\eta - L^{-1}\beta v$. Assume the decomposition $u = \sum_{i=0}^{\infty} u_i$ identifying $u_0 = L^{-1}\eta + \phi$, where $\phi = \sum_{v=0}^{n-1}(t^v/v!)u^{(v)}(0)$ if L is nth order. Similarly assume the decomposition $v = \sum_{i=0}^{\infty} v_i$ identifying $v_0 = L^{-1}\xi + \theta$, where $\theta = \sum_{v=0}^{n-1}(t^v/v!)v^{(v)}(0)$. Now,

$$u_0 = L^{-1}\eta + u(0)$$

$$v_0 = L^{-1}\xi + v(0)$$

Then,

$$u = u_0 - L^{-1}\beta(v_0 + v_1 + \cdots)$$

$$v = v_0 - L^{-1}\alpha(u_0 + u_1 + \cdots)$$

Therefore,

$$u_1 = -L^{-1}\beta v_0$$

$$v_1 = -L^{-1}\alpha u_0$$

88

are clearly calculable since u_0, v_0 are known. Then,

$$u_2 = -L^{-1}\beta v_1$$

$$v_2 = -L^{-1}\alpha u_1$$

etc., so that all terms of both series are obtained concurrently.

EXAMPLE: Two Coupled Riccati Equations

$$Lu + A_1 u + A_2 v + A_3 uv + A_4 u^2 = x_1(t)$$

$$Lv + B_1 v + B_2 u + B_3 uv + B_4 v^2 = x_2(t)$$

where $L = d/dt$, and the A's and B's are nonconstant coefficients. Hence,

$$u(t) = L^{-1}x_1(t) - L^{-1}A_1 u - L^{-1}A_2 v - L^{-1}A_3 uv - L^{-1}A_4 u^2$$

$$v(t) = L^{-1}x_2(t) - L^{-1}B_1 v - L^{-1}B_2 u - L^{-1}B_3 uv - L^{-1}B_4 v^2 \qquad (5.1.1)$$

Let $u = u_0 + u_1 + \cdots$ and $v = v_0 + v_1 + \cdots$. Identify $u_0 = L^{-1}x_1(t) + u(0)$ and $v_0 = L^{-1}x_2(t) + v(0)$

$$u(t) = u_0 - L^{-1}A_1(u_0 + u_1 + \cdots) - L^{-1}A_2(v_0 + v_1 + \cdots)$$
$$\qquad - L^{-1}A_3(u_0 + u_1 + \cdots)(v_0 + v_1 + \cdots) - L^{-1}A_4(u_0 + u_1 + \cdots)^2$$

$$v(t) = v_0 - L^{-1}B_1(v_0 + v_1 + \cdots) - L^{-1}B_2(u_0 + u_1 + \cdots)$$
$$\qquad - L^{-1}B_3(u_0 + u_1 + \cdots)(v_0 + v_1 + \cdots) - L^{-1}B_4(v_0 + v_1 + \cdots)^2$$

Therefore,

$$u_1 = -L^{-1}A_1 u_0 - L^{-1}A_2 v_0 - L^{-1}A_3 u_0 v_0 - L^{-1}A_4 u_0^2$$

$$v_1 = -L^{-1}B_1 v_0 - L^{-1}B_2 u_0 - L^{-1}B_3 u_0 v_0 - L^{-1}B_4 v_0^2$$

and

$$u_2 = -L^{-1}A_1 u_1 - L^{-1}A_2 v_1 - L^{-1}A_3(u_1 v_0 + v_1 u_0) - L^{-1}A_4(2u_0 u_1)$$

$$v_2 = -L^{-1}B_1 v_1 - L^{-1}A_2 u_1 - L^{-1}B_3(u_1 v_0 + v_1 u_0) - L^{-1}B_4(2v_0 v_1).$$

Continuing, we have

$$u_3 = -L^{-1}A_1 u_2 - L^{-1}A_2 v_2 - L^{-1}A_3(u_1 v_1 + u_2 v_0 + v_2 u_0)$$
$$\qquad - L^{-1}A_4(u_1^2 + 2u_0 u_2)$$

$$v_3 = -L^{-1}B_1 v_2 - L^{-1}B_2 u_2 - L^{-1}A_3(u_1 v_1 + u_2 v_0 + v_2 u_0)$$
$$\qquad - L^{-1}B_4(v_1^2 + 2v_0 v_2)$$

and so on. Alternatively, we return to (5.1.1) and write the parametrized equations

$$u(t) = L^{-1}x_1 - \lambda L^{-1}[A_1 u + A_2 v + A_3 uv + A_4 u^2]$$

$$v(t) = L^{-1}x_2 - \lambda L^{-1}[B_1 v + B_2 u + B_3 uv + B_4 v^2] \qquad (5.1.2)$$

We substitute the parametrized decompositions $u = \sum_{n=0}^{\infty} \lambda^n u_n$ and $v = \sum_{n=0}^{\infty} \lambda^n v_n$ and identify terms by powers of λ, thus obtaining the same results as before.

EXAMPLE: Two First-Order Equations.
This is a special case of (5.1.1):

$$du/dt + v = 0, \qquad u(0) = 1$$

$$dv/dt - u = 0, \qquad v(0) = 1$$

or for convenience we write $Lu + v = 0$ and $Lv - u = 0$. Hence,

$$u = u(0) - L^{-1}v$$

$$v = v(0) + L^{-1}u$$

Hence,

$$u = u(0) - L^{-1}(v_0 + v_1 + \cdots)$$

$$v = v(0) + L^{-1}(u_0 + u_1 + \cdots)$$

Thus

$$u_0 = v_0 = 1$$

$$u_1 = -L^{-1}v_0 = -L^{-1}(1) = -\int_0^t dt = -t$$

$$v_1 = L^{-1}u_0 = L^{-1}(-1) = t$$

$$u_2 = -L^{-1}v_1 = -L^{-1}(-t) = -t^2/2!$$

$$v_2 = L^{-1}u_1 = L^{-1}(-t) = -t^2/2!$$

$$u_3 = -L^{-1}v_2 = -L^{-1}(-t^2/2!) = t^3/3!$$

$$v_3 = L^{-1}u_2 = -L^{-1}(-t^2/2!) = t^3/3!$$

$$\vdots$$

Hence,

$$u = 1 - t - (t^2/2!) + (t^3/3!) + \cdots$$

$$v = 1 + t - (t^2/2!) - (t^3/3!) + \cdots$$

EXAMPLE: Coupled Equations with a Nonconstant Coefficient.

$$du/dt + kv = 0, \qquad u(0) = 1 \qquad (k = \text{constant})$$

$$dv/dt + t^2 u - v = 0, \qquad v(0) = 1$$

Let $L = d/dt$; then

$$u = v(0) - L^{-1}k(v_0 + v_1 + \cdots)$$

$$v = v(0) - L^{-1}t^2(u_0 + u_1 + \cdots) + L^{-1}(v_0 + v_1 + \cdots)$$

Identify $u_0 = u(0)$ and $v_0 = v(0)$, then

$$u_1 = -L^{-1}kv_0 = -L^{-1}k(1) = -kt$$

$$v_1 = -L^{-1}t^2u_0 + L^{-1}v_0 = -L^{-1}t^2(1) + L^{-1}(1)$$
$$= -(t^3/3) + t$$

$$u_2 = -L^{-1}kv_1 = -L^{-1}k[(-t^3/3) + t] = k[(t^4/12) - (t^2/2)]$$

$$v_2 = -L^{-1}t^2u_1 + L^{-1}v_1 = -L^{-1}t^2(-kt) + L^{-1}[(-t^3/3) + t]$$
$$= k(t^4/4) - (t^4/12) + (t^2/2)$$

$$u_3 = -L^{-1}kv_2 = -L^{-1}k[k(t^4/4) - (t^4/12) + (t^2/2)]$$
$$= -k^2(t^5/20) + k(t^5/60) - k(t^3/6)$$

$$v_3 = -L^{-1}t^2u_2 + L^{-1}v_2 = -L^{-1}t^2[k(t^4/12) - (t^2/2)]$$
$$+ L^{-1}[k(t^4/4) - (t^4/12) + (t^2/2)]$$
$$= -k(t^7/84) + k(t^5/10) + k(t^5/20) - (t^5/60) + (t^3/6)$$
$$\vdots$$

$$u = 1 - kt + k((t^4/12) - (t^2/2)) - k(t^5/20) + k(t^5/60) - k(t^3/6) + \cdots$$

$$v = 1 - (t^3/3) + t + k(t^4/4) - (t^4/12) + (t^2/2) - k(t^7/84)$$
$$+ k(t^5/10) + k(t^5/70) - (t^5/60) + (t^3/6) + \cdots$$

Note that $t^2u_3 - v_3$ will be cancelled by dv_4/dt etc., i.e., $dv_n/dt + t^2u_{n-1} - v_{n-1} = 0$.

EXAMPLE: Coupled Riccati Equations with Nonlinear Interaction Terms and a Nonconstant Coefficient

$$du/dt + k\,uv = 0, \qquad u(0) = \mu \qquad (k = \text{constant})$$

$$dv/dt + t^2\,uv = 0, \qquad v(0) = v$$

Let $L = d/dt$, then

$$u = u(0) - L^{-1}k\,uv$$

$$v = v(0) - L^{-1}t^2\,uv$$

where we decompose the nonlinear interaction term uv by decomposition as before:

$$uv = N(u, v) = \sum_{n=0}^{\infty} A_n$$

where

$$A_0 = u_0 v_0$$

$$A_1 = u_0 v_1 + v_0 u_1$$

$$A_2 = u_1 v_1 + u_0 v_2 + v_0 u_2$$

$$A_3 = u_0 v_3 + v_0 u_3 + u_1 v_2 + v_1 u_2$$

Hence,

$$u = \mu - L^{-1} k[u_0 v_0 + (u_0 v_1 + v_0 u_1) + (u_1 v_1 + u_0 v_2 + v_0 u_2) + \cdots]$$

$$v = v - L^{-1} t^2[u_0 v_0 + (u_0 v_1 + v_0 u_1) + (u_1 v_1 + u_0 v_2 + v_0 u_2) + \cdots]$$

and by comparison with our series for u and v, we identify $u_0 = \mu$ and $v_0 = v$, then

$$u_1 = -L^{-1} k u_0 v_0 = -\mu v k t$$

$$v_1 = -L^{-1} t^2 u_0 v_0 = -\mu v t^3/3$$

$$u_2 = -L^{-1} k(u_0 v_1 + v_0 u_1) = -L^{-1} k[\mu(-\mu v t^3/3) + v(-\mu v k t)]$$
$$= \mu^2 v k t^4/12 + \mu v^2 k^2 t^2/2$$

$$v_2 = -L^{-1} t^2(u_0 v_1 + v_0 u_1) = L^{-1} t^2[\mu(-\mu v t^3/3) + v(-\mu v k t)]$$
$$= \mu^2 v t^6/18 + \mu v^2 k^2 t^4/4$$

$$u_3 = -L^{-1} k(u_1 v_1 + u_0 v_2 + v_0 u_2)$$
$$= -L^{-1} k\{(-\mu v k t)(-\mu v t^3/3) + (\mu)(\mu^2 v t^6/18 + \mu v^2 k^2 t^4/4)$$
$$+ (v)(\mu^2 v k t^4/12 + \mu v^2 k^2 t^2/2)\}$$
$$= -\mu^2 v^2 k^2 t^5/15 - \mu^3 v k t^7/126 - \mu^2 v^2 k^2 t^5/20$$
$$- \mu^2 v^2 k^2 t^5/60 - \mu v^3 k^3 t^3/6$$

$$v_3 = -L^{-1} t^2(u_1 v_1 + u_0 v_2 + v_0 u_2)$$
$$= -L^{-1} t^2\{(-\mu v k t)(-\mu v t^3/3) + (\mu)(\mu^2 v t^6/18 + \mu v^2 k^2 t^4/4)$$
$$+ (v)(\mu^2 v k t^4/12 + \mu v^2 k^2 t^2/2)$$
$$= -\mu^2 v^2 k t^7/21 - \mu^3 v t^9/162 - \mu^2 v^2 k t^7/28 - \mu^2 v^2 k t^7/84$$
$$- \mu v^3 k^2 t^5/10$$

$$\vdots$$

$$u = \mu - \mu v k t + (\mu^2 v k t^4/12 + \mu v^2 k^2 t^2/2)$$
$$- \{\mu^2 v^2 k^2 t^5/15 + \mu^3 v k t^7/126 + \mu^2 v^2 k^2 t^5/20 + \mu^2 v^2 k^2 t^5/60$$
$$+ \mu v^3 k^3 t^6/6\} - \cdots$$

$$v = v - \mu v t^3/3 + (\mu^2 v t^6/18 + \mu v^2 k^2 t^4/4) - \{\mu^2 v^2 k t^7/2]$$
$$+ \mu^3 v t^9/162 + \mu^2 v^2 k t^7/28 + \mu^2 v^2 k t^7/84 + \mu v^3 k^2 t^5/10\} + \cdots$$

For a quick solution check, notice that $du_n/dt + kA_{n-1} = 0$ and $dv_n/dt + t^2 A_{n-1} = 0$. It is interesting to observe, for this special case of coupled Riccati equations, how both of the concurrent solutions, u and v, depend *nonlinearly* on the simultaneous initial conditions, μ and v, thus suggesting nonlinear superposition formulas.

5.2. STOCHASTIC COUPLED EQUATIONS

Consider the coupled system

$$\mathscr{L}_1 y + \alpha yz = x_1$$

$$\mathscr{L}_2 z + \beta yz = x_2$$

where the linear stochastic operators $\mathscr{L}_1$ and $\mathscr{L}_2$ are decomposable into $L_1 + \mathscr{R}_1$ and $L_2 + \mathscr{R}_2$, respectively, where L_1 and L_2 are deterministic and $\mathscr{R}_1$ and $\mathscr{R}_2$ are random. Thus,

$$(L_1 + \mathscr{R}_1)y + \alpha yz = x_1$$

$$(L_2 + \mathscr{R}_2)z + \beta yz = x_2$$

Hence,

$$y = L_1^{-1}x_1 - L_1^{-1}[\mathscr{R}_1 y - \alpha yz]$$

$$z = L_2^{-1}x_2 - L_2^{-1}[\mathscr{R}_2 z - \beta yz]$$

As before

$$y_0 = L_1^{-1}x_1 + y(0) + \cdots \{t^{n-1}/(n-1)!\}y^{(n-1)}(0)$$

if L is nth order. Similarly,

$$z_0 = L^{-1}x_2 + z(0) + \cdots + \{t^{n-1}/(n-1)!\}z^{(n-1)}(0)$$

Then

$$y_1 = -L_1^{-1}[\mathscr{R}_1 y_0 + \alpha y_0 z_0]$$

$$z_1 = -L_2^{-1}[\mathscr{R}_2 z_0 + \beta y_0 z_0]$$

$$y_{n+1} = -L_1^{-1}[\mathscr{R}_1 y_n + \alpha(y_0 z_n + y_1 z_{n-1} + \cdots + y_n z_0)]$$

$$z_{n+1} = -L_2^{-1}[\mathscr{R}_2 z_n + \beta(y_0 z_n + y_1 z_{n-1} + \cdots + y_n z_0)]$$

5.3. GENERALIZATION TO n COUPLED STOCHASTIC DIFFERENTIAL EQUATIONS

$$Ly + \mathscr{M} \prod y = x$$

where we now define $\mathscr{L}$ to be an $n \times n$ matrix that can be decomposed into a sum of two matrices L and $\mathscr{R}$. Here $\mathscr{M}$ is an $n \times n$ matrix, y a column vector (with components $y_1, y_2, \ldots, y_n$), and x a column vector (with components $x_1, x_2, \ldots, x_n$). The elements of $\mathscr{L}$ are given as

$$\begin{pmatrix} l_{11} & l_{12} & \cdots & l_{1n} \\ l_{21} & & & \\ \vdots & & & \\ l_{n1} & \cdots & & l_{nn} \end{pmatrix}$$

Finally, $\prod y$ will be defined as

$$\begin{pmatrix} y_1 y_2 \cdots y_n \\ y_1 y_2 \cdots y_n \\ \vdots \\ y_1 y_2 \cdots y_n \end{pmatrix}$$

The quantity $\mathscr{M} \prod y$ can express quite general coupling between equations. For example, let

$$\mathscr{M} = \begin{pmatrix} ad/dt & b \\ 0 & c \end{pmatrix}$$

Then

$$\begin{pmatrix} ad/dt & b \\ 0 & c \end{pmatrix} \begin{pmatrix} y_1 & y_2 \\ y_1 & y_2 \end{pmatrix} = \begin{pmatrix} a(d/dt)(y_1 y_2) + b(y_1 y_2) \\ c y_1 y_2 \end{pmatrix}$$

A FINAL EXAMPLE: Consider the equations

$$\dot{\theta} = g v^{-1} \cos \theta \tag{5.3.1}$$

$$\dot{v} = g \sin \theta, \tag{5.3.2}$$

we write

$$L\theta = g v^{-1} \cos \theta$$

$$Lv = g \sin \theta.$$

Thus,

$$\theta = \theta(0) + L^{-1} g f(v, \theta) \tag{5.3.3}$$

where $f(v, \theta) = v^{-1} \cos \theta = \sum_{n=0}^{\infty} A_n$ and

$$v = v(0) + L^{-1} g h(\theta) \tag{5.3.4}$$

where $h(\theta) = \sin \theta = \sum_{n=0}^{\infty} B_n$. Now

$$A_0 = f(v_0, \theta_0) = v_0^{-1} \cos \theta_0$$

$$B_0 = h(\theta_0) = \sin \theta_0$$

$$A_1 = \left(\frac{df}{dv}\frac{dv}{d\lambda} + \frac{df}{d\theta}\frac{d\theta}{d\lambda}\right)_{\lambda=0} = -v_0^{-2}v_1 \cos \theta_0 - v_0^{-1} \theta_1 \sin \theta_0$$

$$B_1 = \left(\frac{dh}{d\theta}\frac{d\theta}{d\lambda}\right)_{\lambda=0} = \theta_1 \cos \theta_0$$

$$A_2 = \frac{1}{2}\left(\frac{d^2f}{dv^2}\left(\frac{dv}{d\lambda}\right)^2 + \frac{df}{dv}\frac{d^2v}{d\lambda^2} + \frac{d^2f}{d\theta^2}\left(\frac{d\theta}{d\lambda}\right)^2 + \frac{df}{d\theta}\frac{d^2\theta}{d\lambda^2}\right)_{\lambda=0}$$

$$= \frac{1}{2}(2v_0^{-3}v_1^2 \cos \theta_0 - 2v_0^{-2}v_2 \cos \theta_0$$

$$-v_0^{-1}\theta_1^2 \cos \theta_0 - 2v_0^{-1} \sin \theta_0 \theta_2)$$

$$= v_0^{-3}v_1^2 \cos \theta_0 - v_0^{-2}v_2 \cos \theta_0 - \frac{1}{2}v_0^{-1}\theta_1^2 \cos \theta_0 - v_1^{-1}\theta_2 \sin \theta_0$$

$$B_2 = \frac{1}{2}\left(\frac{d^2h}{d\theta^2}\left(\frac{d\theta}{d\lambda}\right)^2 + \frac{dh}{d\theta}\frac{d^2\theta}{d\lambda^2}\right)_{\lambda=0} = -\frac{1}{2}\theta_1^2 \sin \theta_0 + \theta_2 \cos \theta_0$$

$$A_3 = \frac{1}{6}\left(\frac{d^3f}{dv^3}\left(\frac{dv}{d\lambda}\right)^3 + \frac{d^2f}{dv^2}\frac{dv}{d\lambda}\frac{d^2v}{d\lambda^2} + \frac{df}{dv}\frac{d^3v}{d\lambda^3}\right.$$

$$+ \frac{d^2f}{dv^2}\frac{dv}{d\lambda}\frac{d^2v}{d\lambda^2} + \frac{d^3f}{d\theta^3}\left(\frac{d\theta}{d\lambda}\right)^3 + 2\frac{d^2f}{d\theta^2}\frac{d\theta}{d\lambda}\frac{d\theta}{d\lambda^2}$$

$$\left. + \frac{d^2f}{d\phi^2}\frac{d^2\theta}{d\lambda^2}\frac{d\theta}{d\lambda} + \frac{df}{d\theta}\frac{d^3\theta}{d\lambda^3}\right)_{\lambda=0}$$

$$= \frac{1}{6}\left(\frac{d^3f}{dv^3}\left(\frac{dv}{dx}\right)^3 + 3\frac{d^2f}{dv^2}\frac{dv}{d\lambda}\frac{d^2v}{d\lambda^2} + \frac{df}{dv}\frac{d^3v}{d\lambda^3}\right.$$

$$\left. + 3\frac{d^2f}{d\theta^2}\frac{d\theta}{d\lambda}\frac{d^2\theta}{d\lambda^2} + \frac{df}{d\theta}\frac{d^3\theta}{d\lambda^3} + \frac{d^3f}{d\theta^3}\left(\frac{d\theta}{d\lambda}\right)^3\right)$$

$$= \frac{1}{6}[-6v_0^{-4}(\cos \theta_0)(v_1^3) + 6v_0^{-3}(\cos \theta_0)(v_1)(2v_2)$$

$$-v_0^{-2}(\cos \theta_0)(6v_3) - v_0^{-1}(\cos \theta_0)(\theta_1)(2\theta_2)$$

$$-v_0^{-1}(\sin \theta_0)(6\theta_3) + v_0^{-1}(\sin \theta_0)(\theta_1)^3]$$

$$= -v_0^{-4}v_1^3 \cos \theta_0 + 2v_0^{-3}v_1v_2 \cos \theta_0$$

$$-v_0^{-2}v_3 \cos \theta_0 - \frac{1}{3}v_0^{-1}\theta_1\theta_2 \cos \theta_0$$

$$-v_0^{-1}\theta_3 \sin \theta_0 + \frac{1}{6}v_0^{-1} \theta_1^3 \sin \theta_0$$

$$B_3 = \frac{1}{6}\left(\frac{d^3h}{d\theta^2}\left(\frac{d\theta}{d\lambda}\right)^3 + \frac{d^2h}{d\theta^2}\left(2\frac{d\theta}{d\lambda}\frac{d^2\theta}{d\lambda^2}\right) + \frac{dh}{d\theta}\frac{d^3\theta}{d\lambda^3} + \frac{d^2h}{d\theta^2}\frac{d^2\theta}{d\lambda^2}\frac{d\theta}{d\lambda}\right)_{\lambda=0}$$

$$= \frac{1}{6}[-(\cos\theta_0)(\theta_1^3) - (\sin\theta_0)(2)(\theta_1)(2\theta_2) + (\cos\theta_0)(6\theta_3)$$

$$- (\sin\theta_0)(2\theta_2)(\theta_1)]$$

$$= -\frac{1}{6}\theta_1^3\cos\theta_0 - \frac{2}{3}\theta_1\theta_2\sin\theta_0 + \theta_3\cos\theta_0 - \frac{1}{3}\theta_1\theta_2\sin\theta_0$$

Thus the solution is given by (5.8.3) and (5.8.4) with the above A_n and B_n or

$$\theta = \theta(0) + L^{-1}g[A_0 + A_1 + A_2 + A_3 + \cdots] \tag{5.3.5}$$

$$v = v(0) + L^{-1}g[B_0 + B_1 + B_2 + B_3 + \cdots] \tag{5.3.6}$$

yielding for the case of $\theta_0 = 0$ and $v(0) = V$

$$v_0 = v(0) = V$$

$$\theta_0 = \theta(0) = 0$$

$$v_1 = L^{-1}gB_0 = L^{-1}g\sin\theta_0 = 0$$

$$\theta_1 = L^{-1}gA_0 = L^{-1}gv_0^{-1}\cos\theta_0 = (g/V)t$$

$$v_2 = L^{-1}gB_1 = L^{-1}g\theta_1\cos\theta_0 = L^{-1}g[(g/V)t] = g^2t^2/2V$$

$$\theta_2 = L^{-1}gA_1 = L^{-1}g[-v_0^{-2}v_1] = 0$$

$$v_3 = L^{-1}gB_2 = L^{-1}\theta_2 = 0$$

$$\phi_3 = L^{-1}gA_2 = L^{-1}g[v_0^{-3}v_1^2\cos\theta_0 - v_0^{-2}v_2\cos\theta_0$$
$$- \tfrac{1}{2}v_0^{-1}\theta_1^2\cos\theta_0 - v_0^{-1}\theta_2\sin\theta_0]$$

$$= L^{-1}g[-v_0^{-2}v_2 - \frac{1}{2}v_0^{-1}\theta_1^2]$$

$$v_4 = L^{-1}gB_3 = -g^4t^4/8V^2.$$

Consequently,

$$\theta = \frac{g}{V}t - \frac{g^3}{3V^3}t^3 + \cdots$$

$$v = V + \frac{g^2}{2V}t^2 + \cdots$$

$$v = V\left[1 + \frac{g^2 t^2}{2V^2} + \frac{g^4 t^4}{8V^3} + \cdots\right]$$

SUGGESTED FURTHER READING

R. E. Bellman and G. Adomian, The Stochastic Riccati Equation, *Journal of Nonlinear Analysis: Theory, Methods, and Applications*, *4*, (6), pp. 1131–1133, 1980.

C. C. Lin, "Mathematics Applied to Deterministic Problems of the Natural Sciences." MacMillan, 1974.

CHAPTER 6

Delay Equations

There must be a simpler way...

R. E. Bellman

6.1. DEFINITIONS

The importance of delay equations is well known. As modeling becomes more sophisticated, increasing realization of their importance will necessarily follow. Problems in electrodynamics, reactor kinetics, behavior of economic systems, weapons fire control from moving platforms, etc., all are modeled by differential delay equations. The delays may be constant, time dependent, stochastic, or state dependent. The equations may be linear or nonlinear, deterministic or stochastic. We shall define various *delay operators* for the solution of equations involving retarded effects. We can define deterministic and random delay operators (respectively, D and $\mathscr{E}$):

$$Dy(t) = \sum_{i=1}^{n} y(t - \tau_i)$$

$$Dy(t, \omega) = \sum_{i=1}^{n} y(t - \tau_i, \omega)$$

$$\mathscr{E}y(t) = \sum_{i=1}^{n} y(t - \tau_i(\omega))$$

Time-dependent delays are treated by letting $\tau = \tau(t)$ or $\tau(t, \omega)$. We can consider also a further extension to nonlinear differential delay operators $D_n y(t) = Ny(t - \tau)$ or even stochastic versions $\mathscr{E}_n y(t) = Ny(t - \tau, \omega)$. The methods to be employed are based, as usual, on the author's decomposition procedure.

98

(a) Simple Delay Operators: Here, we assume delays are *constants*, and the delay operator is a (deterministic) nondifferential operator. Multiple delays can be involved as well. Thus

$$Dy(t) = \sum_{i=1}^{n} y(t - \tau_i) \tag{6.1.1}$$

For the special case of $n = 1$, we then have $Dy = y(t - \tau)$. Extension of the concept to delay operations on stochastic processes causes no problems. If instead of $y(t)$ we consider the operator acting on a stochastic process $y(t, \omega)$, then

$$Dy(t, \omega) = \sum_{i=1}^{n} y(t - \tau_i, \omega) \tag{6.1.2}$$

(b) Random Delay Operators: By the operator $\mathscr{E}$ we shall mean a *simple random delay operator*, i.e., one involving random retardations

$$\mathscr{E}y(t) = \sum_{i=1}^{n} y(t - \tau_i(\omega)) \tag{6.1.3}$$

The special case of $n = 1$ is

$$\mathscr{E}y(t) = y(t - \tau(\omega)) \tag{6.1.4}$$

If the operand y is a stochastic process $y(t, \omega)$, then

$$\mathscr{E}y(t, \omega) = \sum_{i=1}^{n} y(t - \tau_i(\omega), \omega) \tag{6.1.5}$$

(c) Time-Dependent Delays: Here, the delay is time dependent and can be either deterministic or stochastic. Thus, τ can be $\tau(t)$ or $\tau(t, \omega)$. When $n = 1$, $Dy(t) = y(t - \tau(t))$ and $\mathscr{E}y(t) = y(t - \tau(t, \omega))$.

(d) Differential Delay Operators: For the linear (deterministic) differential operator $L_i = \sum_{\nu=0}^{i} a_\nu(t) d^\nu/dt^\nu$, define the linear differential delay operator D_L by

$$D_L y(t) = \sum_{i=0}^{n} a_i(t)\left(\frac{d^i}{dt^i}\right) y(t - \tau_i) = \sum_{i=0}^{n} L_i y(t - \tau_i) \tag{6.1.6}$$

Similarly, let

$$D_{\mathscr{R}} y(t) = \sum_{i=0}^{n} a_i(t, \omega)\left(\frac{d^i}{dt^i}\right) y(t - \tau_i) = \sum_{i=0}^{n} \mathscr{R}_i y(t - \tau_i) \tag{6.1.7}$$

Random delays are dealt with by defining

$$\mathscr{E}_L y(t) = \sum_{i=0}^{n} a_i(t)\left(\frac{d^i}{dt^i}\right) y(t - \tau_i(\omega))$$

$$= \sum_{i=0}^{n} L_i y(t - \tau_i(\omega)) \qquad (6.1.8)$$

$$\mathscr{E}_\mathscr{R} y(t) = \sum_{i=0}^{n} a_i(t, \omega)\left(\frac{d^i}{dt^i}\right) y(t - \tau_i(\omega))$$

$$= \sum_{i=0}^{n} \mathscr{R}_i y(t - \tau_i(\omega)) \qquad (6.1.9)$$

Of course, as before we can replace $y(t)$ by $y(t, \omega)$ in all of the differential delay operations, e.g., $D_L y(t, \omega) = \sum_{i=0}^{n} L_i y(t - \tau_i, \omega)$.

(e) **Nonlinear Differential Delay Operators:** The deterministic non-linear operations $N_i(\cdot)$ and stochastic nonlinear operations $\mathscr{M}_i(\cdot)$ are used to define deterministic and stochastic nonlinear differential delay operations

$$D_N y(t) = \sum_{i=1}^{n} N_i y(t - \tau_i) \qquad (6.1.10)$$

$$D_\mathscr{M} y(t) = \sum_{i=1}^{n} \mathscr{M}_i y(t - \tau_i) \qquad (6.1.11)$$

where N_i and $\mathscr{M}_i$ are (either simple or differential) nonlinear operators. The only difference is that N_i involves deterministic coefficients $a_i(t)$ while $\mathscr{M}_i$ involves stochastic coefficients $\alpha_i(t, \omega)$. An example of a nonlinear differential delay operator is $D_N = y(t - \tau)(d/dt)y(t - \tau)$. If the delays are random as well, we have

$$\mathscr{E}_N y(t) = \sum_{i=1}^{n} N_i y(t - \tau_i(\omega))$$

$$\mathscr{E}_\mathscr{M} y(t) = \sum_{i=1}^{n} \mathscr{M}_i y(t - \tau_i(\omega)) \qquad (6.1.12)$$

Again, $y(t)$ can be replaced by the process $y(t, \omega)$.

6.2. SOLUTION OF DELAY OPERATOR EQUATIONS

The appropriate delay operations can now be added to the operation $\mathscr{F} y$ in the equation $\mathscr{F} y = x$. Let us consider some examples to illuminate our methods.

EXAMPLE: The equation

$$(d^2/dt^2)y(t) + (d/dt)y(t - \tau) + k^2 y(t) = x(t) \qquad (6.2.1)$$

describes the well-known harmonic oscillator problem with the added feature of a delayed damping term. The delay τ is not restricted to a constant but is a function of t. Let us choose the simple case $\tau = t/2$. Furthermore, choose $k^2 = 1$ and $x(t) = 0$. For initial conditions, let $y(0) = 1$ and $y'(0) = 0$. Our specific equation is

$$(d^2/dt^2)y(t) + (d/dt)y(t/2) + y(t) = 0. \qquad (6.2.2)$$

Let $L = d^2/dt^2$ in (6.2.1) or (6.2.2), $\mathscr{R} = k^2$ [or actually 1 in Eq. (6.2.2)]. We represent $(d/dt)y(t - \tau)$ in (6.2.1) by Dy for simplicity—actually a single term of D_L from (6.1.6). Since $\tau = t/2$, this becomes $(d/dt)y(t/2)$ in Eq. (6.2.2). In general then, (6.2.1) becomes $\mathscr{L}y + Dy = x$ or

$$Ly + Dy + \mathscr{R}y = x \qquad (6.2.3)$$

or

$$Ly = x - Dy - \mathscr{R}y \qquad (6.2.4)$$

assuming the existence of a Green's function for L. We can write

$$y = L^{-1}x - L^{-1}Dy - L^{-1}\mathscr{R}y \qquad (6.2.5)$$

To get the complete solution, initial conditions must be incorporated. In this particular case, this simply means adding $y(0)$. For general second-order equations, it is necessary to add $y(0) + ty'(0)$. For the simple problem of (6.2.1) or (6.2.2), it is sufficient to assume a decomposition of y into components $y_0 + y_1 + y_2 + \cdots$ and let $y_0 = y(0) + ty'(0) + L^{-1}x$, or since $y'(0) = 0$ and $x = 0$, $y_0 = y(0) = 1$ for our problem. Now we have

$$y = y_0 - L^{-1}Dy - L^{-1}\mathscr{R}y$$
$$= y_0 - L^{-1}D(y_0 + y_1 + \cdots) - L^{-1}\mathscr{R}(y_0 + y_1 + \cdots) \qquad (6.2.6)$$

We identify

$$y_1 = -L^{-1}Dy_0 - L^{-1}\mathscr{R}y_0$$
$$y_2 = -L^{-1}Dy_1 - L^{-1}\mathscr{R}y_1 \qquad (6.2.7)$$
$$y_3 = -L^{-1}Dy_2 - L^{-1}\mathscr{R}y_2 \cdots$$

Letting $\mathscr{R}$ be 1 as in our specific case and using our $y_0 = 1$,

$$y_1 = -L^{-1}D(1) - L^{-1}(1) = c - \frac{t^2}{2} = \frac{-t^2}{2}$$

The constant vanishes because $y(t)|_{t=0} = y(0) = 1$. Furthermore,

$$y_2 = -L^{-1}D\left(\frac{-t^2}{2}\right) - L^{-1}\left(\frac{-t^2}{2}\right) \qquad (6.2.8)$$

Since $Dy(t) = (d/dt)y(t/2)$, $D(-t^2/2) = (d/dt)(-t^2/8) = -t/4$, then

$$y_2 = -\left(\frac{t^3}{24}\right) - \left(\frac{t^4}{24}\right).$$

The procedure is clear; all terms are calculable in terms of preceding terms.

EXAMPLE: Consider the linear differential delay equation

$$Ly + \mathscr{D}y = x. \tag{6.2.9}$$

We write $Ly = x - \mathscr{D}y$ and assume existence of L^{-1}; then

$$y = L^{-1}x - L^{-1}\mathscr{D}y = L^{-1}x - L^{-1}\mathscr{D}(y_0 + y_1 + \cdots) \tag{6.2.10}$$

Thus,

$$
\begin{aligned}
y_0 &= L^{-1}x \\
y_1 &= -L^{-1}\mathscr{D}y_0 \\
y_2 &= -L^{-1}\mathscr{D}y_1 \\
&\vdots \\
y_n &= -L^{-1}\mathscr{D}y_{n-1} = (-1)^n(L^{-1}\mathscr{D})^n L^{-1}x.
\end{aligned}
\tag{6.2.11}
$$

The usual decomposition series $y(t) = \sum_{i=0}^{\infty} y_i(t)$ is the solution, while $y(t - \tau) = \sum_{i=0}^{\infty} y_i(t - \tau)$ is the delayed form of the same series.

REMARK: If L is an nth-order differential operator, and $\mathscr{R}$ is an mth-order differential operator, $n > m$.

Similar order relations apply to $\mathscr{N}$, D_L, etc., which we can write $[L] > [\mathscr{R}]$, $[L] > [\mathscr{N}]$, $[L] > [D_L]$, etc., where $[\cdot]$ indicates the order of the differential operator.

REMARK: Assume $y(t) = \sum_{i=0}^{\infty} y_i(t)$ and $y(t - \tau) = \sum_{i=0}^{\infty} y_i(t - \tau)$. Equation (6.2.10) becomes

$$y(t) = L^{-1}x(t) - L^{-1}\left(\sum_{i=0}^{\infty} y_i(t - \tau)\right)$$

Thus,

$$y_0(t) = L^{-1}x(t), \qquad y_1(t) = -L^{-1}y_0(t - \tau),\ldots$$

or

$$y_n(t) = -L^{-1}y_{n-1}(t - \tau)$$

Writing $y_n(t)$ in terms of y_0 yields

$$y_n(t) = (-1)^n(L^{-1})^n L^{-1}x(t - n\tau)$$

Finally,

$$y(t) = \sum_{n=0}^{\infty} (-1)^n (L^{-1})^n L^{-1} x(t - n\tau)$$

Notice that the limiting case of zero delay yields the solution of the ordinary linear case as we expect. This corresponds to solution of the equation

$$Ly + y = x$$

instead of (6.2.9). If we write $L_0 = L + 1$ and

$$L_0 y = x(t)$$

then

$$y(t) = L_0^{-1} x(t) = \sum_{i=0}^{\infty} (-1)^n (L^{-1})^n L^{-1} x(t)$$

Thus for $L_0 = L + 1$,

$$L_0^{-1} = \sum_{i=0}^{\infty} (-1)^n (L^{-1})^{n+1} = L^{-1} - (L^{-1})^2 + (L^{-1})^3 - \cdots \quad (6.2.12)$$

The equation $\mathscr{L} y = x$ or $(L + \mathscr{R})y = x$ yields the analogous series

$$\mathscr{L}^{-1} = \sum_{i=0}^{\infty} (-1)^n (L^{-1}\mathscr{R})^n L^{-1} = L^{-1} - (L^{-1}\mathscr{R})L^{-1} + (L^{-1}\mathscr{R})^2 L^{-1} - \cdots$$

$$= [1 - (L^{-1}\mathscr{R}) + (L^{-1}\mathscr{R})^2 - \cdots]L^{-1}$$

REMARK: Since $\mathscr{D} y(t) = y(t - \tau)$, then $\mathscr{D}^{-1}\mathscr{D} y(t) = y(t)$, i.e., $\mathscr{D}^{-1}$ is the operator that advances instead of delays.

EXAMPLE: Let us consider first the simple equation $dy(t)/dt - Ay(t) = 0$, $y(0) = k$ without delay or in our usual form,

$$Ly(t) + \mathscr{R}y(t) = x(t) = 0$$

with $L = d/dt$ and $\mathscr{R} = -A$. Since the $L^{-1}x$ term is zero,

$$y = y_0 + L^{-1}x - L^{-1}\mathscr{R}y = y(0) - L^{-1}\mathscr{R}y = y(0) + L^{-1}Ay.$$

Let $y = \sum_{n=0}^{\infty} y_n$, where $y_0 = y(0) = k$. Then

$$y_1 = L^{-1}Ay_0 = L^{-1}Ak = kAt$$

$$y_2 = L^{-1}Ay_1 = L^{-1}(kAt) = kA^2t^2/2!$$

$$\vdots$$

$$y_n = kA^n t^n / n!$$

Hence, $y(t) = \sum_{n=0}^{\infty} kA^n t^n/n! = ke^{At}$. Supposing now we add a nonlinear delay term $ByDy$, where D is a delay operator defined by $Dy(t) = y(t - \tau)$, $L = d/dt$, $R = -A$. We can now write $Ly + \mathscr{R}y + NDy = 0$, where $NDy(t)$ is a nonlinear delay operation on $y(t)$ given by $By(t)y(t - \tau)$. Then

$$y = y_0 + L^{-1}Ay - L^{-1}ByDy$$
$$= y_0 + L^{-1}A(y_0 + y_1 + \cdots)$$
$$\quad - L^{-1}B(y_0 + y_1 + \cdots)D(y_0 + y_1 + \cdots),$$

$$y_1 = L^{-1}Ay_0 - L^{-1}By_0Dy_0 = L^{-1}Ay_0(t) - L^{-1}By_0(t)y_0(t - \tau),$$

$$y_2 = L^{-1}Ay_1 - L^{-1}By_0Dy_1 - L^{-1}By_1Dy_0.$$

(6.2.13)

Why is the term $-L^{-1}By_1Dy_1$ not in y_2? We take only terms such that the sum of the subscripts is less than the index of the component term to be determined. Each y_i term will then depend on y_{i-1} and ultimately on y_0 which leads to statistical separability in stochastic cases. To verify this, let $y = \sum_{n=0}^{\infty} \lambda^n y_n$ and write

$$y = y_0 + \lambda L^{-1}Ay - \lambda L^{-1}ByDy.$$

Now

$$y = y_0 + \lambda y_1 + \lambda^2 y_2 + \cdots$$
$$= y_0 + \lambda L^{-1}A(y_0 + \lambda y_1 + \cdots)$$
$$\quad - \lambda L^{-1}B(y_0 + \lambda y_1 + \cdots)D(y_0 + \lambda y_1 + \cdots)$$

Hence

$$y_1 = L^{-1}Ay_0 - L^{-1}B[y_0Dy_0]$$
$$y_2 = L^{-1}Ay_1 - L^{-1}B[y_1Dy_0 + y_0Dy_1]$$
$$y_3 = L^{-1}Ay_2 - L^{-1}B[y_1Dy_1 + y_0Dy_2 + y_2Dy_0]$$
$$\vdots$$

Consequently,

$$y_0 = k$$
$$y_1 = L^{-1}Ak - L^{-1}Bk^2 - (Ak - Bk^2)t$$
$$y_2 = L^{-1}A[Ak - Bk^2]t - L^{-1}B\{k[Ak - Bk^2][t - \tau] + [(Ak - Bk^2)t](k)\}$$
$$= (A - 2Bk)(Ak - Bk^2)(t^2/2) + Bk(Ak - Bk^2)\tau t$$

etc., so that

$$y(t) = k + (Ak - Bk^2)t + (A - 2Bk)(Ak - Bk^2)(t^2/2)$$
$$\quad + Bk(Ak - Bk^2)\tau t + \cdots$$

If $B = 0$, we have the previous solution. As a check, one trivially verifies

$$dy/dt = (Ak - Bk^2) + (A - 2Bk)(Ak - Bk^2)t$$
$$+ Bk(Ak - Bk^2)\tau + \cdots$$
$$-Ay(t) = -Ak - A(Ak - Bk^2)t - \cdots$$
$$By(t)y(t - \tau) = Bk^2 + Bk(Ak - Bk^2)(t - \tau) + Bk(Ak - Bk^2)t + \cdots$$

and we easily see the term by term cancellations to yield $dy(t)/dt - Ay(t) + By(t)y(t - \tau) = 0$, i.e., $(d/dt)(y_0 + y_1 + y_2) - A(y_0 + y_1) + B(y_0 y_0(t - \tau) + y_1 y_0(t - \tau) + y_0 y_1(t - \tau)) = 0$ or

$$(d/dt)y_1 - Ay_0 + By_0 y_0(t - \tau) = 0$$

$$(d/dt)y_2 - Ay_1 + B(y_1 y_0(t - \tau) + y_0 y_1(t - \tau)) = 0$$

$$(d/dt)y_3 - Ay_2 + B(y_1 y_1(t - \tau) + y_0 y_2(t - \tau) + y_2 y_0(t - \tau)) = 0$$

Here, we have solved (6.2.13) for constant τ, A, and B. Clearly however, these parameters may be stochastic.

REMARK: Let D_L be a differential delay operator and consider

$$Ly + D_L y = x(t),$$

the order of L being greater than the order of D_L. We have

$$Ly = x - D_L y,$$

$$y = L^{-1}x - L^{-1}D_L y = L^{-1}x - L^{-1}D_L(y_0 + y_1 + \cdots)$$

Thus,

$$y_0 = L^{-1}x$$

$$y_1 = -L^{-1}D_L y_0$$
$$\vdots$$
$$y_n = (-1)^n(L^{-1}D_L)^n L^{-1}x(t)$$

Consequently,

$$y = \sum_{n=0}^{\infty} (-1)^n(L^{-1}D_L)^n L^{-1}x(t)$$

We have seen in this chapter that the methods evolved for solution of linear and nonlinear stochastic differential equations (deterministic being a special case) can be extended to equations involving delays as well. Since effects do not occur simultaneously in all parts of a large complex system, delay effects are important in many applications [1].

REFERENCE

1. G. Adomian, "Applications of Nonlinear Stochastic Systems Theory to Physics," in press.

SUGGESTED FURTHER READING

G. Adomian, and R. Rach, Nonlinear Stochastic Differential-delay Equations, *J. Math. Anal. Appl.* **91** 94-101, (1983).

W. K. Ergen, Kinetics of the circulating-fuel nuclear reactor, *J. Appl. Phys.* **25**(6) 702-711 (1954).

L. E. E'sgol'ts, "Introduction to the Theory of Differential Equations with Deviating Arguments," (translated by R. T. McLaughlin). Holden-Day, San Francisco, 1966.

R. Kakutani and L. Markus, On the nonlinear difference-differential equation $y'(t) = [A - By(t - \tau)]y(t)$, *in* "Contributions to the Theory of Nonlinear Oscillations," Vol. V. Princeton Univ. Press. Princeton, New Jersey, 1950.

A. B. Nersesyan, *Isv. Akad. Nauk Armenian SSR Ser. Mat.* **12**(6), 37-68 (1959).

Y. A. Solodova, A study of the accuracy of a delayed tracking system in the presence of delay time fluctuations in the feedback circuit, *Radio Eng. Electron. Phys.* **24**(3) 84-87 (1979).

CHAPTER 7

Discretization versus Decomposition

Believe nothing even if I said it myself...

Buddha

7.1. DISCRETIZATION

Difference equations occur as recurrence relations in series solutions of ordinary differential equations, in some mathematical applications such as the "gambler's ruin" problem and evaluation of the Euler gamma function, but of most interest to us is the discretization of differential and partial differential equations for solution by computers.

In numerical solutions of physical problems, it is common to make computations at discrete space or time intervals. Computer methods are based on changing continuous problems to discrete problems. Thus, in solving a differential equation, we select a small time interval $\Delta t = t_n - t_{n-1}$, and at each t_n we can indicate the value of y at t_n by y_n. If the differential equation is transformed into difference form, we get a relationship of the form $y_{n+1} = f(y_n, y_{n-1}, \Delta t)$. With the initial conditions, this relationship yields values of y at the points $0, \Delta t, 2\Delta t, \ldots$ Derivatives become difference quotients and clearly we have *linearized approximations* in each interval. It is also clear that laborious computation is involved, which becomes more accurate as the mesh gets finer but at the expense of increasing the computation (and the need for gigaflop computers).

To discuss some simple examples consider the linear equation $d^2y/dt^2 + y = 0$ with $y(0) = 1$ and $y'(0) = 0$ or perhaps the nonlinear equation $dy/dt = y^2 - y$ with $y(0) = 2$. The solution to the first is $y = \cos t$. The solution to the second is $2/(2 - e^x)$, which is singular at $x = \ln 2$.

Now instead of discretizing and linearizing, we will use the decomposition method, which offers considerable advantages. The equation $d^2y/dt^2 + y = 0$

107

is written as $Ly = -y$, where $L = d^2/dt^2$, then $y = y_0 - L^{-1}y$, where $y_0 = y(0) + ty'(0) = 1$, $y_1 = -L^{-1}(1) = -t^2/2$, $y_2 = t^4/4!$, etc., and hence $y = 1 - (t^2/2) + (t^4/4!) - \cdots$. Let us consider the second equation $dy/dt = y^2 - y$. We can write immediately

$$y = y(0) - L^{-1}y + L^{-1} \sum_{n=0}^{\infty} A_n$$

$$y_0 = y(0) = 2$$

$$y_1 = -L^{-1}y_0 + L^{-1}A_0$$
$$\vdots$$

Evaluating the A_n polynomials for the y^2 nonlinearity, $A_0 = y_0^2$, $A_1 = 2y_0y_1$, $A_2 = y_1^2 + 2y_0y_2$, $A_3 = 2y_1y_2 + 2y_0y_3, \ldots$. Hence

$$y_0 = 2$$

$$y_1 = 2x$$

$$y_2 = 3x^2$$
$$\vdots$$

The solution is therefore given by

$$y = 2 + 2x + 3x^2 + (13x^3/3) + (75x^4/12) + \cdots$$

Convergence has been discussed previously in the literature and also in Chapter 12. Consequently, using the ratio test, we find $x < \frac{52}{75}$ or $x < 0.693$. In this region of convergence, any value of x yields a convergent series. Suppose, for example, that $x = 0.1$; then $y = 2 + 0.2 + 0.03 + 0.0039 + \cdots$.

Nonlinear partial differential equations are also very easily calculated. Since the decomposition method does not linearize, solves continuously (which by discrete methods would require infinite computation), and is very computable with no cumbersome integrals as arise in Picard's method, then a new approach to many problems is suggested.

Relationship of Difference and Delay Operators: Delay operators were considered in Chapter 6. The value of y at time t_n or $y(t = t_n)$ will be symbolized by y_n. The delayed function $y(t_n - \tau)$ will be written as $Dy(t_n)$ or Dy_n. If $t_n - \tau = t_{n-1}$ (i.e., $\tau = t_n - t_{n-1}$), then

$$Dy_n = y_{n-1} \tag{7.1.1}$$

Analogously we can write

$$D^{-1}y_n = y_{n+1} \tag{7.1.2}$$

so the inverse of D means an advancing operation as opposed to a delaying operation. Thus, difference equations can be investigated in terms of differential-delay equations as in Chapter 6.

Difference Equations for Computers: We consider here the most common use of difference equations for numerical solution of differential and partial differential equations by discretization.

A *backward difference operator* δ is defined by

$$\delta y_n = y_n - y_{n-1} \tag{7.1.3}$$

A second backward difference of y_n is given by $\delta^2 y_n = \delta(\delta y_n) = \delta(y_n - y_{n-1}) = \delta y_n - \delta y_{n-1}$ or

$$\delta^2 y_n = y_n - 2y_{n-1} + y_{n-2} \tag{7.1.4}$$

Similarly,

$$\delta^3 y_n = y_n - 3y_{n-1} + 3y_{n-2} - y_{n-3} \tag{7.1.5}$$

Analogously a *forward difference operator* η can be written as

$$\eta y_n = y_{n+1} - y_n \tag{7.1.6}$$

i.e., the value of y at time t_{n+1} minus the value at time t_n.

We observe the connection to the delay and inverse delay operators by writing

$$\delta = 1 - D, \qquad \eta = D^{-1} - 1 \tag{7.1.7}$$

Repeated operations by η are easily defined, thus

$$\eta^2 y_n = \eta(\eta y_n) = \eta(y_{n+1} - y_n) \quad \text{or} \quad \eta^2 = y_{n+2} - 2y_{n+1} + y_n \tag{7.1.8}$$

and

$$\eta^3 y_n = y_{n+3} - 3y_{n+2} + 3y_{n+1} - y_n \tag{7.1.9}$$

To relate these difference operators to differential operators, we write the Taylor expansion for $y(t_{n+1})$ or y_{n+1}

$$\begin{aligned} y(t_n + \tau) &= y(t_n) + \tau y'(t_n) + (\tau^2/2!)y''(t_n) \\ &\quad + \cdots + (\tau^n/n!)y^{(n)}(t_n) + \cdots \\ &= y_n + \tau y'_n + (\tau^2/2!)y''_n + \cdots \end{aligned}$$

but the left-hand side, or y_{n+1}, is $D^{-1}y_n$ in terms of our delay operators. Thus

$$D^{-1}y_n = \left\{ 1 + \tau \frac{d}{dt} + \cdots + \frac{\tau^n}{n!} \frac{d^n}{dt^n} + \cdots \right\} y_n \tag{7.1.10}$$

We can write the bracketed quantity as an expansion of the operator exponential $\exp(\tau \, d/dt)$. Hence,

$$D^{-1} = e^{\tau d/dt} \tag{7.1.11}$$

Similarly we can write $Dy_n = y_{n-1}$, or $y(t_n - \tau) = y(t_n) - \tau\, y'(t_n) + \cdots =$ $\exp(-\tau\, d/dt)y(t_n)$ or

$$D = e^{-\tau\, d/dt} \tag{7.1.12}$$

Since the backward difference operator $\delta = 1 - D$, we have $\delta = 1 - D = 1 - \exp(-\tau\, d/dt)$ or

$$e^{-\tau\, d/dt} = 1 - \delta, \qquad -\tau\, d/dt = \ln(1 - \delta) \tag{7.1.13}$$

and expansion of the function in a series yields

$$\frac{d}{dt} = \frac{1}{\tau}\left[\delta + \frac{\delta^2}{2} + \frac{\delta^3}{3} + \cdots + \frac{\delta^{n+1}}{n+1} + \cdots\right] \tag{7.1.14}$$

Thus we have useful (operator) relations between differentials, differences, and delays, and a differential can be given in terms of differences or delays with some truncation of course. We must take a finite (two, for example) number of terms in numerical analysis. Since the grid spacing $\Delta t = \tau$ is small, the series is usually convergent and is generally *assumed to be* convergent, and the first of the neglected terms will be the largest. This is called a finite difference approximation. Since the series is truncated, there is a truncation error which is the sum of the neglected terms. From (7.1.13) the inverse relation for δ as a series in derivatives is easily obtained as

$$\delta = 1 - \left[1 - \tau\frac{d}{dt} + \frac{\tau^2}{2!}\frac{d^2}{dt^2} - \frac{\tau^3}{3!}\frac{d}{dt} + \cdots\right]$$

or

$$\delta = \tau\frac{d}{dt} - \frac{\tau^2}{2!}\frac{d^2}{dt} + \frac{\tau^3}{3!}\frac{d^3}{dt} - \cdots \tag{7.1.15}$$

These relations are easily extended to higher derivatives and differences

$$\delta^2 = [1 - e^{-\tau\, d/dt}]^2$$
$$= 1 + e^{-2\tau\, d/dt} - 2e^{-\tau\, d/dt}$$
$$= 1 + \left[1 - \frac{2\tau\, d/dt}{1!} + \frac{4\tau\, d^2/dt^2}{2!} - \cdots\right]$$
$$- 2\left[1 - \frac{\tau\, d/dt}{1!} + \frac{\tau^2\, d^2/dt^2}{2!} - \cdots\right] \tag{7.1.16}$$

$$\frac{d^2}{dt^2} = (1/\tau^2)[\delta^2 - \delta^3 + \tfrac{11}{12}\delta^4 - \tfrac{5}{6}\delta^5 + \cdots] \qquad (7.1.17)$$

$$\frac{d^3}{d\tau^3} = (1/\tau^3)[\delta^3 - \tfrac{3}{2}\delta^4 + \tfrac{7}{4}\delta^5 - \cdots] \qquad (7.1.18)$$

$$\frac{d^4}{dt^4} = (1/\tau^4)[\delta^4 - 2\delta^5 + \tfrac{17}{6}\delta^6 - \cdots] \qquad (7.1.19)$$

As pointed out by Hovanessian [1], an error of order τ^4 in evaluating δ^2 means we have neglected the term $(\tfrac{7}{12}\tau^4(d^4/dt^4)$ and all the following terms. These higher derivatives were unknown and unevaluated and even the fourth derivative would be unknown in many problems so the absolute value of the error is unknown. Smaller τ and increased computation time are the recourse. Relationships given by Hovanessian [1] for the forward difference operator are

$$\eta = \tau\frac{d}{dt} + \frac{\tau^2}{2!}\frac{d^2}{dt^2} + \frac{\tau^3}{3!}\frac{d^3}{dt^3} + \cdots$$

$$\frac{d}{dt} = \frac{1}{\tau}\left[\eta - \frac{\eta^2}{2} + \frac{\eta^3}{3} - \cdots\right]$$

$$\eta^2 = \tau^2\frac{d^2}{dt^2} + \tau^3\frac{d^3}{dt^3} + \frac{7}{12}\tau^4\frac{d^4}{dt^4} + \cdots \qquad (7.1.20)$$

$$\frac{d^2}{dt^2} = \frac{1}{\tau^2}\left[\eta^2 - \eta^3 + \frac{11}{12}\eta^4 - \cdots\right]$$

Since we do *not* intend to use finite difference methods, we refer interested readers to texts in numerical analysis and computer methods. Our purpose is twofold: first, to connect difference equations to differential equations by using our previously defined delay operator so our decomposition method can deal with difference equations and, second, to make clear the advantages of the decomposition method to avoid the massive computations otherwise required in solving differential equations—if τ is taken small enough for a reasonably accurate solution, the number of equations to be solved then becomes enormous! Let us consider an example:

$$\frac{d^2y}{dt^2} + \frac{dy}{dt} + y = 0$$

with $y(0) = 1$ and $y'(0) = 0$. The discretized version is

$$\frac{d^2y_i}{dt^2} + \frac{dy_i}{dt} + y_i = 0$$

Replace d^2y_i/dt^2 by $[y_{i-1} - 2y_i + y_{i+1}]/\tau^2$ (for an error of order τ^2), where τ (usually written h) is the interval Δt and replace dy_i/dt by $[y_{i+1} - y_{i-1}]/2\tau$ (for an error of order τ^2). The differential equation becomes

$$y_{i+1} = \frac{1}{2 + \tau} [(4 - 2\tau^2)y_i + (\tau - 2)y_{i-1}]$$

which can be used as a recursive relation for y_{i+1} in terms of the previous values y_i and y_{i-1}. Note that for $\Delta t = 0.01$, to get the value of y at $t = 10$ sec requires 1000 solutions of the above equation or 8000 actual computations. For 1 min, this means 6000 solutions or 48,000 actual computations. Note that if we consider an equation in two independent variables x and t we require a Δx and Δt and the computations will go up several orders of magnitude. We can easily visualize a problem leading to a billion coupled difference equations to solve. For a simple scalar elliptic equation, we have one unknown at each mesh point. For more complex problems, there can be many unknowns at each mesh point, and the resulting systems of difference equations (instead of being linear as in the previous case) may be nonlinear, time-dependent, and very large. (Inclusion of stochastic coefficients, etc., is still another matter.) To solve massive systems, iterative procedures are used to solve simpler systems, then substitution is used to get "residuals" and repetitions of the process to produce corrections until the error is (or is felt to be) within tolerable limits. To get accuracy the mesh must become very fine and the computations required must finally exceed any conceivable computer capability for complicated equations in x, y, z, and t.

Our solution, on the other hand, is *continuous* (see also Sarafyan [2]), which would correspond to an infinite number of computations by discretization. *No linearization is involved, and the solution is accurate.* If variable coefficients, several independent variables, and nonlinearities are involved, the decomposition method is to be preferred. For stochastic equations, the case is stronger, since computer results are not correct when stochastic processes are discretized. Since recent results show that the method applies to partial differential equations as well, the comparisons become stronger still. The fact that our solution is analytic means we can see relationships impossible to see with massive printouts and that we can verify the solution.

To solve the same problem by the decomposition method, we write

$$Ly = -y - dy/dt$$

and operating with L^{-1} (a double integral from 0 to t) we get

$$y = y_0 - L^{-1}y - L^{-1}(d/dt)y$$

$$y_0 = y(0) + ty'(0) = 1$$

$$y_1 = -L^{-1}y_0 - L^{-1}(d/dt)\, y_0 = -L^{-1}[1] - L^{-1}[0]$$
$$= -t^2/2$$

$$y_2 = -L^{-1}y_1 - L^{-1}(d/dt)\, y_1$$
$$= -L^{-1}[-(t^2/2)] - L^{-1}[(d/dt)(-t^2/2)]$$
$$= (t^3/6) + (t^4/24)$$

$$y_3 = -L^{-1}y_2 - L^{-1}(d/dt)\, y_2$$
$$= -L^{-1}[(t^3/6) + (t^4/24)] - L^{-1}\{(d/dt)[(t^3/6) + (t^4/24)]\}$$
$$= -(t^4/24) - (t^5/60) - (t^6/720)$$

Verifying by substitution to the same power to t, $y \approx 1 - (t^2/2)$, $y' = -t + (t^2/2)$, $y'' = -1 + t$, which add to zero. If we carry terms to the cubics, $y \simeq 1 - (t^2/2) + (t^3/6)$, $y' = -t + (t^2/2)$, $y'' = -1 + t - (t^3/3)$, which again add to zero. For $t < 2$ the solution is convergent. At $t = 1$, for example, in the convergent region, we have $1 - \frac{1}{2} + \frac{1}{6} - \frac{1}{60} - \frac{1}{720} + \cdots$, which rapidly yields an accurate solution.

7.2. A DIFFERENTIAL-DIFFERENCE EQUATION

$$y'_{n+1}(t) = y_n(t), \qquad y_0(t) = t, \quad y_n(0) = n$$

$$y'_1 = y_0, \qquad Ly_1 = y_0$$

Writing y_{1_0}, or $y_1(0)$, for the first term of y_1,

$$y_1 = y_1(0) + L^{-1}y_0 = 1 + L^{-1}t = 1 + (t^2/2!)$$

$$Ly_2 = y_1$$

$$y_2 = y_2(0) + L^{-1}y_1 = 2 + L^{-1}[1 + (t^2/2)]$$
$$= 2 + [t + (t^3/3!)]$$

$$y_3 = y_3(0) + L^{-1}[2 + t + (t^3/3!)]$$
$$= 3 + 2t + (t^2/2!) + (t^4/4!)$$

Continuing in the same way, we can write immediately

$$y_n(t) = n + (n - 1)t + \frac{(n - 2)t^2}{2!}$$

$$+ \frac{(n - 3)t^3}{3!} + \cdots + \frac{t^{n-1}}{(n - 1)!} + \frac{t^{n+1}}{(n + 1)!}$$

which is the solution.

7.3. DIFFERENCE EQUATIONS AND THE DECOMPOSITION METHOD

It is interesting to contemplate writing analogous differential equations for difference equations and solving the resulting equation. The connection would clearly be to write $y(t_n) = y_n$, or a_n in a difference equation. Thus, the difference equation would simply provide relations between values of y at discrete times and $y'(t)$ would correspond to $\delta y_n / \tau$ if $\tau = \Delta t$. If we consider $t = 1, t = 2, \ldots$ then $y' = a_{n+1} - a_n$ as a first linear approximation, and to the same approximation, $y'' = a_{n+1} - 2a_n + a_{n-1}$. Thus, $a_{n+1} = -a_n$ would be written as $a_{n+1} - a_n = -2a_n$ or $y' = -2y$. If $y(0) = k$, we get $y = k[1 - 2t + 2t^2 - \frac{4}{3}t^3 + \cdots]$. Thus, from $t = 0$, $a_0 = k$. From $t = 1$, $a_1 = k[1 - 2 + 2 - \frac{4}{3} + \cdots]$. We will not investigate the idea further since it is of less interest physically. The difference equations generally arise in using numerical methods to solve differential equations. Since the series obtained will not generally be convergent for all t, we would contemplate this only for the first few a_n or for problems leading to series convergent everywhere.

7.4. SOME REMARKS ON SUPERCOMPUTERS

Supercomputers are developing rapidly because of the urgent need in meteorology, fluid dynamics, fusion research, intelligent missile guidance, and weapons design. In fluid dynamics, for example, they are considered essential for the solution of Navier–Stokes equations, which are relevant to turbulence, internal waves in the ocean, and future development of hypersonic flight vehicles and engines (see Adomian [3]). Supercomputers are also essential for VLSI devices, seismology, reservoir modeling, bioengineering, and studies of the national economy.

To solve an aircraft problem on contemplated next-generation computers, a three-dimensional mesh is generated which discretizes the system of nonlinear partial differential equations into a million, a hundred million, or perhaps a billion coupled difference equations in as many unknowns. We begin to see then the tremendous data-handling problem, the necessity for improved algorithms (see particularly reference [3]), and the need for still greater computational speed. We may also have many unknowns at each point, and, as we have pointed out, the system nonlinearities and random fluctuations need to be taken into consideration. Usual solutions are iterative—first solving an approximation to the original system of differential equations and then improving the solution by repeated substitution of each new solution. Parallel processing is complicated by the difficulty of partitioning the work so that each processor can work independently. Thus the massive computation and complexities are due to the discretization.

In all such problems we need to be able to solve coupled systems of nonlinear (and generally stochastic as well) partial differential equations with complex boundary conditions and possible delayed effects. These systems are *linearized* and *discretized* (and the stochastic aspects are either ignored or improperly dealt with), so that the various numerical approximation methods can be used. This requires faster and faster supercomputers to do these computations in a reasonable time. Fifth-generation computers may operate at speeds up to 1000 megaflops (1 gigaflop) or 10^9 operations per second. NASA's numerical aerodynamic simulator, expected in 1986 or 1987, will operate at 1 gigaflop with a 240-million-word memory.

Unfortunately the further developments in supercomputers can quite possibly give wrong answers faster and faster because even a single one-dimensional nonlinear differential equation without stochasticity in coefficients, inputs, and boundary conditions, let alone vector partial differential equations in space and time with nonlinear and/or stochastic parameters, is not solved exactly. Real systems are nonlinear and stochastic. When you throw out these "complications," you have a different problem! When you linearize and use perturbative methods, you solve a mathematized problem, not the physical problem. The model equations, even before the linearization, discretization, etc., are already wrong because the stochastic behavior is generally not incorporated or is incorporated incorrectly as an afterthought. For example, for a wave propagation in a medium of random index of refraction, we cannot start from the ordinary wave equation derived for the deterministic case and then let c in the d'Alembertian operator be random. We cannot write immediately a Helmholtz equation assuming no spectral spreading. In a real ocean, velocity, density, and pressure are stochastic, not constants. Present treatment of Navier–Stokes equations solves a simplistic model, not real behavior [3]. Turbulence is a strongly nonlinear, strongly stochastic phenomenon not understood using linearized perturbative treatments. Generally the theories of physics are perturbative theories and the theories of mathematics are for linear operators (other than some *ad hoc* methods for special nonlinear equations). What is needed is a way of solving one or more nonlinear stochastic operator equations whether algebraic, differential, delay-differential, partial-differential, or systems of such equations. To solve the national economy or control it, we need to solve systems involving the real fluctuations and nonlinearities that are present. Taxes, for example, are not a linear function of income. A supercomputer is, after all, a fast adding machine and its computational accuracy is dependent on the sophistication of the mathematical methods programmed into it. Typical calculations consider millions of discrete time intervals made small enough so that trajectories between them can be taken as low-order polynomials, e.g., quadratics. If stochasticity is involved, then Monte Carlo methods are used, thus inserting randomness but not the properly correlated randomness that is present in the physical problem.

Recently, efforts are proceeding in extending linear hydrodynamics from the macroscopic scale to the microscopic. This is called generalized hydrodynamics. Essentially the form of Navier–Stokes equations is kept, but time and distance scales are introduced so one can go beyond the continuum approximation and take account of molecular structure. However, application to a real situation becomes simply a test of the validity of the linear approximations as pointed out by Alder and Alley [4]. Fluctuations are, as usual, assumed "small" and delayed effects, due to the fact that responses cannot be instantaneous, are ignored.

When one studies airflow about aircraft surfaces, computations are made at tens of millions of points, and it is felt that increasing the volume of computation to the limit in an ultimate extrapolation of present supercomputers will yield complete accuracy. Not only does this ignore stochasticity, it ignores the sensitivity of nonlinear stochastic systems to very slight changes in the model—in fact, to changes essentially undeterminable by measurement.

REFERENCES

1. S. A. Hovanessian, "Computational Mathematics in Engineering," D. C. Heath, Lexington, Massachusetts, 1976.
2. D. Sarafyan, An investigation concerning fifth-order scalar and vectors Runge–Kutta processes, *Riv. Mat.* 2, 41–45 (1971).
3. G. Adomian, "Applications of Stochastic Systems Theory to Physics," to appear.
4. B. J. Alder and W. E. Alley, Generalized hydrodynamics, *Phys. Today*, 37, 56 (1984).

SUGGESTED FURTHER READING

R. Bellman, Asymptotic series for the solutions of linear differential-difference equations, *Rendi. Circ. Mat. Palermo (2)* 7, 1–9 (1958).
R. Bellman and G. Adomian, "Partial Differential Equations—New Methods for Their Treatment and Applications. Reidel, Dordrecht, Netherlands, 1985.
B. Carnahan, H. A. Luther, and J. A. Wilkes, "Applied Numerical Methods." Wiley, New York, 1969.
G.-C. Rota, "Finite Operator Calculus," Academic Press, New York, 1975.
M. Elrod, Numerical methods for the solution of stochastic differential equations. Ph.D. Dissertation, Center for Applied Mathematics, Univ. of Georgia, Athens, Georgia, 1973.

CHAPTER 8

Random Eigenvalue Equations

We will begin as simply as possible by considering the stochastic Sturm–Liouville problem in the form

$$\mathscr{L}u = \lambda[1 + \eta(x)]u \qquad (8.1)$$

where $\mathscr{L}$ is a linear stochastic second-order differential operator and $\mathscr{L} = L + \mathscr{R}$ with L a deterministic operator and $\mathscr{R}$ a stochastic operator. The general case of nonlinear stochastic operators is considered in the next section. Appropriate smoothness conditions for coefficients are assumed, and L is assumed invertible. If it is not, the operator L is taken to be only the highest-ordered derivative in the deterministic part of the decomposition with the *remainder* being called R. Since this modification has been previously discussed, we can assume for now that $R = 0$. We require that the eigenvalue problem $Lu = \lambda u$ be solvable and that if $\mathscr{R} = 0$ then $\eta(x) = 0$, i.e., if the operator L becomes $L + \mathscr{R}$, then λ becomes $\lambda(1 + \eta(x))$.

In this section we assume that the boundary conditions (at zero and one) are also deterministic. The problem of *this* section has been considered by others, but here also we depart immediately from conventional treatments in that *no restrictive assumption of "smallness"* is made for η limiting perturbative methods and/or (equivalently) hierarchy methods and closure approximations are not used, and no special nature (white noise, etc.) will be assumed for the stochastic process η. Clearly, of course, if the fluctuations *are* small, the same results will be obtained as in the perturbation case.

Suppose, as an example, Lu is given by $-u''$, i.e., $L = -d^2/dx^2$ and we have simple boundary conditions $u(0) = u(\pi) = 0$. Now $1 + \eta$ could symbolize a stochastic density for a taut string fixed at endpoints 0 and π. If $\mathscr{R}$ and η are zero, the equation reduces to $u'' + \lambda u = 0$ which is solved for solutions $u(\lambda)$

117

existing for a discrete set of λ values. The general solution in terms of the fundamental solutions $\sin \sqrt{\lambda} x$ and $\cos \sqrt{\lambda} x$ is

$$u(x, \lambda) = c_1(\lambda) \sin \sqrt{\lambda} x + c_2(\lambda) \cos \sqrt{\lambda} x$$

for $\lambda > 0$, or $\sum_{j=1}^{n} c_j(\lambda) u_j(x, \lambda)$ for arbitrary c_j, where the $u_j(x, \lambda)$ terms are the fundamental solutions. Use of the boundary condition $u(0) = 0$ means that

$$u(x) = c \sin \sqrt{\lambda} x \qquad (8.2)$$

Satisfying the boundary condition $u(\pi) = 0$, we have

$$\sqrt{\lambda} \pi = k\pi, \qquad k = 1, 2, 3, \ldots$$

Hence

$$\lambda_k = k^2 = 1, 4, 9, \ldots$$

are the eigenvalues and the corresponding eigenfunctions are $\sin x$, $\sin 2x$, $\sin 3x, \ldots$. The k eigenfunctions will be identified as the u_{0k}.

Thus, in general, use of the boundary conditions symbolized by $U_i(u) = 0$ yields

$$U_i\left(\sum_{j=1}^{n} c_j u_j \right) = \sum_{j=1}^{n} c_j U_i(u_j) = 0$$

a set of linear algebraic equations whose solution yields the eigenvalues.

Having solved $Lu = \lambda u$ we have the eigenvalues λ for $\eta = 0$. When $\mathcal{R}$ and consequently $\eta \neq 0$ we have (8.1). Assume $u = \sum_{n=0}^{\infty} u_n$, where u_{0k} represents the solutions for $\eta = 0$.

The solutions u_{0k} for $k = 1, 2, \ldots$ for the deterministic problem ($\eta = 0$) will become *randomized* when we include the η. The u_{0k} terms are the solutions of the homogeneous equation $(L - \lambda)u = 0$. Now we have $Lu - \lambda u = \lambda \eta u$ and the right side is like a forcing function or inhomogeneous term. The previous solution, therefore, must be added to the solutions of $u = \lambda L^{-1}(1 + \eta)u$. Using the decomposition method and calling the homogeneous solution u_{0k},

$$\sum_{n=0}^{\infty} u_{nk} = u_{0k} + \lambda L^{-1}(1 + \eta) \sum_{n=0}^{\infty} u_{nk}$$

$$= u_{0k} + \lambda L^{-1}(1 + \eta)[u_{0k} + u_{1k} + \cdots]$$

Thus

$$u_{1k} = \lambda L^{-1}(1 + \eta)u_{0k}$$
$$\vdots \qquad\qquad\qquad (8.3)$$
$$u_{n+1, k} = \lambda L^{-1}(1 + \eta)u_{nk}$$

Thus, for any particular "unperturbed" eigenfunction, we find $\sum_{n=0}^{\infty} u_{nk}$ to get the randomized solution. The $k = 1$ solution was $\sin x$. Hence for this k (and dropping k)

$$u_0 = \sin x$$
$$u_1 = \lambda L^{-1}(1 + \eta) \sin x$$
$$u_2 = \lambda L^{-1}(1 + \eta)u_1 \tag{8.4}$$
$$u_3 = \lambda L^{-1}(1 + \eta)u_2$$

etc, and the sum indicates the randomized eigenfunction for the first eigenvalue

$$u_1 = \sin x + \lambda L^{-1}(1 + \eta) \sin x + \lambda L^{-1}(1 + \eta)\lambda L^{-1}(1 + \eta) \sin x + \cdots \tag{8.5}$$

which is a stochastic series since η and u are stochastic. We can now average to get $\langle u \rangle$ or get correlations, variances, etc., by taking a finite number of terms. The errors have been thoroughly discussed (Adomian [1]) and the series converges. Let us look at a few terms. Suppose η is zero-mean. Then

$$\langle u \rangle = \sin x + \lambda L^{-1} \sin x + \lambda L^{-1} \lambda L^{-1} \sin x + \cdots$$

thus the mean is not the deterministic solution. Similarly, u_2 is found by using the $u_{02} = \sin 2x$ solution, etc.

If we replace $\lambda(1 + \eta)$ by Λ, a stochastic eigenvalue, we can decompose Λ into $\Lambda_0 + \Lambda_r$, where Λ_0 is the deterministic part corresponding to the previous λ and Λ_r is the random part corresponding to the previous $\lambda\eta$.

If the linear operator is not easily invertible, L^{-1} will represent only the invertible portion. Then

$$u = \lambda L^{-1}(1 + \eta)u - Ru$$

and proceed as before. Then $u_{n+1} = \lambda L^{-1}(1 + \eta)u_n - Ru_n$.

Now consider stochastic nonlinear eigenvalue problems given by

$$\mathscr{F}u = \Lambda u \tag{8.6}$$

where $\mathscr{F}$ is a nonlinear stochastic operator, and the eigenvalues are random. Then with $\mathscr{R}$ a random operator, N a nonlinear operator, and Λ decomposed into deterministic and random parts λ, and λ_r,

$$Lu + \mathscr{R}u + Nu = (\lambda + \lambda_r)u \tag{8.7}$$

Again assume L is invertible. (If not, the invertible part only is taken as L and the remainder is R.) Solving for Lu

$$Lu = (\lambda + \lambda_r)u - \mathscr{R}u - Nu - Ru \tag{8.8}$$

$$u = u_0 + L^{-1}(\lambda + \lambda_r)u - L^{-1}\mathscr{R}u - L^{-1}\sum_{n=0}^{\infty} A_n - L^{-1}Ru$$

where $Nu = \sum_{n=0}^{\infty} A_n$ is defined in terms of Adomian's polynomials for the particular nonlinearity and u_0, or generally u_{0k}, is the solution of $Lu = \lambda u$ as before. Since generally we have a set of k eigenvalues, a subscript k is also necessary but suppressed for now. Then, since $u - \sum_{n=0}^{\infty} u_n$,

$$u_1 = L^{-1}(\lambda + \lambda_r)u_0 - L^{-1}\mathscr{R}u_0 - L^{-1}A_0 - L^{-1}Ru_0 \qquad (8.9)$$

etc., as before, i.e., u_{1k} in terms of the u_{0k} so each $u_{n+1,k}$ can be found in terms of the $u_{n,k}$, and are therefore determinable having first found the k eigenvalues in the linear deterministic case.

The harmonic oscillator is a well-used application in physics. A mass m attached to a fixed point by an elastic spring or pendulum is generally represented linearly with a force $F = -k\xi$, where ξ is the displacement. A particle moving near a point of stable equilibrium approximates these conditions since, near this point, the potential energy function $V(\xi)$, or $V(x - a)$, where a is the equilibrium point, is a "well" of parabolic shape, and, expanding it in powers of ξ, the first derivative is proportional to the force and must vanish when evaluated at $\xi = 0$, where V is taken as zero, yielding $V = k\xi^2/2$ to second-order terms. Near equilibrium points, systems are often represented as harmonic oscillators. In quantum mechanics, the time-independent Schrödinger equation is an eigenvalue equation in the form $L\psi = \lambda\psi$, where the eigenvalues λ represent energy levels and L represents the Hamiltonian operator written as $H = -(h^2/2m)\,\nabla^2 + V$, and if $V = kx^2/2$, we have

$$-\frac{h^2}{2m}\,\nabla^2\psi + \frac{kx^2}{2}\,\psi = E\psi$$

In the one-dimensional case one writes

$$-\frac{h^2}{2m}\frac{d^2\phi}{dx^2} + \frac{k}{2}\,x^2\psi = E\psi$$

Transformation of the independent variable yields the Sturm–Liouville form

$$\frac{d^2\psi}{dx^2} + (\lambda - x^2)\psi = 0 \qquad (8.10)$$

A further transformation—this time of the dependent variable using $\psi(x) = v(x)y(x)$, where $v(x) = e^{-x^2/2}$—to satisfy behavior at $\pm\infty$ yields

$$\frac{d^2y}{dx^2} - 2x\frac{dy}{dx} - (1 - \lambda)y = 0$$

which is Hermite's equation with eigenvalues determined as $\lambda = 2n + 1$, $n = 0, 1, 2, 3,\ldots$.

Consider now the Sturm–Liouville form (8.1) with $L = d^2/dx^2$:[1]

$$Ly - x^2y + \lambda y = 0$$

This comes from the general form:

$$\frac{d}{dx}\left(p(x)\frac{dy}{dx}\right) - s(x)y + \lambda r(x)y = 0$$

if $s(x) = x^2$, $r(x) = 1$, and $p(x) = 1$. Instead of finding the Green's function for the Sturm–Liouville operator, we seek only to invert $L = d^2/dx^2$ writing

$$Ly = x^2y - \lambda y \qquad (8.11)$$

Since we choose L as only the highest-ordered derivative d^n/dx^n or in this case d^2/dx^2, we do not need the Green's function of the entire Sturm–Liouville operator [2] but only the simple Green's function for L. Thus,

$$\frac{d^2G(x, \xi)}{dx^2} = \xi(x - \xi)$$

and integrating twice,

$$G(x, \xi) = (x - \xi)H(x - \xi) + x\alpha(\xi) + \beta(\xi)$$

Specification of the boundary conditions now determines the arbitrary functions α and β. For example, if $y(0) = y(1) = 0$, then

$$G(x, \xi) = (x - \xi)H(x - \xi) - x(1 - \xi)$$

i.e., the inverse of the differential operator d^2/dx^2 with boundary conditions $y(0) = y(1) = 0$ is the integral operator whose kernel is $G(x, \xi)$ as given. Different boundary conditions will, of course, yield a different G since α and β will change.

We now have

$$y = L^{-1}x^2y - (\lambda + \lambda_r)L^{-1}y$$

$$= y_0 + \int_a^b G(x, \xi)x^2y\,dx - (\lambda + \lambda_r)\int_a^b G(x, \xi)y\,dx$$

with y_0, or y_{0k}, the solution of $Ly = \lambda y$ and appropriate G for the given boundary conditions, since we can assume the deterministic eigenvalue problem previously solved, treat the y_k obtained as y_{0k}, and use decomposition to see the effect of randomization as well as nonlinear terms.

---

[1] L^{-1} is the double integration from a to b.

REFERENCES

1. G. Adomain, "Stochastic Systems." Academic Press, New York, 1983.

SUGGESTED FURTHER READING

R. Bellman, Eigenvalues and Functional Equations, *Proc. Amer. Math. Soc.* **8**, 68–72 (1957).
W. A. Boyce, Random eigenvalue problems *in* "Probabilistic Methods in Applied Mathematics,"
(A. T. Bharucha-Reid, ed.), pp. 2–71. Academic Press, New York, 1968.

CHAPTER 9

Partial Differential Equations

> "On the one hand, their analytical methods were not powerful enough to deal with the problem of nonlinearity; on the other hand, purely numerical techniques were not far advanced nor were they feasible from the standpoints of economics and engineering. Taking the only possible way out, they changed the problem, tailoring it to fit their modest mathematical means. Specifically, they "linearized" the equations using the perturbation methods ..."
>
> *Philip Duncan Thompson*

9.1. SOLVING m-DIMENSIONAL EQUATIONS

The subject of (nonlinear) partial differential equations has been aptly described by J. L. Kazdan as a wilderness. This chapter deals with frontier applications of science which lead us naturally to the study of partial differential equations in space and time. Current developments in mathematical physics, energy problems, and other areas have given impetus to such research and to linearization techniques. The techniques employed assume essentially that a nonlinear system is "almost linear" in order to take advantage of well-known techniques. Often, unfortunately, the assumption has little *physical* justification. It has become vital, not only to mathematics but to the areas of application, that further advances be made. Fluid mechanics, soliton physics, quantum field theory, and nonlinear evolution equations are all areas that can benefit from such advances. In fluid mechanics, for example, the usual analyses are far indeed from any physical reality when they deal with a "mathematized" ocean bearing no resemblance to a real ocean in which strong nonlinearities and strong stochasticity are clearly involved in a reasonable model.

123

In some areas, such as turbulence studies (and, quite possibly, many or all of the other areas), once possibilities are recognized, *stochasticity* is also a significant factor in the actual behavior.

Let us begin with the general form $\mathscr{F}u = g$, where g may be a function of space variables x, y, and z, and time t

$$[\mathscr{L}_x + \mathscr{L}_y + \mathscr{L}_z + \mathscr{L}_t]u + \mathscr{N}u = g(x, y, z, t) \qquad (9.1.1)$$

where $\mathscr{N}(u)$ indicates any nonlinear term possibly involving derivatives of u, products, etc. Since $\mathscr{L} = L + \mathscr{R}$, we have

$$(L_x + L_y + L_z + L_t)u + (\mathscr{R}_x + \mathscr{R}_y + \mathscr{R}_z + \mathscr{R}_t)u + \mathscr{N}u = g \quad (9.1.2)$$

We emphasize that $\mathscr{R}_x$, $\mathscr{R}_y$, $\mathscr{R}_z$, and $\mathscr{R}_t$, as well as g, are not necessarily random. They may be, or they may simply be a part of an entirely deterministic operator and be chosen only to make the remaining part easily invertible. We solve for L_xu, L_yu, L_zu, and L_tu, in turn, and then assuming inverses L_x^{-1}, L_y^{-1}, L_z^{-1}, and L_t^{-1} exist

$$\begin{aligned}
L_x^{-1}L_xu &= L_x^{-1}[g - L_yu - L_zu - L_tu] \\
&\quad - L_x^{-1}[\mathscr{R}_x + \mathscr{R}_y + \mathscr{R}_z + \mathscr{R}_t]u - L_x^{-1}\mathscr{N}u \\
L_y^{-1}L_yu &= L_y^{-1}[g - L_xu - L_zu - L_tu] \\
&\quad - L_y^{-1}[\mathscr{R}_x + \mathscr{R}_y + \mathscr{R}_z + \mathscr{R}_t]u - L_y^{-1}\mathscr{N}u \\
L_z^{-1}L_zu &= L_z^{-1}[g - L_xu - L_yu - L_tu] \\
&\quad - L_z^{-1}[\mathscr{R}_x + \mathscr{R}_y + \mathscr{R}_z + \mathscr{R}_t]u - L_z^{-1}\mathscr{N}u \\
L_t^{-1}L_tu &= L_t^{-1}[g - L_xu - L_yu - L_zu] \\
&\quad - L_t^{-1}[\mathscr{R}_x + \mathscr{R}_y + \mathscr{R}_z + \mathscr{R}_t]u - L_t^{-1}\mathscr{N}u
\end{aligned} \qquad (9.1.3)$$

A linear combination of these solutions is necessary. Therefore, adding and dividing by four, we write

$$\begin{aligned}
u = u_0 &- \tfrac{1}{4}[(L_x^{-1}L_y + L_y^{-1}L_x) + (L_x^{-1}L_z + L_z^{-1}L_x) \\
&+ (L_x^{-1}L_t + L_t^{-1}L_x) + (L_y^{-1}L_z + L_z^{-1}L_y) \\
&+ (L_t^{-1}L_y + L_y^{-1}L_t) + (L_z^{-1}L_t + L_t^{-1}L_z)]u \\
&- \tfrac{1}{4}[L_x^{-1} + L_y^{-1} + L_z^{-1} + L_t^{-1}][\mathscr{R}_x + \mathscr{R}_y + \mathscr{R}_z + \mathscr{R}_t]u \\
&- \tfrac{1}{4}[L_x^{-1} + L_y^{-1} + L_z^{-1} + L_t^{-1}]Nu
\end{aligned} \qquad (9.1.4)$$

where the term u_0 includes

$$\tfrac{1}{4}[L_x^{-1} + L_y^{-1} + L_z^{-1} + L_t^{-1}]g$$

as well as terms arising from the initial conditions which depend on the number of integrations involved in the inverse operators. Thus, $L_x^{-1}L_xu = u(x, y, z, t) - \theta_x$, where $L_x\theta_x = 0$. Thus, $L_x^{-1}L_xu = u(x, y, z, t) - u(0, y, z, t)$ if

L_x involves a single differentiation; $L_x^{-1}L_x u = u(x, y, z, t) - u(0, y, z, t) - x \, \partial u(0, y, z, t)/\partial x$ for a second order operator, etc. Similarly $L_y^{-1}L_y u = u - \theta_y$, where $\theta_y = u(x, 0, z, t)$ for a single differentiation in L_y, etc. Thus, we have the partial homogeneous solutions θ_x, θ_y, θ_z, and θ_t analogous to the one-dimensional problems considered in earlier work where we wrote $L_t^{-1}L_t u(t) = \int_0^t (du/dt) \, dt = u(t) - u(0)$ when $L_t \equiv d/dt$. Thus

$$u_0 = \tfrac{1}{4}[\theta_x + \theta_y + \theta_z + \theta_t] + \tfrac{1}{4}[L_x^{-1} + L_y^{-1} + L_z^{-1} + L_t^{-1}]g \quad (9.1.5)$$

We now write the nonlinear term Nu as $Nu = \sum_{n=0}^{\infty} A_n$ and assume our usual decomposition of u into $\sum_{n=0}^{\infty} u_n$, or equivalently, of $\mathcal{F}^{-1}g$ into $\sum_{n=0}^{\infty} \mathcal{F}_n^{-1}g$ to determine the individual components.

For m dimensional problems, we can write in a more condensed form,

$$u = u_0 - \frac{1}{m} \sum_{\substack{j=1+1 \\ (i \neq j)}}^{m} \sum_{i=1}^{m} [L_{x_i}^{-1}L_{x_j} + L_{x_j}^{-1}L_{x_i}]u$$

$$- \frac{1}{m}\left[\sum_{i=1}^{m} L_{x_i}^{-1}\right]\left[\sum_{i=1}^{m} \mathcal{R}_{x_i}\right]u - \frac{1}{m}\left[\sum_{i=1}^{m} L_{x_i}^{-1}\right]\sum_{n=0}^{\infty} A_n \quad (9.1.6)$$

where

$$u_0 = \frac{1}{m}\left[\sum_{i=1}^{m} \theta_i + \sum_{i=1}^{m} L_{x_i}^{-1}g\right]$$

Thus u_0 is easily calculated. The following components of the decomposition follow in terms of u_0. (There are no statistical separability problems in the stochastic case.) Thus,

$$u_1 = -\frac{1}{m} \sum_{\substack{j=i+1 \\ (i \neq j)}}^{m} \sum_{i=1}^{m-1} [L_{x_i}^{-1}L_{x_j} + L_{x_j}^{-1}L_{x_i}]u_0$$

$$- \frac{1}{m}\left[\sum_{i=1}^{m} L_{x_i}^{-1}\right]\left[\sum_{i=1}^{m} \mathcal{R}_{x_i}\right]u_0 - \frac{1}{m}\left[\sum_{i=1}^{m} L_{x_i}^{-1}\right]A_0$$

$$\vdots$$

$$u_n = -\frac{1}{m} \sum_{\substack{i=1 \\ (i \neq j)}}^{m} \sum_{j=1}^{m-1} [L_{x_i}^{-1}L_{x_j} + L_{x_j}^{-1}L_{x_i}]u_{n-1}$$

$$- \frac{1}{m}\left[\sum_{i=1}^{m} L_{x_i}^{-1}\right]\left[\sum_{i=1}^{m} \mathcal{R}_{x_i}\right]u_{n-1} - \frac{1}{m}\left[\sum_{i=1}^{m} L_{x_i}^{-1}\right]A_{n-1}$$

The complete solution is $u = \sum_{n=0}^{\infty} u_n$, and our n-term approximation ϕ_n is given by

$$\phi_n = \sum_{i=0}^{n-1} u_i$$

For the particular problem here,

$$u_0 = \tfrac{1}{4}[\theta_x + \theta_y + \theta_z + \theta_t] + \tfrac{1}{4}[L_x^{-1} + L_y^{-1} + L_z^{-1} + L_t^{-1}]g$$
$$\vdots$$
$$\begin{aligned}
u_n = &-\tfrac{1}{4}[(L_x^{-1}L_y + L_y^{-1}L_x) + (L_x^{-1}L_z + L_z^{-1}L_x) \\
&+ (L_x^{-1}L_t + L_t^{-1}L_x) + (L_y^{-1}L_z + L_z^{-1}L_y) \\
&+ (L_t^{-1}L_y + L_y^{-1}L_t) + (L_z^{-1}L_t + L_t^{-1}L_z)]u_{n-1} \\
&-\tfrac{1}{4}[L_y^{-1} + L_y^{-1} + L_z^{-1} + L_t^{-1}][\mathscr{R}_x + \mathscr{R}_y + \mathscr{R}_z + \mathscr{R}_t]u_{n-1} \\
&-\tfrac{1}{4}[L_x^{-1} + L_y^{-1} + L_z^{-1} + L_t^{-1}]A_{n-1}
\end{aligned}$$

In the one-dimensional ($m = 1$) case, the general solution reduces to the previous result for an ordinary differential equation:

$$u_0 = \theta_t + L_t^{-1}g$$
$$u_1 = -L_t^{-1}\mathscr{R}_t u_0 - L_t^{-1}A_0$$

etc. For simplicity in writing, we define

$$(L_x^{-1} + L_y^{-1} + L_z^{-1} + L_t^{-1})/4 \equiv L^{-1}$$

and

$$\begin{aligned}
\tfrac{1}{4}[&(L_x^{-1}Ly + L_y^{-1}L_x) + (L_x^{-1}L_z + L_z^{-1}L_x) \\
&+ (L_x^{-1}L_t + L_t^{-1}L_x) + (L_y^{-1}L_z + L_z^{-1}L_y) \\
&+ (L_t^{-1}L_y + L_y^{-1}L_t) + (L_z^{-1}L_t + L_t^{-1}L_z)] \equiv G
\end{aligned}$$

and

$$(\mathscr{R}_x + \mathscr{R}_y + \mathscr{R}_z + \mathscr{R}_t)/4 = \mathscr{R}$$

Then for $m = 4$

$$u = u_0 - Gu - L^{-1}\mathscr{R}u - L^{-1}Nu$$

In a one-dimensional case, Gu vanishes, the $\tfrac{1}{4}$ or $1/m$ factor is, of course, equal to one, and we have

$$u = u_0 - L^{-1}\mathscr{R}u - L^{-1}Nu$$

which is precisely the basis of earlier solutions of nonlinear ordinary differential equations.

For m dimensions, we write

$$L^{-1} = \frac{1}{m} \sum_{i=1}^{m} L_{x_i}^{-1}$$

$$\mathscr{R} = \frac{1}{m} \sum_{i=1}^{m} \mathscr{R}_{x_i}$$

Now

$$u = u_0 - \frac{1}{m} \sum_{j=i+1}^{m} \sum_{i=1}^{m-1} [L_{x_i}^{-1}L_{x_j} + L_{x_j}^{-1}L_{x_i}]u - L^{-1}\mathscr{R}u - L^{-1}Nu \quad (9.1.8)$$

which reduces to

$$u = u_0 - L^{-1}\mathscr{R}u - L^{-1}Nu$$

as previously written for ordinary differential equations when $m = 1$ since the second term vanishes.

PARAMETRIZATION AND THE A_n POLYNOMIALS: A parametrization of equation (9.1.8) into

$$u = u_0 - \left(\frac{1}{m}\right)\lambda \sum_{j=i+1}^{m} \sum_{i=1}^{m-1} [L_{x_i}^{-1}L_{x_j} + L_{x_j}^{-1}L_{x_i}]u - \lambda L^{-1}\mathscr{R}u - \lambda L^{-1}Nu \quad (9.1.9)$$

and $u = \mathscr{F}^{-1}g = \sum_{n=0}^{\infty} u_n$ into

$$u = \sum_{n=0}^{\infty} \lambda^n \mathscr{F}_n^{-1}g = \sum_{n=0}^{\infty} \lambda^n u_n \quad (9.1.10)$$

has been convenient in determining the components of u and also in finding the A_n polynomials originally. We will later set $\lambda = 1$ so $u = \sum_{n=0}^{\infty} u^n$. The λ is *not a perturbation parameter*. It is simply an identifier helping us to collect terms in a way that will result in each u_i depending only on $u_{i-1}, u_{i-2}, \ldots, u_0$, for the nonlinear case.

Now $\mathscr{N}(u)$ is a nonlinear function and $u = u(\lambda)$. We assume $\mathscr{N}(u)$ is analytic and write it as $\sum_{n=0}^{\infty} A_n \lambda^n$ if $\mathscr{N}(u) = Nu$, i.e., if N is deterministic. (If the nonlinear *stochastic* term $\mathscr{M}u$ appears, we simply carry that along as a second "stochastically analytic" expansion $\sum_{n=0}^{\infty} B_n \lambda^n$.)

Equation (9.1.9) now becomes

$$\sum_{n=0}^{\infty} \lambda^n \mathscr{F}_n^{-1}g = u_0 - \left(\frac{1}{m}\right)\lambda \sum_{j=i+1}^{m} \sum_{i=1}^{m-1} [L_{x_i}^{-1}L_{x_j} + L_{x_j}^{-1}L_{x_i}] \sum_{n=0}^{\infty} \lambda^n \mathscr{F}_n^{-1}g$$

$$- \lambda L^{-1}\mathscr{R} \sum_{n=0}^{\infty} \lambda^n \mathscr{F}_n^{-1}g - \lambda L^{-1} \sum_{n=0}^{\infty} \lambda^n A_n$$

Equating powers of λ

$$\mathscr{F}_0^{-1}g = u_0$$

$$\mathscr{F}_1^{-1}g = -\left(\frac{1}{m}\right) \sum_{j=i+1}^{m} \sum_{i=1}^{m-1} [L_{x_i}^{-1}L_{x_j}$$
$$+ L_{x_j}^{-1}L_{x_i}](\mathscr{F}_0^{-1}g) - L^{-1}\mathscr{R}(\mathscr{F}_0^{-1}g) - L^{-1}A_0 \qquad (9.1.12)$$

$$\vdots$$

$$\mathscr{F}_n^{-1}g = -\left(\frac{1}{m}\right) \sum_{j=i+1}^{m} \sum_{i=1}^{m-1} [L_{x_i}^{-1}L_{x_j}$$
$$+ L_{x_j}^{-1}L_{x_i}](\mathscr{F}_{n-1}^{-1}g) - L^{-1}\mathscr{R}(\mathscr{F}_{n-1}^{-1}g) - L^{-1}A_{n-1}$$

Hence, all terms are calculable. If there is both a deterministic and a stochastic term which are nonlinear, i.e., $\mathscr{N}u = Nu + \mathscr{M}u$, we also have $-L^{-1}B_{n-1}$ calculated the same way but involving randomness. If randomness is involved anywhere in any part of the equation, we will then calculate the statistical measures, e.g., the expectation and covariance of the solution process.

Thus, each $\mathscr{F}_{n+1}^{-1}g$ depends on $\mathscr{F}_n^{-1}g$ and ultimately on $\mathscr{F}_0^{-1}g$. Hence, the stochastic nonlinear inverse $\mathscr{F}^{-1}$ has been determined. The quantities A_n and B_n have been calculated for general classes of nonlinearities, and explicit formulas have been developed. Their calculation is as simple as writing down a set of Hermite or Legendre polynomials. They depend, of course, on the particular nonlinearity.

If stochastic quantities are involved, the above series then involves processes and can be averaged for $\langle u \rangle$ or multiplied and averaged to form the correlation $\langle u(t_1)\overset{*}{u}(t_2) \rangle = \mathscr{R}_u(t_1, t_2)$ as discussed in Adomian [1]. Thus, the solution statistics, or *statistical measures*, are obtained when appropriate statistical knowledge of the random quantities is available.

Summarizing, we have decomposed the solution process for the output of a physical system into additive components, the first being the solution of a simplified linear deterministic system which takes account of initial conditions. Each of the other components is then found in terms of a *preceding* component and, thus, ultimately in terms of the first.

The usual statistical separability problems requiring closure approximations are eliminated with the reasonable assumption of statistical independence of the system *input* and the system itself (although this assumption can be modified in some cases). Quasi-monochromaticity assumptions are *unnecessary*, and processes can be assumed to be general physical processes rather than white noise. White noise is not a physical process. Physical inputs are neither unbounded nor do they have zero correlation times. In any event, the results can be obtained as a special case. If fluctuations are small, the results of perturbation theory are exactly obtained, but again this is a special case, as are the diagrammatic methods of physicists.

Just as spectral spreading terms are lost by a quasi-monochromatic approximation, when a random or scattering medium is involved or terms are lost in the use of closure approximations, Boussinesq approximations, and replacement of stochastic quantities by their expectations, significant terms may be lost by the usual linearizations unless, of course, the behavior is actually close to linear.

One hopes, therefore, that physically more realistic and accurate results and predictions will be obtained in many physical problems by this method of solution, as well as interesting new mathematics from the study of such operators and relevant analysis.

9.2. FOUR-DIMENSIONAL LINEAR PARTIAL DIFFERENTIAL EQUATION

Consider $(\partial u/\partial x) + (\partial u/\partial y) + (\partial u/\partial z) + (\partial u/\partial t) = 0$. Assume initial conditions

$$u(0, y, z, t) = \theta_x = f_1(y, z, t) = -y + z - t$$

$$u(x, 0, z, t) = \theta_y = f_2(x, z, t) = x + z - t$$

$$u(x, y, 0, t) = \theta_z = f_3(x, y, t) = x - y - t$$

$$u(x, y, z, 0) = \theta_t = f_4(x, y, z) = x - y + z$$

[We note that $u(0, 0, 0, 0) = 0$.] In our usual notation we write

$$L_x + L_y + L_z + L_t = \mathscr{L}_{x,y,z,t}$$

and

$$\mathscr{L}u = 0$$

By the decomposition method, $u(x, y, z, t)$ is given by

$$u = \sum_{n=0}^{\infty} (-1)^n \left(\frac{1}{4}\right)^n \left[\sum_{j=i+1}^{4} \sum_{i=1}^{3} (L_{x_i}^{-1}L_{x_j} + L_{x_j}^{-1}L_{x_i})\right]^n \left(\frac{1}{4}\right)\left(\sum_{m=1}^{4} \theta_n\right)$$

The last sum $\sum_{m=1}^{4} \theta_m = 3x - 3y + 3z - 3t$, and the double summation within the square brackets is

$$[(L_x^{-1}L_y + L_y^{-1}L_x) + (L_x^{-1}L_z + L_z^{-1}L_x) + (L_x^{-1}L_t + L_t^{-1}L_x)$$
$$+ (L_y^{-1}L_z + L_z^{-1}L_y) + (L_y^{-1}L_t + L_t^{-1}L_y) + (L_z^{-1}L_t + L_t^{-1}L_z)]$$

We seek to find our approximate solution ϕ_n

$$\phi_n = u_0 + u_1 + \cdots + u_{n-1}$$

as far as we wish to calculate it. We have

$$u_0 = \tfrac{1}{4} \sum_{m=1}^{4} \phi_m = \tfrac{1}{4}(3x - 3y + 3z - 3t) = \tfrac{3}{4}(x - y + z - t)$$

$$u_1 = -\tfrac{3}{16}\{\cdot\}(x - y + z - t)$$

where the double summation in the curly brackets $\{\cdot\}$ is easily evaluated. Thus,

$$(L_x^{-1}L_y)(x - y + z - t) = L_x^{-1}(-1) = \int_0^x (-1)\, dx = -x$$

$$(L_y^{-1}L_x)(x - y + z - t) = (L_y^{-1})(1) = \int_0^y dy = y$$

Hence $(L_x^{-1}L_y + L_y^{-1}L_x)(x - y + z - t) = -x + y$. Similarly evaluating the other five quantities in the double summation,

$$u_1 = -\tfrac{3}{16}(-x + y + x + z - x + t + y - z - t - y - z + t)$$

$$u_1 = -\tfrac{3}{16}(-x + y - z + t) = \tfrac{3}{16}(x - y + z - t)$$

Thus, a two-term approximation $\phi_2 = u_0 + u_1$ would be given by

$$\phi_2 = \tfrac{3}{4}(x - y + z - t) + \tfrac{3}{16}(x - y + z - t) = \tfrac{15}{16}(x - y + z - t)$$

Continuing in the same manner, we get

$$u_n = \frac{3}{4^{n+1}}(x - y + z - t)$$

and since $u = \sum_{n=0}^{\infty} u_n$, then

$$u = k(x - y + z - t)$$

where

$$k = \sum_{n=0}^{\infty} \frac{3}{4^{n+1}}.$$

The series for k is given by

$$3\left(\frac{1}{4^1} + \frac{1}{4^2} + \frac{1}{4^3} + \frac{1}{4^4} + \frac{1}{4^5} + \frac{1}{4^6} + \cdots\right)$$

or

$$3\left(\frac{1}{2^2} + \frac{1}{2^4} + \frac{1}{2^6} + \frac{1}{2^8} + \cdots\right) = \tfrac{3}{4}\left(\frac{1}{2^0} + \frac{1}{2^2} + \frac{1}{2^4} + \cdots\right)$$

The series for

$$k = \tfrac{3}{4}\left(\frac{1}{2^0} + \frac{1}{2^2} + \frac{1}{2^4} + \cdots\right)$$

$$= 0.75 + 0.1875 + 0.046875$$

$$+ 0.01171875 + 0.0029296815 + 0.0007324219 + \cdots$$

The sum of the first five terms is 0.9990 and for six terms the sum is 0.9998 to four places. Thus, the correct solution is

$$u = x - y + z - t$$

to within 0.02 % error. Of course it is trivial to verify that this answer is indeed the correct solution.

9.3.   NONLINEAR PARTIAL DIFFERENTIAL EQUATION

Consider the nonlinear equation[1]

$$\nabla^2 p = k^2 \sinh p$$

or

$$[L_x + L_y + L_z]p = k^2 Np$$

where $Np = \sinh p$.

The notation L_x symbolizes a linear (deterministic) differential operator $\partial^2/\partial x^2$. Similarly, $L_y = \partial^2/\partial y^2$, $L_z = \partial^2/\partial z^2$ and $N(p)$ (or Np for convenience) symbolizes the nonlinear (deterministic) operator acting on p to give $\sinh p$

$$L_x p = k^2 Np - L_y p - L_z p$$

$$L_y p = k^2 Np - L_x p - L_z p$$

$$L_z p = k^2 Np - L_x p - L_y p$$

---

[1] In the usual form, this is $Fp = Lp - Np = g$, where the inhomogeneous term is zero in this case. If $g \neq 0$, the solution has an additional $\tfrac{1}{3}[L_x^{-1} + L_y^{-1} + L_z^{-1}]g(x, y, z)$.

Assuming the inverses L_x^{-1}, L_y^{-1}, L_z^{-1} exist[2]

$$L_x^{-1}L_xp = L_x^{-1}k^2Np - L_x^{-1}L_yp - L_x^{-1}L_zp$$

$$L_y^{-1}L_yp = L_y^{-1}k^2Np - L_y^{-1}L_xp - L_y^{-1}L_zp \qquad (9.3.1)$$

$$L_z^{-1}L_zp = L_z^{-1}k^2Np - L_z^{-1}L_xp - L_z^{-1}L_yp$$

However,

$$L_x^{-1}L_xp = p - p(0, y, z) - x\frac{\partial p}{\partial x}(0, y, z)$$

$$L_y^{-1}L_yp = p - p(x, 0, z) - y\frac{\partial p}{\partial y}(x, 0, z) \qquad (9.3.2)$$

$$L_z^{-1}L_zp = p - p(x, y, 0) - z\frac{\partial p}{\partial z}(x, y, 0).$$

Consequently, summing (9.3.1) with the substitution (9.3.2) and dividing by three, we get

$$p = \frac{1}{3}\left[p(0, y, z) + x\frac{\partial p}{\partial x}(0, y, z) + p(x, 0, z) + y\frac{\partial p}{\partial y}(x, 0, z)\right.$$

$$\left. + p(x, y, 0) + z\frac{\partial p}{\partial z}(x, y, 0)\right] + \frac{1}{3}[(L_x^{-1}L_y + L_y^{-1}L_z) + (L_x^{-1}L_z + L_z^{-1}L_x)$$

$$+ (L_y^{-1}L_z + L_z^{-1}L_y)]p + \frac{1}{3}[L_x^{-1} + L_y^{-1} + L_z^{-1}]\sum_{n=0}^{\infty} A_n \qquad (9.3.3)$$

Here $N(u)$ has been replaced by the A_n polynomials. We take for the first term of our approximation

$$p_0 = \frac{1}{3}\left[p(0, y, z) + x\frac{\partial p}{\partial x}(0, y, z) + p(x, 0, z) + y\frac{\partial p}{\partial y}(x, 0, z)\right.$$

$$\left. + p(x, y, 0) + z\frac{\partial p}{\partial z}(x, y, 0)\right] \qquad (9.3.4)$$

with the following terms given by

$$p_1 = \tfrac{1}{3}[(L_x^{-1}L_y + L_y^{-1}L_z) + (L_x^{-1}L_z + L_z^{-1}L_x) + (L_y^{-1}L_z + L_z^{-1}L_y)]p_0$$

$$+ \tfrac{1}{3}[L_x^{-1} + L_y^{-1} + L_z^{-1}]A_0$$

$$\vdots \qquad\qquad (9.3.5)$$

$$p_n = \tfrac{1}{3}[(L_x^{-1}L_y + L_y^{-1}L_z) + (L_x^{-1}L_z + L_z^{-1}L_x) + (L_y^{-1}L_z + L_z^{-1}L_y)p_{n-1}]$$

$$+ \tfrac{1}{3}[L_x^{-1} + L_y^{-1} + L_z^{-1}]A_{n-1}$$

[2] They do in this case; when they do not, we can decompose each of the L_x, L_y, L_z into an invertible operator and a remainder term taken to the right-hand side of the equation.

We must now evaluate the A_n. We use the fact that $(d/dx)(\sinh x) = \cosh x$ and $(d/dx) \cosh x = \sinh x$ to obtain

$$h_0(p_0) = \sinh p_0$$
$$h_1(p_0) = \cosh p_0$$
$$h_2(p_0) = \sinh p_0$$
$$\vdots$$
$$h_n(p_0) = \sinh p_0 \quad \text{for even} \quad n$$
$$h_n(p_0) = \cosh p_0 \quad \text{for odd} \quad n$$

Then

$A_0 = \sinh p_0$

$A_1 = p_1 \cosh p_0$

$A_2 = p_2 \cosh p_0 + \frac{1}{2} p_1^2 \sinh p_0$ $\qquad\qquad\qquad\qquad$ (9.3.6)

$A_3 = p_3 \cosh p_0 + p_1 p_2 \sinh p_0 + \frac{1}{6} p_1^3 \cosh p_0$

$A_4 = p_4 \cosh p_0 + [\frac{1}{2} p_2^2 + p_1 p_3] \sinh p_0 + \frac{1}{2} p_1^2 p_2 \cosh p_0 + \frac{1}{24} p_1^4 \sinh p_0$

$\vdots$

The A_n are easily written down by the procedures given for as many terms as desired. From (9.3.5)–(9.3.7) we have the complete decomposition $p = \sum_{n=0}^{\infty} p_i$ and hence the solution.

EXERCISE

Consider the equation

$$\partial^2 u/\partial x^2 - \partial u/\partial t = 0$$
$$u(0, t) = t$$
$$u(x, 0) = x^2/2$$
$$\partial u(0, t)/\partial x = 0$$

Show the solution is $u = t + (x^2/2)$ with six terms providing a solution within a 2% error. (Ten terms brings the error down to 0.1%.)

9.4. SOME GENERAL REMARKS

The author's approach to these problems began in 1960 with linear *stochastic operator* equations and has evolved since 1976 to nonlinear stochastic operator equations. Consider, for example

$$\frac{\partial u}{\partial t} + a(t, x) \frac{\partial u}{\partial x} + b(t, x) \frac{\partial^2 u}{\partial x^2} = g(t, x)$$

which is rewritten in terms of operators as

$$L_t u + L_x u = g(t, x)$$

where $L_t = \partial/\partial t$ and $L_x = a\partial/\partial x + b\partial^2/\partial x^2$. A similar *stochastic* equation,

$$\frac{\partial u(x, t, \omega)}{\partial t} + A(x, t)u(x, t, \omega) + B(x, t, \omega)u(x, t, \omega) = f(x, t, \omega)$$

(where $\omega \in (\Omega, F, \mu)$, a probability space, f is a stochastic process, A is a deterministic coefficient, but B is a stochastic process) can similarly be written

$$Lu + \mathscr{R}u = f$$

where $L = (\partial/\partial t) + A(x, t)$ is a deterministic operator and $\mathscr{R} = \mathscr{B}(x, t, \omega)$ is a stochastic operator, or

$$\mathscr{L}u = f$$

where $\mathscr{L}$ is a stochastic operator with deterministic and random parts, L being $\langle \mathscr{L} \rangle$ if $\mathscr{R}$ is zero-mean.

Let us consider then the operator equation

$$\mathscr{F}u = g$$

where $\mathscr{F}$ represents an ordinary or partial differential operator. (In the deterministic case, we would write $Fu = g$.) We suppose that $\mathscr{F}$ has linear and nonlinear parts [i.e., $\mathscr{F}u = \mathscr{L}u + \mathscr{N}u$, where $\mathscr{L}$ is a linear (stochastic) operator and $\mathscr{N}$ is a nonlinear (stochastic) operator]. We may, of course, have a nonlinear term that depends upon derivatives of u as well as u. Such nonlinear terms are considered elsewhere.

Since $\mathscr{L}$ may have deterministic and stochastic components, let $\mathscr{L} = L + \mathscr{R}$, where conveniently $L = \langle \mathscr{L} \rangle$ and $\mathscr{R} = \mathscr{L} - L$. This is not a limitation on the method but a convenience in explanation. It is necessary that L be invertible. If the above choice makes this difficult, we choose a simpler L and let $\mathscr{R}$ incorporate the remainder. Let $\mathscr{N}u = Nu + \mathscr{M}u$, where Nu indicates a deterministic part and $\mathscr{M}u$ indicates a stochastic nonlinear term.

$\mathscr{F}$ may involve derivatives with respect to x, y, z, t or mixed derivatives. To avoid difficulties in notation which tend to obscure rather than clarify, we will assume the same probability space for each process and let $L = L_x + L_y + L_z + L_t$, where the operators indicate quantities such as $\partial^2/\partial x^2$, $\partial/\partial y$, etc. Similarly, $\mathscr{R}$ is written as $\mathscr{R}_x + \mathscr{R}_y + \mathscr{R}_z + \mathscr{R}_t$. Mixed derivatives and product nonlinearities such as $u^2u'^3$, uu'', and $f(u, u', \ldots, u^{(m)})$ can also be handled but will not be discussed here. A simple Langevin equation is written $Lu = g$, where $L = (d/dt) + \beta$ and g is a white noise process. Langevin equations as used for modeling complex nonlinear phenomena in physics of the form

$\Psi = f(\Psi) + \xi$ are represented by $Lu + Nu = g$; however, *we will not make any Markovian or white-noise restrictions.* All processes will be physical processes without restriction to being Gaussian or stationary. In the $K\,dV$ equation, for example, $\mathscr{F}u$ would become $L_t u + L_x u + Nu$, where Nu is of the form uu_x (again a product nonlinearity). In equations of the Satsuma–Kaup type for soliton behavior, we have also such products as uu_x, uu_{xxx}, and $u_x u_{xx}$. Stochastic transport equations will fit nicely into our format since $\nabla^2 = L_x + L_y + L_z$, and stochastic behavior in coefficients or inputs is easily included. For example, instead of $Ly(\bar{\imath}, t) = \xi(\bar{\imath}, t, \omega)$, where ξ is a random source and $L = (\partial/\partial t) - d\nabla^2$ or $(\partial/\partial t) - \Lambda_{xyz}$, we can include nonlinear terms or stochastic behavior in the operator. In the double sine–Gordon equation we have $u_{tt} - u_{xx} - \sin u + \sin 2u = 0$ or $L_t + L_x + N(u)$, where $N(u)$ includes the trigonometric nonlinearities. We can also allow polynomial, exponential, and product nonlinearities as well as terms such as $N(u) = f(u, u_x, u_{xx}, \ldots)$. We remark that the Itô equation

$$dy = f(t, y)\,dt + g(t, y)\,dz$$

where z is the Wiener process, can be written as

$$dy/dt = f(t, y) + g(t, y)u(t)$$

Here, we can write $dz/dt = u$ since we do not insist that z is a Wiener process. This equation can, consequently, be put into the author's standard form. The nondifferentiability of the Wiener process is, of course, a *mathematical* property. We are interested in *physical* solutions. In the Itô integral, $\int f\,dz$, the z process is not of bounded variation; however, a Lipschitz condition on z is reasonable for physical processes, so the integral will be a well-defined Riemann–Stieltjes integral. Physically reasonable models and mathematically tractable models are not necessarily the same. This point of view offers interesting and different mathematics for systems characterized by linear or nonlinear stochastic operator equations in which the operator may be an ordinary or partial differential operator, an integral operator, or other, where the operator itself is stochastic (e.g., in the case of the differential operator of nth order, one or more coefficient processes may be stochastic processes).

9.5.   THE HEAT EQUATION

Consider $\partial^2 u/\partial x^2 - \partial u/\partial t = 0$ given the conditions

$$u(x, 0) = x^2/2, \qquad u(0, t) = t, \qquad \partial u(0, t)/\partial x = 0$$

Write $L_x = \partial^2/\partial x^2$ and $L_t = \partial/\partial t$. Then, $L_x^{-1} = \int_0^x dx \int_0^x dx$ and $L_t^{-1} = \int_0^t dt$. Solving alternately for the operators

$$L_x u = L_t u \tag{9.5.1}$$

$$L_t u = L_x u \tag{9.5.2}$$

(9.5.1) results in

$$u - u(0, t) = L_x^{-1} L_t u \tag{9.5.3}$$

and (9.5.2) results in

$$u - u(x, 0) = L_t^{-1} L_x u \tag{9.5.4}$$

Hence,

$$u = u(0, t) + L_x^{-1} t_t u$$

$$u = u(x, 0) + L_t^{-1} L_x u$$

Adding these and dividing by 2, we get

$$u = \tfrac{1}{2}[u(0, t) + u(x, 0)] + \tfrac{1}{2}[L_x^{-1}L_t + L_t^{-1}L_x]u$$

With decomposition, $u = \sum_{n=0}^{\infty} u_n$

$$u_0 = \tfrac{1}{2}[u(0, t) + u(x, 0)] = \tfrac{1}{2}[t + (x^2/2)]$$

$$u_1 = \tfrac{1}{2}[L_x^{-1}L_t + L_t^{-1}L_x]u_0$$

$$\vdots$$

$$u_n = \tfrac{1}{2}[L_x^{-1}L_t + L_t^{-1}L_x]u_{n-1}$$

(Note that in this specific case with the given initial conditions

$$[L_x^{-1}L_t + L_t^{-1}L_x][u(0, t) + u(x, 0)]$$
$$= L_x^{-1}L_t u(0, t) + L_x^{-1}L_t u(x, 0) + L_t^{-1}L_x u(0, t) + L_t^{-1}L_x u(x, 0)$$
$$= (x^2/2) + t$$
$$= u(0, t) + u(x, 0)$$

i.e., for *this* case, $[L_x^{-1}L_t + L_t^{-1}L_x]$ is an identity operator, a special case which makes calculation particularly simple.)

Now, continuing the determination of the individual terms of the decomposition,

$$u_1 = \frac{1}{4}[L_x^{-1}L_t + L_t^{-1}L_x]\left[t + \left(\frac{x^2}{2}\right)\right]$$

$$= \frac{1}{4}\left[\int_0^x dx \int_0^x dx\left(\frac{\partial}{\partial t}\right)\right]\left[t + \left(\frac{x^2}{2}\right)\right] + \frac{1}{4}\left[\int_0^t dt\left(\frac{\partial^2}{\partial x^2}\right)\right]\left[t + \left(\frac{x^2}{2}\right)\right]$$

$$= \frac{1}{4}\left(\frac{x^2}{2}\right) + \frac{1}{4}(t)$$

$$= \frac{1}{4}\left[t + \left(\frac{x^2}{2}\right)\right]$$

$$u_2 = \frac{1}{2}[L_x^{-1}L_t + L_t^{-1}L_x]u_1$$

$$= \frac{1}{8}[L_x^{-1}L_t + L_t^{-1}L_x]\left[t + \left(\frac{x^2}{2}\right)\right]$$

Since we have shown the behavior of the above as an identity operation, the calculation becomes trivial and

$$u_2 = \frac{1}{8}[t + (x^2/2)]$$
$$\vdots$$
$$u_n = (\tfrac{1}{2})^{n+1}[t + (x^2/2)]$$

Hence,

$$u = \left[t + \left(\frac{x^2}{2}\right)\right]\sum_{n=0}^{\infty}\frac{1}{2^{n+1}}$$

is the solution.

If we denote the approximation to n terms by ϕ_n we have the improving approximations:

$$\phi_1 = 0.5[t + (x^2/2)] = u_0$$
$$\phi_2 = 0.75[t + (x^2/2)] = u_0 + u_1$$
$$\phi_3 = 0.875[t + (x^2/2)] = u_0 + u_1 + u_2$$
$$\vdots$$
$$u = \lim_{n\to\infty}\phi_n = (1)[t + (x^2/2)]$$

which clearly satisfies the problem. We note that six terms already yield the solution to better than 98%. With ten terms the approximation is within 99.9% of the correct solution.

9.6.   INHOMOGENEOUS HEAT EQUATION

Now consider

$$\frac{\partial^2 u}{\partial x^2} - \frac{\partial u}{\partial t} = g(x, t) \tag{9.6.1}$$

or

$$L_x u - L_t u = g$$

Assume g is given along with appropriate conditions on u. We now write

$$L_x u = g + L_t u \tag{9.6.2}$$

$$L_t u = -g + L_x u \tag{9.6.3}$$

Remembering that $L_x = \partial^2/\partial x^2$ and $L_t = \partial/\partial t$, (9.6.2) and (9.6.3) become

$$u = a + bx + L_x^{-1} g + L_x^{-1} L_t u \tag{9.6.4}$$

$$u = c - L_t^{-1} g + L_t^{-1} L_x u \tag{9.6.5}$$

where a, b, and c must be evaluated from the given conditions on u. (They arise from the solutions of $L_x u = 0$ and $L_t u = 0$.) Adding (9.6.4) and (9.6.5), we get

$$u = \tfrac{1}{2}(a + bx + L_x^{-1} g - L_t^{-1} g) + \tfrac{1}{2}(L_x^{-1} L_t + L_t^{-1} L_x)u \tag{9.6.6}$$

We rewrite this as

$$u = u_0 + \tfrac{1}{2}(L_x^{-1} L_t + L_t^{-1} L_x)u \tag{9.6.7}$$

with $u_0 = \tfrac{1}{2}(a + bx + L_x^{-1} g - L_t^{-1} g)$. Let $u = \sum_{n=0}^{\infty} u_n$. Then

$$u = u_0 + \tfrac{1}{2}\{L_x^{-1} L_t + L_t^{-1} L_x\} \sum_{n=0}^{\infty} u_n \tag{9.6.8}$$

Since u_0 is known when the conditions on u are specified, we have

$$u_1 = \tfrac{1}{2}(L_x^{-1} L_t + L_t^{-1} L_x)u_0$$

$$u_2 = \tfrac{1}{2}(L_x^{-1} L_t + L_t^{-1} L_x)u_1$$

$$\vdots$$

$$u_{n+1} = \tfrac{1}{2}(L_x^{-1} L_t + L_t^{-1} L_x)u_n, \qquad n \geq 0$$

so all terms of u are easily evaluated once u_0 is determined. If, for example, we have initial conditions,

$$a = u(x, 0), \qquad b = u(0, t), \qquad c = \partial u(0, t)/\partial x.$$

At any stage of approximation, we write

$$\phi_n = u_0 + u_1 + \cdots + u_{n-1}$$

and can easily verify that

$$\frac{\partial^2 \phi_n}{\partial x^2} - \frac{\partial \phi_n}{\partial t} = g$$

9.7. ASYMPTOTIC DECOMPOSITION FOR PARTIAL DIFFERENTIAL EQUATIONS

We discussed asymptotic decomposition solutions in Chapter 4. The technique can apply also to partial differential equations and avoid boundary conditions.

Thus, in an equation such as $[L_x + L_y]u + Nu = g$ we write $\sum_{n=0}^{\infty} A_n$ for Nu then solve for the A_n (or for u if $Nu = u$)

$$\sum_{n=0}^{\infty} A_n = g - L_x u - L_y u$$

For example, if $Nu = u^2$, we get $u_0 = g^{1/2}$ and $u_1 = -L_x u_0 - L_y u_0$, etc. Use of this method for various classes of partial differential equations is under investigation at this time.

EXAMPLE: Consider the equation

$$u_{xx} + u_{yy} + u = g, \qquad g = x^2 y^2 + 2x^2 + 2y^2$$

Write

$$u = g - u_{xx} - u_{yy}$$

$$\sum_{n=0}^{\infty} u_n = g - \frac{\partial^2}{\partial x^2} \sum_{n=0}^{\infty} u_n - \frac{\partial^2}{\partial y^2} \sum_{n=0}^{\infty} u_n$$

$$u_0 = g = x^2 y^2 + 2x^2 + 2y^2$$

$$u_1 = -\frac{\partial^2}{\partial x^2} u_0 - \frac{\partial^2}{\partial y^2} u_0 = -2y^2 - 2x^2 - 8$$

$$u_2 = -\frac{\partial^2}{\partial x^2} u_1 - \frac{\partial^2}{\partial y^2} u_1 = 4 + 4 = 8$$

$$u_3 = 0 \quad \text{and} \quad u_n = 0 \quad \text{for} \quad n > 3$$

Thus, we have a terminating series, which is the solution

$$u = u_0 + u_1 + u_2 = x^2 y^2$$

Suppose that instead of u the last term on the left is $Nu = \sum_{n=0}^{\infty} A_n$. If $Nu = u^2$, the A_0 term is u_0^2, so we have $u_0 = g^{1/2}$, $A_1 = 2u_0 u_1 = -(\partial^2/\partial x^2)u_0 - (\partial^2/\partial y^2)u_0$, and we can solve for u_1, etc.

EXAMPLE: Consider

$$u_{xx} + u_{yy} + u^2 = x^2 y^2$$

$$\sum_{n=0}^{\infty} A_n = x^2 y^2 - \left(\frac{\partial^2}{\partial x^2}\right) \sum_{n=0}^{\infty} u_n - \left(\frac{\partial^2}{\partial y^2}\right) \sum_{n=0}^{\infty} u_n$$

$$A_0 = u_0^2 = x^2 y^2$$

$$u_0 = xy$$

$$A_1 = 2u_0 u_1 = -\left(\frac{\partial^2}{\partial x^2}\right)(xy) - \left(\frac{\partial^2}{\partial y^2}\right)(xy)$$

$$u_1 = u_2 = \cdots = 0$$

Thus $u = xy$.

EXERCISES

1. $\nabla^2 u + u = g(x, y, z)$. Use asymptotic decomposition to see that $u_0 = g$, $u_1 = -\nabla^2 u_0, \ldots$
2. For $\nabla^2 u + Nu = g$, with $Nu = u^2$, show by asymptotic decomposition that $u_0 = \sqrt{g}$, $u_1 = -(\nabla^2 u_0)/2u_0, \ldots$

Thus, both forms, the decomposition and asymptotic decomposition, offer a new and powerful way of gaining insight into the behavior of very complicated nonlinear equations.

NOTE

Very recent work (to be published) has now proved that an analytic $f(u)$ can be written as a convergent summation $\sum_{n=0}^{\infty} A_n$ in terms of the A_n polynomials and that the resulting *decomposition solution* of a nonlinear partial differential equation $Fu = Lu + Nu = g(x, y, z, t)$, where $Nu = f(u)$ and $L = L_x + L_y + L_z + L_t$ is a sum of partial differential operators with respect to x, y, z, t, for example, $u_t + \nabla^2 u$ or $u_{tt} + \nabla^2 u$, is precisely the solution of the differential equation.

REFERENCE

1. G. Adomian, "Stochastic Systems." Academic, New York, 1983.

SUGGESTED FURTHER READING

G. Adomian, A new approach to the heat equation—an application of the decomposition method, *J. Math. Anal. Appl.*, in press.

R. Bellman and G. Adomian, "Partial Differential Equations—New Methods for Their Treatment and Application. Reidel, Dordrecht, Netherlands, 1984.

R. Bellman, R. Kalaba, and B. Kotkin, On a new approach to the computational solution of partial differential equations, *Proc. Nat. Acad. Sci.* **4**, 1325–1327 (1962).

G. F. Carrier, "Partial Differential Equations: Theory and Technique." Academic Press, New York, 1976.

P. R. Garabedian, "Partial Differential Equations." Wiley, New York, 1964.

N. S. Koshlyakov, M. M. Smirnov, and E. B. Gliner, "Differential Equations of Mathematical Physics." Wiley, New York, 1964.

CHAPTER 10

Algebraic Equations

"Read the masters, not the pupils..."

Abel

PART I: POLYNOMIALS

10.1. QUADRATIC EQUATIONS BY DECOMPOSITION

If we write an ordinary quadratic equation $ax^2 + bx + c = 0$ in the form $Lu + Nu = g$ and identify $Nx = ax^2$, $L = b$, and $g = -c$, we have $Lu = g - Nu$ or $bx = -c - ax^2$. The operation L^{-1} for differential equations is an integral operator. Here it is simply division by b. Hence,

$$x = (-c/b) - (a/b)x^2$$

in our standard format. The solution x is now decomposed into components $x_0 + x_1 + \cdots$, where x_0 is taken as $(-c/b)$ and $x_1, x_2, \ldots$ are still to be identified. Thus, $x_0 = -c/b$. We now have

$$x = x_0 - (a/b)x^2$$

with x_0 known. The nonlinear term without the coefficient—in this case x^2—is replaced by $\sum_{n=0}^{\infty} A_n$, where $A_n(x_0, x_1, \ldots, x_n)$ refers to our A_n polynomials. These are found for the particular nonlinearity. For the example $Nx = x^2$ we have

$$A_0 = x_0^2$$

$$A_1 = 2x_0 x_1$$

$$A_2 = x_1^2 + 2x_0 x_2$$

142

$$A_3 = 2x_1x_2 + 2x_0x_3$$

$$A_4 = x_2^2 + 2x_1x_3 + 2x_0x_4$$

$$A_5 = 2x_0x_5 + 2x_1x_4 + 2x_2x_3$$

$$A_6 = x_3^2 + 2x_0x_6 + 2x_1x_5 + 2x_2x_4$$

$$A_7 = 2x_0x_7 + 2x_1x_6 + 2x_2x_5 + 2x_3x_4$$

$$A_8 = x_4^2 + 2x_0x_8 + 2x_1x_7 + 2x_2x_6 + 2x_3x_5$$

$$\vdots$$

Examining the subscripts we note that the sum of subscripts in each term is n. Now $x = x_0 - (a/b) \sum_{n=0}^{\infty} A_n$ requires

$$x_1 = -(a/b)A_0 = -(a/b)x_0^2$$

$$x_2 = -(a/b)A_1 = -(a/b)(2x_0x_1)$$

$$x_3 = -(a/b)A_2 = -(a/b)(x_1^2 + 2x_0x_2)$$

$$x_4 = -(a/b)A_3 = -(a/b)(2x_1x_2 + 2x_0x_3)$$

$$x_5 = -(a/b)A_4 = -(a/b)(x_2^2 + 2x_1x_3 + 2x_0x_4)$$

$$\vdots$$

and thus the x_i are determined.

We note in the example $Nx = x^2$ that if we expand $(x_0 + x_1 + \cdots)^2$ into $x_0^2 + x_1^2 + x_2^2 + \cdots + 2x_0x_1 + 2x_0x_2 + \cdots + 2x_1x_2 + \cdots$, we must choose $A_0 = x_0^2$, but A_1 could be $x_1^2 + 2x_0x_1$. The sum of the subscripts for x_1^2, or x_1x_1, is higher than for the x_0x_1 term. By choosing for any x_n only terms summing to $n - 1$, we get consistency with our more general schemes which, as we shall see, we can use with high-ordered polynomials, trigonometric or exponential terms, and negative or irrational powers, as well as multidimensional differential equations.

When the Nx (or in the quadratic case, x^2) term is written in terms of the A_n polynomials, the decomposition method solves the equation. (Although it is not necessary to discuss it here, if stochastic coefficients are involved, the decomposition method achieves statistical separability in the averaging process for desired statistics, and no truncations are required.) Let us look at some examples.

EXAMPLE: Consider $x^2 + 3x + 2 = 0$ whose solutions are obviously $(-1, -2)$. Write it in the form

$$3x = -2 - x^2$$

$$x = -\frac{2}{3} - \frac{1}{3}x^2 = x_0 + x_1 + x_2 + \cdots$$

$$= x_0 - \frac{1}{3}\sum_{n=0}^{\infty} A_n$$

$$= x_0 - \frac{1}{3}A_0 - \frac{1}{3}A_1 - \cdots$$

Substituting the A_n we have

$$x_0 = -0.667, \qquad x_7 = -0.00765$$
$$x_1 = -0.148, \qquad x_8 = -0.00567$$
$$x_2 = -0.069, \qquad x_9 = -0.0043$$
$$x_3 = -0.037, \qquad x_{10} = -0.0033$$
$$x_4 = -0.023, \qquad x_{11} = -0.00268$$
$$x_5 = -0.015, \qquad x_{12} = -0.0020$$
$$x_6 = -0.0106,$$

Since an n-term approximation (symbolized by ϕ_n) is given by $\sum_{i=0}^{n-1} x_i$, we define the error as $\psi_n = (x - \phi_n)/x$. We now have

$$\phi_1 = -0.667, \qquad \psi_1 = 33.3\%$$
$$\phi_2 = -0.815, \qquad \psi_2 = 18.5\%$$
$$\phi_3 = -0.884, \qquad \psi_3 = 11.6\%$$
$$\phi_4 = -0.921, \qquad \psi_4 = 7.9\%$$
$$\phi_5 = -0.944, \qquad \psi_5 = 5.6\%$$
$$\phi_6 = -0.959, \qquad \psi_6 = 4.1\%$$
$$\phi_7 = -0.970, \qquad \psi_7 = 3.0\%$$
$$\phi_8 = -0.977, \qquad \psi_8 = 2.3\%$$
$$\phi_9 = -0.983, \qquad \psi_9 = 1.7\%$$
$$\phi_{10} = -0.987, \qquad \psi_{10} = 1.2\%$$

which is approaching the smaller root which is -1. The error ψ_n becomes less than 0.5% by $m = 12$. If we take the equation $x^2 - 3x + 2 = 0$ we get the same numbers as above for the x_i terms except that they will all be positive.

EXAMPLE: Consider $x^2 - 1.25x + 0.25 = 0$ or $(x - \frac{1}{4})(x - 1) = 0$. In our form it becomes $-\frac{5}{4}x = -\frac{1}{4} - x^2$ or $x = \frac{1}{5} + \frac{4}{5}x^2$. Thus

$$x_0 = 0.2$$
$$x_1 = (0.8)(0.2)^2 = 0.032$$
$$x_2 = (0.8)(2)(0.2)(0.032) = 0.01024$$
$$x_3 = (0.8)[(0.032)^2 + 2(0.2)(0.01)] = 0.004$$

Thus $\phi_m = \sum_{n=0}^{m-1} x_n$ is

$$\phi_1 = 0.2$$
$$\phi_2 = 0.232$$
$$\phi_3 = 0.242$$
$$\phi_4 = 0.246$$

which converges to 0.25 as expected.

EXAMPLE: Consider $x^2 - 20x + 36 = 0$ which has the roots $(2, 18)$. Write

$$-20x = -36 - x^2, \qquad x = \frac{36}{20} + \frac{1}{20}x^2$$

By the same procedure we get $x_0 = 1.8$, $x_1 = 0.16$. Hence the approximation to only two terms is given by

$$\phi_2 = x_0 + x_1 = 1.96$$

A three-term approximation is $\phi_3 = 1.98$ which is already close to the smaller root $x = 2$.

EXAMPLE: Consider $(x - \frac{1}{4})(x - 100) = 0$ and write

$$\frac{401}{4}x = 25 + x^2$$
$$x = \frac{100}{401} + \frac{4}{401}x^2$$
$$x_0 = 0.2493$$
$$x_1 = (0.0099)(0.2493)^2 = 0.0006$$
$$\phi_2 = x_0 + x_1 = 0.2499 = 0.25$$

From these examples we observe that the method yields the smaller root and that the farther apart the two roots, the faster the convergence to the correct solution. (We will discuss this further in the next section.) Of course, the second root is found by factoring once we have one root.

Consider the example $x^2 - 8x + 15 = 0$ which has roots $(3, 5)$. We now write immediately

$$x_0 = -c/b = \frac{15}{8} = 1.875$$

and $x_n = (a/b)x^2$ for $n \geq 1$. Thus

$$x_1 = -(a/b)x_0^2 = \tfrac{1}{8}x_0^2 = 0.439$$

$$x_2 = -(a/b)(2x_0 x_1) = \tfrac{1}{8}(2x_0 x_1) = 0.206$$

$$x_3 = \tfrac{1}{8}(x_1^2 + 2x_0 x_2) = 0.121$$

$$x_4 = \tfrac{1}{8}(2x_1 x_2 + 2x_0 x_3) = 0.079$$

$$x_5 = \tfrac{1}{8}(x_2^2 + 2x_1 x_3 + 2x_0 x_4) = 0.056$$

$$x_6 = \tfrac{1}{8}(2x_0 x_5 + 2x_1 x_4 + 2x_2 x_3) = 0.041$$

$$x_7 = \tfrac{1}{8}(x_3^2 + 2x_0 x_6 + 2x_1 x_5 + 2x_2 x_4) = 0.031$$

$$x_8 = \tfrac{1}{8}(2x_0 x_7 + 2x_1 x_6 + 2x_2 x_5 + 2x_3 x_4) = 0.024$$

$$x_9 = \tfrac{1}{8}(x_4^2 + 2x_0 x_8 + 2x_1 x_7 + 2x_2 x_6 + 2x_3 x_5) = 0.019$$

The sum of these 10 terms is 2.89 as compared with the correct solution $x = 3$, which is approximately 3.6% off. Further terms can be computed to approach 3 more closely.

EXAMPLE: The equation $x^2 - 8x + 7 = 0$ is solved by writing $x_0 = -c/b = \tfrac{7}{8} = 0.875$. Then

$$x_1 = \tfrac{1}{8}(0.875^2) = 0.096$$

$$x_2 = \tfrac{1}{8}(2)(0.096)(0.875) \simeq 0.021$$

Thus, $\phi_3 \approx 0.99$ so only three terms already result in an answer within 1% of the smaller root.

EXAMPLE: Consider the equation $(x - 2)(x - 5) = 0$ or $x^2 - 7x + 10 = 0$. We write $x = \tfrac{10}{7} + \tfrac{1}{7}x^2$. Then

$$x_0 = 1.429$$

$$x_1 = \tfrac{1}{7}(1.429)^2 = 0.29155$$

$$x_2 = \tfrac{1}{7}(2x_0 x_1) = \tfrac{1}{7}(2)\tfrac{1}{429}(0.29155) = 0.1190$$

Thus

$$\phi_1 = x_0 = 1.429$$

$$\phi_2 = x_0 + x_1 = 1.721$$

$$\phi_3 = x_0 + x_1 + x_2 = 1.840$$

and

$$\psi_3 = (x - \phi_3)/3 = 8.02\%$$

We can try more terms.

$$x_3 = \tfrac{1}{7}[(0.292)^2 + 2(1.429)(0.119)] \simeq 0.06$$

This brings it to approximately 1.9 for the root $x = 2$ or about a 5% error. (Noting the decrease of terms we might simply try $x = 2$ in the equation.)

An Interesting Observation: Suppose we look at several simple quadratics whose roots get farther and farther apart such as

(a) $(x - 1)(x - 2) = 0$ or $x^2 - 3x + 2 = 0$

(b) $(x - 1)(x - 3) = 0$ or $x^2 - 4x + 3 = 0$

(c) $(x - 1)(x - 4) = 0$ or $x^2 - 5x + 4 = 0$

$\vdots$ $\vdots$ $\vdots$

(d) $(x - 1)(x - R) = 0$ or $x^2 - (1 + R)x + R = 0.$

The solutions in our form are given by

(a) $x = \tfrac{2}{3} + \tfrac{1}{3}x^2$

(b) $x = \tfrac{3}{4} + \tfrac{1}{4}x^2$

(c) $x = \tfrac{4}{5} + \tfrac{1}{5}x^2$

$\vdots$ $\vdots$

(d) $x = (R/(1 + R)) + (1/(1 + R))x^2$

Thus taking the limit:

$$\lim_{R \to \infty} x = \lim_{R \to \infty} \frac{R}{1 + R} + \lim_{R \to \infty} \frac{1}{1 + R} \sum_{n=0}^{\infty} A_n$$

$$= 1$$

which is the first root, and since $x_n = (1/(1 + R))A_{n-1}$

$$\lim_{R \to \infty} x_1 = \lim_{R \to \infty} \frac{1}{1 + R} A_0$$

$$= \lim_{R \to \infty} \frac{1}{1 + R} \frac{R}{1 + R} \frac{R}{1 + R} = 0$$

$$\lim_{R \to \infty} x_2 = \lim_{R \to \infty} \frac{2R^3}{(1 + R)^4} = 0$$

$\vdots$

Since the decomposition method yields a converging series for the smaller root (in this case, unity), we can construct many series for the number 1 with the speed of convergence increasing as the roots get farther apart. Analogously, we can write for roots R_1 and R_2

$$(x - R_1)(x - R_2) = 0$$

Then

$$x = \frac{R_1 R_2}{R_1 + R_2} + \frac{1}{R_1 + R_2} \sum_{n=0}^{\infty} A_n(x^2)$$

and if we let $R_1 \ll R_2$,

$$\lim_{R_2 \to \infty} x = \lim_{R_2 \to \infty} \frac{R_1 R_2}{R_1 + R_2} = \lim_{R_2 \to \infty} \frac{R_1}{(R_1/R_2) + 1} = R_1$$

and analogously

$$\lim_{R_2 \to \infty} \left[\left(\frac{1}{R_1 + R_2} \right) \sum_{n=0}^{\infty} A_n \right] = 0$$

so our series approaches R_1 in the limit.

Let us examine the quadratic equation in the form $(x - r_1)(x - r_2) = 0$, where r_1, and r_2 are real roots. We have then $x^2 - (r_1 + r_2)x + r_1 r_2 = 0$. Then in the standard form

$$(r_1 + r_2)x = r_1 r_2 + x^2$$

or

$$x = \frac{r_1 r_2}{r_1 + r_2} + \frac{1}{r_1 + r_2} x^2$$

Now since $x = \sum_{n=0}^{\infty} x_n$ and we identify $x_0 = (r_1 r_2)/(r_1 + r_2)$, the x_{n+1} terms for $n = 0, 1, \ldots$ are given by

$$x_{n+1} = \frac{1}{r_1 + r_2} A_n \quad \text{or} \quad x = x_0 + \sum_{n=0}^{\infty} \frac{1}{r_1 + r_2} A_n$$

where the A_n have already been given for $N_x = x^2$. Thus

$$x_1 = \frac{r_1^2 r_2^2}{(r_1 + r_2)^3}$$

$$x_2 = \frac{2 r_1^3 r_2^3}{(r_1 + r_2)^5}$$

$$x_3 = \frac{5 r_1^4 r_2^4}{(r_1 + r_2)^7}$$

$$\vdots$$

or, in general, $x_n = k_n(r_1 r_2)^{n+1}/(r_1 + r_2)^{2n+1}$ where in general $k_n = k_n(k_0, k_1, \ldots, k_{n-1})$

$$k_0 = 1$$
$$k_1 = 1^2 = 1$$
$$k_2 = 2 \cdot 1 \cdot 1 = 2$$
$$k_3 = 1^2 + 2 \cdot 1 \cdot 2 = 5$$
$$k_4 = 2 \cdot 1 \cdot 2 + 2 \cdot 1 \cdot 5 = 14$$
$$k_5 = 2^2 + 2 \cdot 1 \cdot 5 + 2 \cdot 1 \cdot 14 = 42$$
$$k_6 = 2 \cdot 2 \cdot 5 + 2 \cdot 1 \cdot 14 + 2 \cdot 1 \cdot 42 = 132$$
$$k_7 = 429$$
$$k_8 = 1430$$
$$k_9 = 4862$$
$$k_{10} = 16{,}796$$
$$k_{11} = 58{,}786$$
$$k_{12} = 208{,}012$$

(For $k_0 \equiv 1$ and $m \geq 1$, $k_m = \sum_{n=0}^{m-1} k_n k_{m-1-n}$. Thus the k_n are determined by the A_n polynomials for x^2.) If we compare the case of equal roots $r_1 = r_2$ with the case $r_2 = 2r_1$, it is easy to see that convergence is much faster in the case of unequal roots and the solution for the smaller root is obtained first. If we take $r_2 = 1000r_1$, we get $\phi_1 = 0.999r_1$, $\phi_2 = 0.999997999r_1$, and essentially an exact answer of r_1 by ϕ_3. If $r_1 = r_2$ we have the following:

$$x_0 = \frac{r_1^2}{2r_1} = \frac{1}{2} r_1$$

$$x_1 = \frac{r_1^4}{(2r_1)^3} = \frac{1}{2^3} r_1$$

$$x_2 = \frac{2r_1^6}{(2r_1)^5} = 2\left(\frac{1}{2^5}\right) r_1$$

$$x_3 = 5\left(\frac{1}{2^7}\right) r_1$$

$$x_4 = 14\left(\frac{1}{2^9}\right) r_1$$

$$\vdots$$

or

$$x = r_1\left[\frac{1}{2} + \frac{1}{2^3} + \frac{2}{2^5} + \frac{5}{2^7} + \frac{14}{2^9} + \frac{42}{2^{11}} + \frac{132}{2^{13}} + \frac{429}{2^{15}} + \frac{1430}{2^{17}} + \frac{4862}{2^{19}}\right.$$
$$\left. + \frac{16796}{2^{21}} + \frac{58786}{2^{23}} + \cdots\right] = r_1[0.84]$$

By ψ_{12} there is still 16% error while in the case of $r_2 = 1000r_1$, one term, i.e., the x_0 term with no computation is accurate to three decimal places. If we take $r_2 = mr_1$, where m is any real positive number, then

$$x_n = (k_n m^{n+1}/(m + 1)^{2n+1})r_1$$

where $\sum_{n=0}^{\infty}\{k_n m^{n+1}/(m + 1)^{2n+1}\} = 1$. Arbitrarily choosing $m = \pi$ and computing only terms to ϕ_5, we obtained $\phi_5 = 0.984$ (an error of 1.6%).

Since $r_1 r_2 = c/a$ and $r_1 + r_2 = -b/a$ in the standard $ax^2 + bx + c$ form,* we have

$$x = -(c/b) - (a/b)x^2$$

where

$$x_0 = c/b$$

$$x_1 = (a/b)x_0^2$$

$$x_2 = (a/b)(2x_0 x_1)$$
$$\vdots$$

Note, for example, that in solving $(x - \pi)(x - r) = 0$, where we have deliberately chosen the second root to be only a little larger than the root π, we have $x^2 - (\pi + 4)x + 4\pi = 0$ or

$$x = \frac{4\pi}{\pi + 4} + \frac{1}{\pi + 4}x^2$$

so that $x_0 = 1.76$. If we consider $(x - \pi)(x - 10) = 0$, we get $x_0 = 2.39$. If we take the second root as 100, $x_0 = 3.05$ and for the second root $x = 1000$, $x_0 = 3.13$, an error of 0.3% with only the x_0 term to obtain the smaller root. Thus, the results converge to the desired solution more and more quickly, i.e., for smaller n, as the roots are farther apart. In general, for $(x - r_1)$ $(x - r_2) = 0$, or, $x^2 - (r_1 + r_2)x + r_1 r_2 = 0$, we have the first term $x_0 = r_1 r_2/(r_1 + r_2)$. If $r_2 \gg r_1$, we have $x_0 \simeq r_1 r_2/r_2 = r_1$. Since the following terms involving the A_n are divided by the factor $1/(r_1 + r_2)$ or approximately $1/r_2$, the other terms vanish early.

---

* The only case of nonconvergence of a quadratic equation for real roots (occurring if $b^2 < 4|ac|$) was discussed in [ ]. Examples are: $(x - 10)(x + 9) = x^2 - x + 90 = 0$, or, $(x - 10)(x + 10.01) = x^2 + .01x - 100.1 = 0$. However, this is a trivial case; easily recognized and easily solved. The method was, of course, developed for difficult systems and extended down to the trivial case of quadratics only to show the generality.

Decimal Roots: Finally as we have previously stated, the roots are not limited to integers. Consider, for example,

$$x^2 - 5.15x + 2.37 = 0$$

$$5.15x = 2.37 + x^2$$

$$x = \frac{2.37}{5.15} + \frac{1}{5.15} \sum_{n=0}^{\infty} A_n$$

We get immediately

$$x_0 = 0.460, \qquad x_1 = 0.0411, \qquad x_2 = 0.00735$$

Thus, the three-term approximation $\phi_3 = x_0 + x_1 + x_2 = 0.50845$. We will call this r_2; but $r_1 r_2 = 2.37$, hence, $r_1 = 2.37/0.50845 = 4.66$. The sum of the roots now constitutes a check by comparison with the coefficient of the middle term of the quadratic equation. We observe in doing this an error less than 0.3%, and considering that we only used a three-term approximation, the result is excellent.

Complex Roots: If we have complex roots z_1 and z_2 then

$$(x - z_1)(x - z_2) = 0 \quad \text{or} \quad x^2 - (z_1 + z_2)x + z_1 z_2 = 0.$$

Thus, the sum of the roots is the coefficient of the x term and the product of roots is the constant term. Consider an example with complex roots but real coefficients

$$x^2 - 2x + 2 = 0$$

Solving it in the usual manner with decomposition, we have

$$x = 1 + \frac{1}{2}x^2 = 1 + \frac{1}{2} \sum_{n=0}^{\infty} A_n.$$

Therefore, we take $x_0 = 1$ and obtain immediately

$$x_1 = \tfrac{1}{2}, \qquad x_2 = \tfrac{1}{2}, \qquad x_3 = \tfrac{5}{8}, \qquad x_4 = \tfrac{7}{8}, \qquad x_5 = \tfrac{21}{16}, \dots$$

i.e., a diverging series (for an equation with real coefficients) may indicate complex roots. In that case, since complex roots occur in conjugate pairs (e.g., $a + bi$ and $a - bi$), their sum is $2a$ and their product is $a^2 + b^2$. Comparison with the coefficients in the equation shows $2a = 2$ or $a = 1$ and $a^2 + b^2 = 2$, hence $b = 1$. Therefore, the roots are $1 + i$ and $1 - i$.

We considered here the equation $x^2 - 2x + 2 = 0$. Consider now what we call the associated equation $x^2 - 2x - 2 = 0$, which is similar except for the sign of the last term. By decomposition in the usual manner we get

$$x = -1 + \frac{1}{2} \sum_{n=0}^{\infty} A_n(x^2)$$

where $A_n(x^2)$ means A_n for $Nx = x^2$. The terms of the decomposition are:

$$x_0 = -1, \quad x_1 = \tfrac{1}{2}, \quad x_2 = -\tfrac{1}{2}, \quad x_3 = \tfrac{5}{8}, \quad x_4 = -\tfrac{7}{8}, \quad x_5 = \tfrac{21}{16}, \dots$$

This is also a diverging series, but this equation has real roots. (In the previous case the quadratic discriminant $b^2 - 4ac < 0$ indicating complex roots; in this case, $b^2 - 4ac > 0$, i.e., we have real roots, which are $1 + \sqrt{3}$ and $1 - \sqrt{3}$). Suppose that having suspected complex roots from noting divergence, we write $r_1 = a + ib$ and $r_2 = a - ib$ for the roots. We then find $2a = 2$ or $a = 1$ and $a^2 + b^2 = -2$ or $1 + b^2 = -2$, hence $b^2 = -3$ and finally $b = i\sqrt{3}$. Consequently,

$$r_1 = 1 + i(i\sqrt{3}) = 1 - \sqrt{3}$$
$$r_2 = 1 - i(i\sqrt{3}) = 1 + \sqrt{3}$$

We have obtained the roots anyway. Thus, when we have divergence, we may have either of these cases arising in such associated equations and assuming complex values will give us the roots in either case.

Quadratic Equation With Complex Roots: Consider c_1 and c_2 given by $(x - c_1)(x - c_2) = 0$ or $x^2 - (c_1 + c_2)x + c_1 c_2 = 0$, where $c_1, c_2 \in C$, the set of complex numbers. In our standard form, we get

$$x = \mu + vx^2$$

where $\mu = \alpha + i\beta$ and $v = \gamma + i\delta$ can, of course, be written in terms of real and imaginary components of c_1 and c_2. We write

$$\sum_{n=0}^{\infty} x_n = \mu + v \sum_{n=0}^{\infty} A_n$$

where

$$A_0 = x_0^2$$
$$A_1 = 2x_0 x_1$$
$$A_2 = x_1^2 + 2x_0 x_2$$
$$A_3 = 2x_0 x_3 + 2x_1 x_2$$
$$\vdots$$

Thus,

$$x_0 = \mu$$
$$x_1 = vA_0 = vx_0^2 = v\mu^2$$
$$x_2 = vA_1 = v(2x_0 x_1) = 2v^2\mu^3$$

$$x_3 = vA_2 = v(x_1^2 + 2x_0x_2) = 5v^3\mu^4$$

$$x_4 = vA_3 = v(2x_0x_3 + 2x_1x_2) = 14v^4\mu^5$$

$$\vdots$$

$$x_m = k_m v^m \mu^{m+1} \qquad \text{for} \quad m \geq 0$$

where the k_m are constants. The solution is

$$x = \sum_{n=0}^{\infty} k_n v^n \mu^{n+1}$$

The k_n are real numbers and the μ and v are complex numbers, i.e., $\mu = \alpha + i\beta$ and $v = \gamma + i\delta$. An m-term approximation is $\phi_m = \sum_{n=0}^{m-1} x_n$. Now let $c_1 = 1 + i$ and let $c_2 = 10 + 10i$. In the equation in standard form

$$x = \mu + vx^2$$

where $\mu = \alpha + i\beta$ and $v = \gamma + i\delta$ we find that $\alpha = \frac{10}{11}$, $\beta = \frac{10}{11}$, $\gamma = \frac{1}{22}$, and $\delta = -\frac{1}{22}$. Thus $\mu = \frac{10}{11}(1 + i)$ and $v = \frac{1}{22}(1 - i)$ and $x = \frac{10}{11}(1 + i) + \frac{1}{22}(1 - i)x^2$. Then

$$x_0 = \frac{10}{11}(1 + i)$$

$$x_1 = v\mu^2 = (10^2/11^3)(1 + i)$$

$$x_2 = 2v^2\mu^3 = 2(10^3/11^5)(1 + i)$$

$$x_3 = 5(10^4/11^7)(1 + i)$$

$$x_4 = 14(10^5/11^9)(1 + i)$$

$$\vdots$$

$$x_m = k_m v^m \mu^{m+1} \qquad (m \geq 0)$$

$$= k_m(1/22)^m(1 - i)^m(10/11)^{m+1}(1 + i)^{m+1}$$

where the coefficients k_m are easily calculated not only for the quadratic case but also for cubics in the form $x = \mu + vx^3$, quartics in the form $x = \mu + vx^4$, etc.; similarly we can find coefficients for $x = \mu + v_1x^2 + v_2x^3 + v_3x^4 + \cdots + v_{n-1}x^n$ for real or complex cases. By factoring x_m we have

$$x_m = k_m(\tfrac{1}{2})^m(10^{m+1}/11^{2m+1})[(1 - i)(1 + i)]^m(1 + i)$$
$$= k_m(\tfrac{1}{2})^m(10^{m+1}/11^{2m+1})(2^m)(1 + i)$$
$$= k_m(10^{m+1}/11^{2m+1})(1 + i).$$

Computing the components x_m, we get

$$x_0 = \tfrac{10}{11}(1 + i) = 0.9090(1 + i)$$

$$x_1 = (10^2/11^3)(1 + i) = (100/1331)(1 + i) = 0.0751(1 + i)$$

$$x_2 = (2)(10^3/11^5)(1 + i) = (2000/161{,}051)(1 + i) = 0.0124(1 + i)$$

$$x_3 = (5)(10^4/11^7)(1 + i) = 0.0025(1 + i)$$

$$x_4 = 0.00059(1 + i).$$

Thus

$$\phi_1 = 0.9090(1 + i)$$

$$\phi_2 = 0.9842(1 + i)$$

$$\phi_3 = 0.9966(1 + i)$$

$$\phi_4 = 0.9992(1 + i)$$

$$\phi_5 = 0.9998(1 + i)$$

$\phi_n \to (1 + i) = c_1$, the root of smallest magnitude. We see that the convergence is very rapid. Even by ϕ_2 we have an adequate solution and the method applies well to quadratic equations with complex coefficients (and is easily extended to polynomial equations). The real and imaginary components generally converge at different rates. Suppose $c_1 = 1 + i$ and $c_2 = m_1 + m_2 i$, where for illustration we choose $m_1 = 1$ and $m_2 = 2$ so that $c_2 = 1 + 2i$. Now $\alpha = \tfrac{7}{13}$, $\beta = \tfrac{9}{13}$, $\gamma = \tfrac{2}{13}$, and $\delta = -\tfrac{3}{13}$. Hence $\mu = \tfrac{7}{13} + \tfrac{9}{13}i$ and $v = \tfrac{2}{13} - \tfrac{3}{13}i$ so that

$$x = \left(\frac{7 + 9i}{13}\right) + \left(\frac{2 - 3i}{13}\right)x^2 = \mu + vx^2$$

Then

$$x_0 = \mu = \tfrac{7}{13} + \tfrac{9}{13}i = 0.5385 + 0.6923i$$

$$x_1 = v\mu^2 = 0.1429 + 0.1584i$$

$$x_2 = 2v^2\mu^3 = 0.0749 + 0.0718i$$

$$x_3 = 5v^3\mu^4$$

$$x_4 = 14v^4\mu^5$$

$$\vdots$$

The n-term approximate solutions are

$$\phi_1 = 0.5385 + 0.6923i$$
$$\phi_2 = 0.6814 + 0.8507i$$
$$\phi_3 = 0.7564 + 0.9225i$$
$$\vdots$$
$$\phi_\infty = 1 + i$$

It is clear that the imaginary component is converging more rapidly than the real component and so we have a differing convergence for the real and imaginary components of complex roots.

Convergence for algebraic operators with complex coefficients is to the complex root of smallest modulus.

10.2. CUBIC EQUATIONS

Consider now equations of the type $z^3 + A_2 z^2 + A_1 z + A_0 = 0$. The z^2 term is ordinarily eliminated by substituting $z = x - A_2/3$ to get an equation in the form $x^3 - qx - r = 0$. Thus, the equation

$$z^3 + 9z^2 + 23z + 14 = 0$$

becomes (substituting $z = x - 3$)

$$x^3 - 4x - 1 = 0$$

whose roots are 2.11, -1.86, and -0.254. If we solve this by decomposition, we write the equation in the form $-qx = r - x^3$ or

$$-4x = 1 - x^3$$

$$x = -\frac{1}{4} + \frac{1}{4}x^3$$

$$x = x_0 + \frac{1}{4}\sum_{n=0}^{\infty} A_n.$$

For this nonlinearity

$$A_0 = x_0^3$$
$$A_1 = 3x_0^2 x_1$$
$$A_2 = 3x_0^2 x_2 + 3x_0 x_1^2$$
$$A_3 = 3x_0^2 x_3 + 6x_0 x_1 x_2 + x_1^3$$
$$A_4 = 3x_0^2 x_4 + 3x_0 x_2^2 + 6x_0 x_1 x_3 + 3x_1^2 x_2$$
$$A_5 = 3x_0^2 x_5 + 6x_0 x_1 x_4 + 6x_0 x_2 x_3 + 3x_1^2 x_3 + 3x_1 x_2^2$$
$$\vdots$$

Thus $x_0 = -0.25$, $x_1 = \frac{1}{4}A_0 = -(\frac{1}{4})^4 = -0.004$, etc. The one-term approximation $\phi_1 = -0.25$, the two-term approximation, $\phi_2 = -0.254$, and $x_2 \simeq 0$ for an answer to three decimal places so that the correct solution is obtained already with ϕ_2 (again for the smallest root). Here ϕ_3 gives -0.254 with no more change to three decimal places. Computing six terms gives -0.25410168 which does not change any further to eight place accuracy.

If we now divide $x^3 - 4x - 1$ by $x - 0.254$, we obtain $x^2 + 0.254x - 3.9375$, which yields the other two roots by either the quadratic formula or the decomposition method.

The equation $x^3 - 6x^2 + 11x - 6 = 0$ has roots $(1, 2, 3)$. Written in the form $x = \frac{6}{11} + \frac{6}{11}x^2 - \frac{1}{11}x^3$ and solving by the decomposition method, it yields $x_0 = 0.5455$, $x_1 = 0.1475, \ldots$ and the solution $x = 1$ in eight terms.

EXAMPLE: $x^3 + 4x^2 + 8x + 8 = 0$ is satisfied by $x = -2$. Calculating this with appropriate A_n for the x^2 and x^3 terms, we get

$$x_0 = -1.0$$

$$x_1 = -0.375$$

$$x_2 = -0234375$$

$$x_3 = -0.1640625$$

$$x_4 = -01179199$$

$$x_5 = -0.0835876$$

If we sum these terms we get approximately $x = -1.98$ which makes us guess $x = -2.0$ and try it in the equation. (It is interesting to note, however, that we actually have an oscillating convergence due to the cubic term. If we sum 10 terms, we get $x = -2.0876342$, which is a peak departure from $x = -2$. At 20 terms we have a peak departure in the opposite direction with $x = -1.9656587$. At 100 terms we have $x = -1.997313$.)

EXAMPLE: Consider

$$x^3 - 6x^2 + 11x - 6 = 0$$

$$x = \tfrac{6}{11} + \tfrac{6}{11}x^2 - \tfrac{1}{11}x^3$$

$$\sum_{n=0}^{\infty} x_n = x_0 + \frac{6}{11}\sum_{n=0}^{\infty} A_n - \frac{1}{11}\sum_{n=0}^{\infty} B_n$$

expanding the x^2 and x^3 terms in our usual polynomials but using A_n and B_n to distinguish the two:

$$x_0 = \tfrac{6}{11} = 0.5455$$

$$x_1 = (\tfrac{6}{11})A_0 - (\tfrac{1}{11})B_0 = (\tfrac{10}{11})(6^3/11^4) = 0.147531$$

$$x_2 = (\tfrac{6}{11})A_1 - (\tfrac{1}{11})B_1 = (19)(10)(6^5/11^7) = 0.0758160$$

$$x_3 = (\tfrac{6}{11})A_2 - (\tfrac{1}{11})B_2 = (6^7/11^{10})(3610) = 0.038962$$

$$\phi_1 = 0.5455$$

$$\phi_2 = 0.693031$$

$$\phi_3 = 0.768847$$

$$\phi_4 = 0.80780$$
$$\vdots$$

where $\phi_n \to 1.0$ as $n \to \infty$.

We can write $x^3 - (r_1 + r_2 + r_3)x^2 + (r_1r_2 + r_1r_3 + r_2r_3)x - r_1r_2r_3 = 0$, then

$$x = \frac{(r_1r_2r_3)}{(r_1r_2 + r_1r_3 + r_2r_3)} + \frac{(r_1 + r_2 + r_3)}{(r_1r_2 + r_1r_3 + r_2r_3)}x^2 - \frac{1}{(r_1r_2 + r_1r_3 + r_2r_3)}x^3$$

Choose $r_1 < r_2 < r_3$ or $r_2 = \alpha r_1$ and $r_3 = \beta r_1$, where α and β are appropriate real fractions. The equation for x will become then

$$x = (r_1)\left[\frac{\alpha\beta + (1 + \alpha + \beta)(x^2/r_2^1) - (x^3/r_1^3)}{\alpha + \beta + \alpha\beta}\right]$$

where the bracketed quantity approaches unity and the first solution found is r_1. Thus, letting $\psi = (x/r_1)$

$$\psi = \left(\frac{\alpha\beta}{\gamma}\right) + \left(\frac{1 + \alpha + \beta}{\gamma}\right)\psi^2 - \left(\frac{1}{\gamma}\right)\psi^3$$

where $\gamma = \alpha + \beta + \alpha\beta$. Then if $\psi = \sum_{n=0}^{\infty}\psi_n$ and $\psi^2 = \sum_{n=0}^{\infty}A_n$ and $\psi^3 = \sum_{n=0}^{\infty}B_n$,

$$\psi_0 = \left(\frac{\alpha\beta}{\gamma}\right)$$

$$\psi_1 = \left(\frac{1 + \alpha + \beta}{\gamma}\right)\left(\frac{\alpha\beta}{\gamma}\right)^2 - \left(\frac{1}{\gamma}\right)\left(\frac{\alpha\beta}{\gamma}\right)^3$$
$$\vdots$$

If, for example, $r_1 < \frac{1}{10}r_2$ and $r_2 < \frac{1}{10}r_3$, then

$$\psi_0 = \frac{(10)(100)}{(10 + 100 + 1000)} = \frac{1000}{1110} \approx 1$$

$$\psi_1 = \left(\frac{111}{1110}\right)\left(\frac{1000}{1110^2}\right) - \left(\frac{1}{1110}\right)\left(\frac{1000^3}{1110^3}\right)$$

so that terms are indeed rapidly approaching zero, and r_1 will be the root calculated.

10.3.   HIGHER-DEGREE POLYNOMIAL EQUATIONS

Higher-degree polynomial equations are similarly solved. In the cubic case it was not necessary, of course, to eliminate the quadratic term. We can solve the original equation simply by substituting the appropriate A_n polynomial summations for both x^2 and x^3 terms. Even higher-degree equations (or non-integral powers or negative powers) can be equally well handled by substituting appropriate A_n polynomials for each nonlinearity. Consider an equation in the form

$$\sum_{\mu=0}^{n} \gamma_\mu x^\mu = 0$$

with γ_μ as given constants and seek the roots $r_1, r_2, \ldots, r_n$ (assumed to be real) satisfying $\prod_{\nu=1}^{n} (x - r_\nu) = 0$. We found if Nx or $f(x) = x^2$, for example, $A_0 = x_0^2$ or $f(x_0)$.

Now we have $Nx = \sum_{\mu=0}^{n} \gamma_\mu x^\mu$ so $A_0 = \sum_{\mu=0}^{n} \gamma_\mu x_0^\mu$. Since $\sum_{\mu=0}^{n} \gamma_\mu x^\mu = \gamma_0 + \gamma_1 x + \gamma_2 x^2 + \cdots + \gamma_n x^n$, we can write the A_n for each term or for the entire polynomial. Let us consider a specific example of the form $f(x) = \sum_{\mu=0}^{n} \gamma_\mu x^\mu = \gamma_n x^n + \gamma_{n-1} x^{n-1} + \cdots + \gamma_1 x + \gamma_0$ with $\gamma_n \neq 0$ and γ_i constant for $0 \leq i \leq n$.

EXAMPLE: It is interesting to consider a fifth-order polynomial operator since no formula exists for $n = 5$ or higher. The equation $x^5 - 15x^4 + 85x^3 - 225x^2 + 274x - 120 = 0$ has the roots 1, 2, 3, 4, 5. To calculate all the roots we rewrite the equation in the author's usual form as

$$x = \frac{120}{274} + \frac{225}{274}x^2 - \frac{85}{274}x^3 + \frac{15}{274}x^4 - \frac{1}{274}x^5$$

$$x = 0.43796 + 0.82117x^2 - 0.31022x^3 + 0.054745x^4 - 0.0036496x^5$$

or

$$x = k + \sum_{n=2}^{5} \gamma_n x^n$$

where

$$k = 0.43796$$
$$\gamma_2 = 0.82117$$
$$\gamma_3 = -0.31022$$
$$\gamma_4 = 0.054745$$
$$\gamma_5 = -0.0036496$$

We have the first approximation $\phi_1 = x_0 = k = 0.43796$. Then

$$x_1 = \gamma_2 A_0(x^2) + \gamma_3 A_0(x^3) + \gamma_4 A_0(x^4) + \gamma_5 A_0(x^5).$$

(The notation $A_0(x^2)$ means the A_0 for the x^2 term, etc.) Thus,

$$x_1 = 0.82117x_0^2 - 0.31022x_0^3 + 0.054745x_0^4 - 0.0036496x_0^5$$
$$= 0.15751 - 0.026060 + 0.0020141 - 0.00005881$$
$$= 0.13341$$

Hence $\phi_2 = x_0 + x_1 = 0.57137$.

$$x_2 = \gamma_2 A_1(x^2) + \gamma_3 A_1(x^3) + \gamma_4 A_1(x^4) + \gamma_5 A_1(x^5)$$

where

$$A_1(x^2) = 2x_0 x_1$$
$$A_1(x^3) = 3x_0^2 x_1$$
$$A_1(x^4) = 4x_0^3 x_1$$
$$A_1(x^5) = 5x_0^4 x_1$$

Consequently,

$$x_2 = [(0.82117)(2)x_0 - (0.31022)(3)x_0^2 + (0.05745)(4)x_0^3$$
$$- (0.0036496)(5)x_0^4]x_1$$
$$x_2 = 0.0746299.$$

Then $\phi_3 = 0.6459999 = 0.6460$. Continuing we have

$$x_3 = \gamma_2 A_2(x^2) + \gamma_3 A_2(x^3) + \gamma_4 A_2(x^4) + \gamma_5 A_2(x^5)$$

etc., as necessary.

The A_n are given by:

$$A_0 = h_0(x_0)$$
$$A_1 = h_1(x_0)x_1$$

$A_2 = \frac{1}{2}\{h_2(x_0)x_1^2 + 2h_1(x_0)x_2\}$

$A_3 = \frac{1}{6}\{h_3(x_0)x_1^3 + 6h_2(x_0)x_1x_2 + 6h_1(x_0)x_3\}$

$A_4 = \frac{1}{24}\{h_4(x_0)x_1^4 + 12h_3(x_0)x_1^2x_2 + h_2(x_0)[12x_2^2 + 24x_1x_3] + 24h_1(x_0)x_4\}$

$A_5 = \frac{1}{120}\{h_5(x_0)x_1^5 + 20h_4(x_0)x_1^3x_2 + 60h_3(x_0)[x_1x_2^2 + x_1^2x_3]$
$\qquad + 120h_2(x_0)[x_2x_3 + x_1x_4] + 120h_1(x_0)x_5\}$

$\vdots$

where $h_i = d^i f/dx_i$ for the function $f(x)$.

We now list final results for the fifth degree equation above to ten digit accuracy.

$$x_0 = 0.4379562044, \qquad \phi_1 = 0.4379562044$$

$$x_1 = 0.1334006838, \qquad \phi_2 = 0.5713568882$$

$$x_2 = 0.0745028484, \qquad \phi_3 = 0.6458597366$$

$$x_3 = 0.0500356263, \qquad \phi_4 = 0.6958953629$$

$$x_4 = 0.0449342233, \qquad \phi_5 = 0.7408295862$$

$$x_5 = 0.0446966625, \qquad \phi_6 = 0.7855262487$$

$$x_6 = 0.0331390668, \qquad \phi_7 = 0.8186653155$$

$$x_7 = 0.0272374949, \qquad \phi_8 = 0.8459028104$$

$$x_8 = 0.022258001, \qquad \phi_9 = 0.8681608114$$

$$x_9 = 0.0196274208, \qquad \phi_{10} = 0.8877882322$$

$$x_{10} = 0.0166467228, \qquad \phi_{11} = 0.904434955$$

$$\psi_1 = 56.2\%, \qquad \psi_7 = 18.1\%$$

$$\psi_2 = 42.9\%, \qquad \psi_8 = 15.4\%$$

$$\psi_3 = 35.4\%, \qquad \psi_9 = 13.9\%$$

$$\psi_4 = 30.4\%, \qquad \psi_{10} = 11.2\%$$

$$\psi_5 = 25.9\%, \qquad \psi_{11} = 9.5\%$$

$$\psi_6 = 21.4\%,$$

The error ψ decreases gradually to less than 10% by ψ_{11}, but it can easily be carried further by computer. The convergence in this case of a quintic operator is relatively poor because of the greater number of more closely spaced roots and the case of equal roots will be the worst case.

For $f(x) = x^k$, where k is an integer ≥ 2, write $h_n = d^n f/dx^n$ for $n \geq 0$. [We will write $h_n(x_0)$ for $d^n f/dx^n|_{\lambda = 0}$ for the computation of the A_n.] Then for x^k,

$$h_0 = x^k$$
$$h_1 = kx^{k-1}$$
$$\vdots$$
$$h_n = k(k-1)\cdots(k-n+1)x^{k-n} = \binom{k}{n}x^{k-n}$$

where $\binom{k}{n} = k!/(k-n)!$. Consequently, the A_n for $f(x) = x^k$ are given by

$$A_0 = x_0^k$$

$$A_1 = \left\{\binom{k}{1}x_0^{k-1}\right\}x_1$$

$$A_2 = \frac{1}{2}\left\{\binom{k}{2}x_0^{k-2}\right\}x_1^2 + \left\{\binom{k}{1}x_0^{k-1}\right\}x_2$$

$$A_3 = \frac{1}{6}\left\{\binom{k}{3}x_0^{k-3}\right\}x_1^3 + \left\{\binom{k}{2}x_0^{k-2}\right\}x_1 x_2 + \left\{\binom{k}{1}x_0^{k-1}\right\}x_3$$

$$A_4 = \frac{1}{24}\left\{\binom{k}{4}x_0^{k-4}\right\} + \frac{1}{2}\left\{\binom{k}{3}x_0^{k-3}\right\}x_1^2 x_2 + \left\{\binom{k}{2}x_0^{k-2}\right\}\left[\frac{1}{2}x_2^2 + x_1 x_3\right]$$
$$\qquad + \left\{\binom{k}{1}x_0^{k-1}\right\}x_4$$

$$A_5 = \frac{1}{120}\left\{\binom{k}{5}x_0^{k-5}\right\}x_1^5 + \frac{1}{6}\left\{\binom{k}{4}x_0^{k-4}\right\}x_1^3 x_2 + \frac{1}{2}\left\{\binom{k}{3}x_0^{k-3}\right\}[x_1 x_2^2 + x_1^2 x_3]$$
$$\qquad + \left\{\binom{k}{2}x_0^{k-2}\right\}[x_2 x_3 + x_1 x_4] + \left\{\binom{k}{1}x_0^{k-1}\right\}x_5.$$

We observe that the subscripts for A_n always add to n and superscripts of the x_i terms always add to k. The above work will yield the lowest root, reducing the equation to the $(k-1)$th, etc., power. We can do the problem more rapidly as follows.

Consider a general polynomial in x with constant nonzero coefficients

$$f(x) = \sum_{i=k}^{0} \gamma_i x^i = \gamma_k x^k + \cdots + \gamma_0$$

Now

$$h_0 = \sum_{i=k}^{0} \gamma_i x^i$$

$$h_1 = \sum_{i=k}^{1} i\gamma_i x^{i-1}$$

$$\vdots$$

$$h_n = \sum_{i=k}^{n} \binom{i}{n} \gamma_i x^{i-n} \quad k > n$$

$$\vdots$$

$$h_k = \binom{k}{k} \gamma_k x^{k-k} = \gamma_k k! \quad k = n$$

$$h_{k+1} = 0 \quad \text{or} \quad h_n = 0 \quad n > k$$

The A_n can now be given as

$$A_0 = \sum_{i=k}^{0} \gamma_i x_0^i$$

$$A_1 = \left\{ \sum_{i=k}^{1} \binom{i}{1} \gamma_i x_0^{i-1} \right\} x_1$$

$$A_2 = \frac{1}{2} \left\{ \sum_{i=k}^{2} \binom{i}{2} \gamma_i x_0^{i-2} \right\} x_1^2 + \left\{ \sum_{i=k}^{1} \binom{i}{1} \gamma_i x_0^{i-1} \right\} x_2$$

$$A_3 = \frac{1}{6} \left\{ \sum_{i=k}^{3} \binom{i}{3} \gamma_i x_0^{i-3} \right\} x_1^3 + \left\{ \sum_{i=k}^{2} \binom{i}{2} \gamma_i x_0^{i-2} \right\} x_1 x_2 + \left\{ \sum_{i=k}^{1} \binom{i}{1} \gamma_i x_0^{i-1} \right\} x_3$$

$$A_4 = \frac{1}{24} \left\{ \sum_{i=k}^{4} \binom{i}{4} \gamma_i x_0^{i-4} \right\} + \frac{1}{2} \left\{ \sum_{i=k}^{3} \binom{i}{3} \gamma_i x_0^{i-3} \right\} x_1^2 x_2$$

$$+ \left\{ \sum_{i=k}^{2} \binom{i}{2} \gamma_i x_0^{i-2} \right\} \left(\frac{1}{2} x_2^2 + x_1 x_3 \right) + \left\{ \sum_{i=k}^{1} \binom{1}{1} \gamma_i x_0^{i-1} \right\} x_4$$

$$A_5 = \frac{1}{120} \left\{ \sum_{i=k}^{5} \binom{i}{5} \gamma_i x_0^{i-5} \right\} x_1^5 + \frac{1}{6} \left\{ \sum_{i=k}^{4} \binom{i}{4} \gamma_i x_0^{i-4} \right\} x_1^3 x_2$$

$$+ \frac{1}{2} \left\{ \sum_{i=k}^{3} \gamma_i x_0^{i-3} \right\} (x_1 x_2^2 + x_1^2 x_3) + \left\{ \sum_{i=k}^{2} \binom{i}{2} \gamma_i x_0^{i-2} \right\} (x_2 x_3 + x_1 x_4)$$

$$+ \left\{ \sum_{i=k}^{1} \binom{i}{1} \gamma_i x_0^{i-1} \right\} x_5$$

$$\vdots$$

from which polynomial equations can be solved more rapidly than with individual substitutions for the various powers as we did earlier in this chapter.

10.4. EQUATION WITH NEGATIVE POWER NONLINEARITIES

Consider an example like $x = 2 + x^{-2}$ or the slightly more general form $x = k + x^{-m}$. We write

$$\sum_{n=0}^{\infty} x_n = k + \sum_{n=0}^{\infty} A_n$$

with $x_0 = k$ and $x_n = A_{n-1}$ for $n \geq 1$. Then

$$x_1 = A_0 = x_0^{-m} = k^{-m}$$

$$x_2 = A_1 = -m x_0^{-(m+1)} x_1$$

$$x_3 = A_2 = \tfrac{1}{2} m(m + 1) x_0^{-(m+2)} x_1^2 - m x_0^{-(m+1)} x_2$$

$$x_4 = A_3 = -\tfrac{1}{6} m(m + 1)(m + 2) x_0^{-(m+3)} x_1^3 + m(m + 1) x_0^{-(m+2)} x_1 x_2$$
$$\quad - m x_0^{-(m+1)} x_3$$

$$x_5 = A_4 = \tfrac{1}{24} m(m + 1)(m + 2)(m + 3) x_0^{-(m+4)} x_1^4$$
$$\quad - \tfrac{1}{2} m(m + 1)(m + 2) x_0^{-(m+3)} x_1^2 x_2$$
$$\quad + m(m + 1) x_0^{-(m+2)} [\tfrac{1}{2} x_2^2 + x_1 x_3] - m x_0^{-(m+1)} x_4$$

If $k = 2$ and $m = 2$, then $x_0 = 2$ and

$$x_1 = 2^{-2} = 0.25$$

$$x_2 = -2(2)^{-3}(0.25) = -0.0625$$

$$x_3 = \tfrac{1}{2}(2)(3)(2)^{-4}(0.25)^2 - (2)(2)^{-3}(-0.0625) = 0.02734375$$

$$x_4 = -0.0146484375$$

$$x_5 = -0.0087280273$$

By ϕ_6 we get an excellent approximation to the solution (2.205569431).

$$\phi_1 = 2, \qquad \psi_1 = 9.32\%$$

$$\phi_2 = 2.25, \qquad \psi_2 = -2.02\%$$

$$\phi_3 = 2.1875, \qquad \psi_3 = 0.82\%$$

$$\phi_4 = 2.21484375, \qquad \psi_4 = -0.42\%$$

$$\phi_5 = 2.200189063, \qquad \psi_5 = 0.24\%$$

$$\phi_6 = 2.20891709, \qquad \psi_6 = -0.15\%$$

EXAMPLE: Consider

$$x = 10 + x^{-10}$$

$$\sum_{n=0}^{\infty} x_n = 10 + \sum_{n=0}^{\infty} A_n$$

$$x_0 = 10$$

$$x_n = A_{n-1} \quad \text{for} \quad n \geq 1$$

$$x_1 = 1 \times 10^{-10}$$

$$x_2 = -1 \times 10^{-20}$$

$$\vdots$$

$$\phi_1 = 10$$

$$\phi_2 = 10.0000000001$$

The value of ϕ_3 is 10 followed by 10 zeros and 9 nines and the series is very rapidly convergent. An even more extreme case is $x = 100 + x^{-100}$, where $x_0 = 100$, $x_1 = 100^{-100}$ or 10^{-200}, $x_2 = -100^{-200}$ or -10^{-400}, etc. Then $\phi_1 = 100$, $\phi_2 = 10^2 + 10^{-200}$, $\phi_3 = 10^2 + 10^{-200} - 10^{-400}$. Finally, consider

$$x = 10^m + x^{-10^m}$$

$$x_0 = 10^m$$

$$x_1 = (10^m)^{-10^m} = 10^{-m(10)^m}$$

$$x_2 = -(10^m)^{-2m(10)^m}$$

$$\vdots$$

$$x = 10^m + 10^{-m(10)^m} - 10^{-2m(10)^m} + \cdots$$

For large m, $x \simeq 10^m$ as expected.

REMARK. It should be clear now that if we have a differential equation with a negative power nonlinearity, it is also solvable (see Section 4.6). Thus, this material on A_n for various kinds of nonlinearities is applicable whether the equation is algebraic, differential, or partial differential.

EXAMPLE: Consider

$$y' - ty^{-1} = 0 \qquad y(0) = a$$

$$Ly = ty^{-1}$$

$$L^{-1}Ly = L^{-1}ty^{-1}$$

$$y = y(0) + L^{-1}t \sum_{n=0}^{\infty} A_n(y^{-1})$$

$$y_0 = y(0) = a$$

$$y_1 = L^{-1}[tA_0(y^{-1})] = L^{-1}[ty_0^{-1}] = \frac{t^2}{2a}$$

$$y_2 = L^{-1}[tA_1(y^{-1})] = L^{-1}[-ty_0^{-2}y_1] = \frac{-t^4}{8a^3}$$

$$y_3 = L^{-1}[tA_2(y^{-1})] = L^{-1}[t\{y_0^{-3}y_1^2 - y_0^{-2}y_2\}] = \frac{3t^5}{8^5 a^5}$$

$$\vdots$$

$$y = a + \frac{t^2}{2a} - \frac{t^4}{8a^3} + \frac{3t^5}{8a^5} - \cdots = \sqrt{a^2 + t^2}$$

which is easily verified to be the Taylor expansion.

10.5.   EQUATIONS WITH NONINTEGER POWERS

Consider now the inversion of algebraic operator equations involving fractional or noninteger powers, e.g., consider $x = k + x^{1/2}$. Write

$$\sum_{n=0}^{\infty} x_n = k + \sum_{n=0}^{\infty} A_n$$

where $x_0 = k$ and $x_n = A_{n-1}$ for $n \geq 1$. Then

$$x_1 = A_0 = x_0^{1/2} = k^{1/2}$$

$$x_2 = A_1 = \tfrac{1}{2}x_0^{-1/2}x_1 = \tfrac{1}{2}(k)^{-1/2}(k)^{1/2} = \tfrac{1}{2}$$

$$x_3 = A_2 = \tfrac{1}{2}x_0^{-1/2}x_2 - \tfrac{1}{8}x_0^{-3/2}x_1^2 = \tfrac{1}{8}k^{-1/2}$$

$$x_4 = A_3 = 0$$

$$x_5 = A_4 = -\tfrac{1}{128}k^{-3/2}$$

$$\vdots$$

$$\phi_6 = (k) + (k^{1/2}) + \tfrac{1}{2} + \tfrac{1}{8}k^{-1/2} + 0 - \tfrac{1}{128}k^{-3/2}$$

If $k = 2$ we expect the solution to converge to $x = 4$. As verification, we get

$$x_0 = 2$$

$$x_1 = 1.414213562$$

$$x_2 = 0.50$$

$$x_3 = 0.0883883476$$

$$x_4 = 0$$

$$x_5 = -0.0027621359$$

and

$$\phi_1 = 2, \qquad\qquad \psi_1 = 50\%$$

$$\phi_2 = 3.414213562, \qquad \psi_2 = 14.65\%$$

$$\phi_3 = 3.914213562, \qquad \psi_3 = 2.15\%$$

$$\phi_4 = 4.00260191, \qquad \psi_4 = -0.065\%$$

$$\phi_5 = \cdots \qquad\qquad \psi_5 = \cdots$$

$$\phi_6 = 3.99839774, \qquad \psi_6 = 0.0040\%$$

Thus, ϕ_6 is an excellent approximation (in fact ϕ_4 is!). With ϕ_6 we have $\frac{4}{1000}$ of 1% error. To be more general, consider nonlinear terms $Nx = x^{1/m}$, where m belongs to the set of positive integers.

EXAMPLE: Consider

$$x = k + x^{1/m}, \qquad \sum_{n=0}^{\infty} x_n = k + \sum_{n=0}^{\infty} A_n$$

where the A_n are the usual Adomian polynomials generated for the specific nonlinearity under consideration. Then

$$x_0 = k$$

$$x_n = A_{n-1} \qquad \text{for} \quad n \geq 1$$

The A_n are given by

$$A_0 = x_0^{1/m}$$

$$A_1 = (1/m)x_0^{(1/m)-1}x_1$$

$$A_2 = \tfrac{1}{2}(1/m)((1/m)-1)x_0^{(1/m)-2}x_1^2 + (1/m)x_0^{(1/m)-1}x_2$$

$$A_3 = \tfrac{1}{6}(1/m)((1/m)-1)((1/m)-2)x_0^{(1/m)-3}x_1^3$$
$$\qquad + (1/m)((1/m)-1)x_0^{(1/m)-2}x_1 x_2$$
$$\qquad + (1/m)x_0^{(1/m)-1}x_3$$
$$\vdots$$

Since $x_n = A_{n-1}$ in this problem, we now have the x_n. Their general form of x_n is $\sigma(1/m)k^{(n/m)-n+1}$, where $\sigma(1/m)$ has the form $\sum_i \prod_j \alpha_i[(1/m) - \beta_j]$. If $m = 2$ and $k = 2$, then we get precisely the results in the preceding example. We now see also that we can consider operators involving a cube root, a fourth root, etc.

10.6. EQUATIONS WITH DECIMAL POWERS

Now consider solution of algebraic equations involving (rational or irrational) decimal powers, first taking up the case of rational powers

$$x = k + x^{a/b}$$

where k is real and a and b are positive integers. Write

$$\sum_{n=0}^{\infty} x_n = k + \sum_{n=0}^{\infty} A_n$$

where $x_0 = k$ and $x_n = A_{n-1}$ for $n \geq 1$. (Thus we have $Nx = x^{a/b} = \sum_{n=0}^{\infty} A_n$.)
Now

$$A_0 = x_0^{a/b}$$

$$A_1 = (a/b)x_0^{(a/b)-1}x_1$$

$$A_2 = (a/b)x_0^{(a/b)-1}x_2 + \tfrac{1}{2}(a/b)((a/b) - 1)x_0^{(a/b)-2}x_1^2$$

$$A_3 = (a/b)x_0^{(a/b)-1}x_3 + (a/b)((a/b) - 1)x_0^{(a/b)-2}x_1x_2$$
$$+ \tfrac{1}{6}(a/b)((a/b) - 1)((a/b) - 2)x_0^{(a/b)-3}x_1^3$$

Hence,

$$x_0 = k$$

$$x_1 = A_0 = k^{a/b}$$

$$x_2 = A_1 = (a/b)k^{2(a/b)-1}$$

$$x_3 = A_2 = \{(a/b)^2 + \tfrac{1}{2}(a/b)((a/b) - 1)\}k^{3(a/b)-2}$$
$$\vdots$$

As a specific case, choose $a = 3$, $b = 11$, and $k = 2$. Then $a/b = 0.272727\ldots$
and $x = 2 + x^{3/11}$

$x_0 = 2$	$\phi_1 = 2$
$x_1 = 1{,}208089444$	$\phi_2 = 3.208089444$
$x_2 = 0.1990200144$	$\phi_3 = 3.407109458$
$x_3 = -0.0109288172$	$\phi_4 = 3.396180641$

Notice ϕ_3 and ϕ_4 differ very little as we try substitution into the original equation of ϕ_4 as an approximate solution. Then

$$\tilde{\phi}_4 = 2 + \phi_4^{3/11} = 3.395775811$$

We see that $\tilde{\phi}_4$ is very close to ϕ_4 differing by about 0.01 %. (We have defined $\tilde{\phi}_n \equiv k + \phi_n^{a/b}$ to see if the approximate solution satisfies the original equation.)

Now we consider the case of *irrational* powers. Write

$$x = k - x^{\gamma}$$

letting k be real and γ an irrational number such as e or π. Now

$$\sum_{n=0}^{\infty} x_n = k - \sum_{n=0}^{\infty} A_n$$

where $x_0 = k$ and $x_n = -A_{n-1}$ for $n \geq 1$. Since $Nx = x^{\gamma} = \sum_{n=0}^{\infty} A_n$,

$$A_0 = x_0^{\gamma}$$

$$A_1 = \gamma x_0^{\gamma-1} x_1$$

$$A_2 = \gamma x_0^{\gamma-1} x_2 + \tfrac{1}{2}\gamma(\gamma - 1)x_0^{\gamma-2} x_1^2$$

$$A_3 = \gamma x_0^{\gamma-1} x_3 + \gamma(\gamma - 1)x_0^{\gamma-2} x_1 x_2 + \tfrac{1}{6}\gamma(\gamma - 1)(\gamma - 2)x_0^{\gamma-3} x_1^3$$

Now the components x_n of the solution $x = \sum_{n=0}^{\infty} x_n$ can be computed as

$$x_0 = k$$

$$x_1 = -k^{\gamma}$$

$$x_2 = \gamma k^{2\gamma-1}$$

$$x_3 = -\{\gamma^2 + \tfrac{1}{2}\gamma(\gamma - 1)\}k^{3\gamma-2}$$

$$x_4 = \{\gamma^2(\gamma - 1) + \tfrac{1}{6}\gamma(\gamma - 1)(\gamma - 2) + \gamma^3 + \tfrac{1}{2}\gamma^2(\gamma - 1)\}k^{4\gamma-3}$$

For a specific example we now choose $k = 1/\pi$ and $\gamma = \pi$

$$x = (1/\pi) - x^{\pi}$$

(letting $\pi = 3.1415927$ and $1/\pi = 0.3183099$ for the computation). We get

$$x_0 = 0.3183099$$

$$x_1 = -0.0274257$$

$$x_2 = 0.0074236$$

$$x_3 = -0.0026943$$

$$x_4 = 0.0011225$$

The five-term approximation $\phi_5 = \sum_{i=0}^{4} x_i = 0.296736$. As a check

$$\tilde{\phi}_5 = (1/\pi) - \phi_5^{\pi} = 0.296311$$

a difference of about 0.01 %.

10.7. RANDOM ALGEBRAIC EQUATIONS

The treatment of algebraic equations by the decomposition method suggests further generalization to random algebraic equations. Such equations, with random coefficients, arise in engineering, physics, and statistics whenever random errors are involved. Random matrices, too, are found in finite-dimensional approximation models for random Hamiltonian operators and various engineering applications concerned with systems of linear random equations; these are discussed in a following section. Thus, suppose we have the equation

$$x^3 + \alpha x^2 + \beta x + \gamma = 0$$

where α is stochastic. Then we have

$$x = -(\gamma/\beta) = (1/\beta)x^3 - (\alpha/\beta)x^2$$

where α is a stochastic process and β and γ are constants. We now write

$$x = x_0 - \frac{1}{\beta} \sum_{n=0}^{\infty} A_n - \frac{\alpha}{\beta} \sum_{n=0}^{\infty} B_n$$

where the A_n and B_n are our appropriate polynomials computed for the nonlinear term x^3 and x^2. For example,

$$x_1 = -(1/\beta)x_0^3 - (\alpha/\beta)x_0^2$$

hence x_1 involves a stochastic coefficient in the second term. Continuing we write ϕ_n and appropriate statistics such as $\langle \phi_n \rangle$.

If we consider a quadratic equation with a forcing term

$$y^2 + by + c = x(t)$$

where b and c can be functions of t, we can write immediately $y = (1/b)(x - c) - (1/b)\sum_{n=0}^{\infty} A_n(y^2)$, or, since $y_0 = (1/b)(t - c)$ and $y_1 = -(1/b)A_0$, etc.,

$$y_1 = -\frac{1}{b^3}(x - c)^2$$

$$y_2 = \frac{2}{b^5}(x - c)^3$$

$$y_3 = -\frac{5}{b^7}(x - c)^4$$

$$\vdots$$

$$y = \sum_{n=0}^{\infty} \frac{(-1)^n k_n}{b^{2n+1}}(x - c)^{n-1}$$

with k_n as appropriately defined constants. Clearly $x(t)$ can be stochastic [or $x(t, \omega)$]. The $b(t)$ coefficient can have a fluctuating or random component and be written as $b_0(t) + \beta(t, \omega)$ in which case,

$$y^2 + (b_0 + \beta)y + c = x$$

$$y^2 + b_0 y + c = x - \beta y$$

$$b_0 y = (x - c) - \beta y - y^2$$

$$y = \frac{1}{b}(x - c) - \frac{\beta}{b} y - \frac{1}{b} \sum_{n=0}^{\infty} A_n(y^2)$$

$$y_0 = \frac{1}{b}(x - c)$$

$$y_1 = -\frac{1}{b}\beta y_0 - \frac{1}{b} y_0^2$$
$$\vdots$$

10.8. GENERAL REMARKS

We have seen that algebraic equations can be handled by the decomposition method and that it provides a useful method for computation of roots of polynomial equations, often yielding a very rapid convergence. We have here a computational and highly convergent system to solve problems of the real world more realistically without assumptions that change the essential nonlinear nature. Whether we deal with differential or partial differential equations, or algebraic systems as in this chapter, an accurate methodology is available for physical applications and more realistic modeling.

PART II: TRANSCENDENTAL EQUATIONS

10.9. TRIGONOMETRIC EQUATIONS

Let $f(x) = \sin x$. Then $h_0 = \sin x$, $h_1 = \cos x$, $h_2 = -\sin x$, $h_3 = -\cos x$, $h_4 = \sin x$, etc. (i.e., $h_{n-4} = h_n$). Consequently,

$$A_0 = \sin x_0$$

$$A_1 = x_1 \cos x_0$$

$$A_2 = -\frac{x_1^2}{2} \sin x_0 + x_2 \cos x_0$$

$$A_3 = -\frac{x_1^3}{6} \cos x_0 - x_1 x_2 \sin x_0 + x_3 \cos x_0$$

$$= \left(x_3 - \frac{x_1^3}{6} \right) \cos x_0 - x_1 x_2 \sin x_0$$

$$\vdots$$

If $f(x) = \cos x,\ h_0 = \cos x,\ h_1 = -\sin x,\ h_2 = -\cos x,\ h_3 = \sin x,\ h_4 = \cos x = h_0$. Then

$$A_0 = \cos x_0$$

$$A_1 = -x_1 \sin x_0$$

$$A_2 = -\frac{x_1^2}{2} \cos x_0 - x_2 \sin x_0$$

$$A_3 = \left(\frac{x_1^3}{6} - x_3 \right) \sin x_0 - x_1 x_2 \cos x_0$$

$$\vdots$$

(For any particular A_n derived for either the sin x or cos x nonlinearity, we can get the A_n for cos x from sin x by replacing sines with cosines and cosines with negative sines. Similarly, we can get the A_n for sin x from cos x by replacing cosines with sines and sines with negative cosines.)

If $f(x) = \sin \alpha x$, where α is a positive integer, $h_0 = \sin \alpha x$ or $\alpha^0 \sin \alpha x$, $h_1 = \alpha \cos \alpha x$ or $\alpha^1 \cos \alpha x$, $h_2 = -\alpha^2 \sin \alpha x$, $h_3 = -\alpha^3 \cos \alpha x$, $h_4 = \alpha^4 \sin \alpha x = \alpha^4 h_0$. Thus, $h_n = \alpha^4 h_{n-4}$. Then

$$A_0 = \sin \alpha x_0$$

$$A_1 = \alpha x_1 \cos \alpha x_0$$

$$A_2 = -\frac{\alpha^2}{2} x_1^2 \sin \alpha x_0 + \alpha x_2 \cos \alpha x_0$$

$$A_3 = -\frac{\alpha^3}{6} x_1^3 \cos \alpha x_0 - \alpha^2 x_1 x_2 \sin \alpha x_0 + \alpha x_3 \cos \alpha x_0$$

$$\vdots$$

For $f(x)$ and $\cos \alpha x$, $h_0 = \alpha^0 \cos \alpha x$, $h_1 = -\alpha^1 \sin \alpha x$, $h_2 = -\alpha^2 \cos \alpha x$, $h_3 = \alpha^3 \sin \alpha x$, $h_4 = \alpha^4 \cos \alpha x = \alpha^4 h_0$; thus $h_n = \alpha^4 h_{n-4}$. Then

$$A_0 = \cos \alpha x_0$$

$$A_1 = -\alpha x_1 \sin \alpha x_0$$

$$A_2 = -\frac{\alpha^2 x_1^2}{2} \cos \alpha x_0 - \alpha x_2 \sin \alpha x_0$$

$$A_3 = \frac{\alpha^3 x_1^3}{6} \sin \alpha x_0 - \alpha^2 x_1 x_2 \cos \alpha x_0 - \alpha x_3 \sin \alpha x_0$$

$$\vdots$$

Consider the example $x = k + \sin x$. We write it as

$$\sum_{n=0}^{\infty} x_n = k + \sum_{n=0}^{\infty} A_n$$

The x_0 term is k and $\sin x$ is the term Nx in Adomian's notation, which is now written in terms of the A_n. Thus, $x_n = A_{n-1}$ for $n \geq 1$. For a specific numerical solution let us take $x_0 = k = \pi/4$. Then

$x_0 = 0.7854,$	$\phi_1 = 0.7859,$	$\psi_1 = \quad 55.5\%$
$x_1 = 0.7071,$	$\phi_2 = 1.4925,$	$\psi_2 = \quad 15.5\%$
$x_2 = 0.5000,$	$\phi_3 = 1.9925,$	$\psi_3 = -12.8\%$
$x_3 = 0.1768,$	$\phi_4 = 2.1693,$	$\psi_4 = -22.8\%$
$x_4 = -0.1667,$	$\phi_5 = 2.0026,$	$\psi_5 = -13.4\%$
$x_5 = -0.3757,$	$\phi_6 = 1.6269,$	$\psi_6 = \quad 7.8\%$

$$\vdots$$

The correct solution is 1.766. The error $\psi_n = (x - \phi_n)/x$ is expressed as a percentage, where x is the correct solution. Each ϕ_n represents an n-term approximation to the solution. What is happening here is an oscillating convergence like a damped sinusoid. If we plot the ψ_n versus n, we see this clearly. The curve crosses the axis first between $n = 2$ and $n = 3$, again between $n = 5$ and $n = 6$, then $n = 8$ and $n = 9$, etc., as it decreases in amplitude. We note that $\phi_2 = 1.4925$ and $\phi_3 = 1.9925$. The difference is 0.5. If we interpolate, we get 1.74, which is very close to the correct solution. Of course, we can simply calculate more terms as well, but recognition of the phenomena above yields a fair solution by $n = 3$.

EXAMPLE: Consider the equation $x = k + \sin \mu x$. To be specific, we choose $k = (\pi/4) = 0.7853981634\ldots$ and $\mu = \frac{1}{2}$. Our nonlinearity $Nx = \sin \mu x = \sum_{n=0}^{\infty} A_n$. Evaluating the A_n, we get

$$A_0 = \sin \mu x_0$$

$$A_1 = x_1 \mu \cos \mu x_0$$

$$A_2 = x_2 \mu \cos \mu x_0 - \tfrac{1}{2} x_1^2 \mu^2 \sin \mu x_0$$

$$A_3 = x_3 \mu \cos \mu x_0 - x_1 x_2 \mu^2 \sin \mu x_0 - \tfrac{1}{6} x_1^3 \mu^3 \cos \mu x_0$$

$$A_4 = x_4 \mu \cos \mu x_0 - [\tfrac{1}{2} x_2^2 + x_1 x_3] \mu^2 \sin \mu x_0$$
$$- \tfrac{1}{2} x_1^2 x_2 \mu^3 \cos \mu x_0 + \tfrac{1}{24} x_1^4 \mu^4 \sin \mu x_0$$

$$A_5 = x_5 \mu \cos \mu x_0 - [x_2 x_3 + x_1 x_4] \mu^2 \sin \mu x_0$$
$$- \tfrac{1}{2} [x_1 x_2^2 + x_1^2 x_3] \mu^3 \cos \mu x_0 + \tfrac{1}{6} x_1^3 x_2 \mu^4 \sin \mu x_0$$
$$+ \tfrac{1}{120} x_1^5 \mu^5 \cos \mu x_0$$

$$A_6 = x_6 \mu \cos \mu x_0 - [\tfrac{1}{2} x_3^2 + x_2 x_4 + x_1 x_5] \mu^2 \sin \mu x_0$$
$$- [\tfrac{1}{6} x_2^3 + x_1 x_2 x_3 + \tfrac{1}{2} x_1^2 x_4] \mu^3 \cos \mu x_0$$
$$+ [\tfrac{1}{4} x_1^2 x_2^2 + \tfrac{1}{6} x_1^3 x_3] \mu^4 \sin \mu x_0$$
$$+ \tfrac{1}{24} x_1^4 x_2 \mu^5 \cos \mu x_0 - \tfrac{1}{720} x_1^6 \mu^6 \sin \mu x_0$$

$$A_7 = x_7 \mu \cos \mu x_0 - [x_3 x_4 + x_2 x_5 + x_1 x_6] \mu^2 \sin \mu x_0$$
$$- [\tfrac{1}{2} x_2^2 x_3 + \tfrac{1}{2} x_1 x_3^2 + x_1 x_2 x_4 + \tfrac{1}{2} x_1^2 x_5] \mu^3 \cos \mu x_0$$
$$+ [\tfrac{1}{6} x_1 x_2^3 + \tfrac{1}{2} x_1^2 x_2 x_3 + \tfrac{1}{6} x_1^3 x_4] \mu^4 \sin \mu x_0$$
$$+ [\tfrac{1}{12} x_1^3 x_2^2 + \tfrac{1}{24} x_1^4 x_3] \mu^5 \cos \mu x_0$$
$$- \tfrac{1}{120} x_1^5 x_2 \mu^6 \sin \mu x_0 - \tfrac{1}{5040} x_1^7 \mu^7 \cos \mu x_0$$

$$A_8 = x_8 \mu \cos \mu x_0 - [\tfrac{1}{2} x_4^2 + x_3 x_5 + x_2 x_6 + x_1 x_7] \mu^2 \sin \mu x_0$$
$$- [\tfrac{1}{2} x_2 x_3^2 + \tfrac{1}{2} x_2^2 x_4 + x_1 x_3 x_4 + x_1 x_2 x_5 + \tfrac{1}{2} x_1^2 x_6] \mu^3 \cos \mu x_0$$
$$+ [\tfrac{1}{24} x_2^4 + \tfrac{1}{2} x_1 x_2^2 x_3 + \tfrac{1}{4} x_1^2 x_3^2 + \tfrac{1}{2} x_1^2 x_2 x_4 + \tfrac{1}{6} x_1^3 x_5] \mu^4 \sin \mu x_0$$
$$+ [\tfrac{1}{12} x_1^2 x_2^3 + \tfrac{1}{6} x_1^3 x_2 x_3 + \tfrac{1}{24} x_1^4 x_4] \mu^5 \cos \mu x_0$$
$$- [\tfrac{1}{48} x_1^4 x_2^2 + \tfrac{1}{120} x_1^5 x_3] \mu^6 \sin \mu x_0$$
$$- [\tfrac{1}{720} x_1^6 x_2] \mu^7 \cos \mu x_0 + [\tfrac{1}{40320}] x_1^8 \mu^8 \sin \mu x_0$$

$$\vdots$$

Results of computation $x = (\pi/4) + \sin(x/2)$ (see Table 1).

Thus, the error in ϕ_{11}, the result of computing the ten values $x_1, x_2, \ldots, x_{10}$, yields the approximation $\phi_{11} = 1.447573642$ versus the correct solution of 1.447655855, an error of 0.005%! Computation yields a damped oscillating convergence. The error is negative up to $n = 5$ and positive from $n = 6$ to $n = 10$ and negative again beginning with $n = 11$; each oscillation, however, decreases in amplitude, but continues in cycles of five. The ϕ_n, of course, is $\sum_{v=0}^{n-1} x_v$ and $\phi_\infty = 1.447655855$. It is interesting to note that computing only four values (x_1 to x_4) yields an error less than 2% and five values yields an error less than 0.1%. Because of the oscillating

TABLE 1

n	x_n	ϕ_n	ψ_n
0	0.7853981634	—	—
1	0.3826834324	0.7853981634	-45.75%
2	0.1767766953	1.168081596	-19.31%
3	0.0746548489	1.344858291	-7.10%
4	0.0269352751	1.419513140	-1.94%
4	0.0067408961	1.446448415	-0.0834%
6	-0.0004152046	1.453189311	$+0.3822\%$
7	-0.0020294996	1.452774106	$+0.3536\%$
8	-0.0017197035	1.450744606	$+0.2134\%$
9	-0.0010092361	1.449024903	$+0.09457\%$
10	-0.0004420255	1.448015667	$+0.02485\%$
11	—	1.447573642	-0.005679%

convergence it can increase after that (however, remaining much less than 0.5%) then decrease again to 0.005% by $n = 11$. The error passes cyclically through zero, thus, $n = 5$ yields -0.0834% and $n = 6$ yields $+0.3822\%$. If the values of ψ_n are plotted, we find the crossing at $n = 5.15$. The difference in ϕ_n values is 0.00674 and 0.15(0.00674) = 0.00100. Subtracting from ϕ_5 yields 1.445 for the solution (an error less than 0.2%). It is also interesting to note the cyclical pattern for ψ_n: negative from $n = 1$ to 5, positive from $n = 6$ to 10, negative from $n = 11$ to 15, etc. and decreasing in amplitude. Noting the peaks of the curve for ψ_n versus n, we see the successive peaks are steadily decreasing. These are approximately at $\psi_6, \psi_{12}, \psi_{18}, \psi_{24}$, etc., with $|\psi_6| > |\psi_{12}| > |\psi_{18}|$, etc. In the first (negative) region $|\psi_1| > |\psi_m|$ for $m \in \{2, 3, 4, 5\}$. In the second (positive) region, $|\psi_6| > |\psi_m|$ for $m \in \{7, 8, 9, 10\}$. In the third (negative) region, $|\psi_{12}| > |\psi_m|$ for $m \in \{11, 13, 14, 15\}$. In the fourth region, $|\psi_{18}| > |\psi_m|$ for $m \in \{16, 17, 19, 20\}$, etc. By noting the crossing points we can get the solution long before the ϕ_n reach a stable solution.

10.10. EXPONENTIAL CASES

Let $f(x) = e^x$; then $h_n = e^x$ for $n \geq 0$ and

$$A_0 = e^{x_0}$$

$$A_1 = x_1 e^{x_0}$$

$$A_2 = \tfrac{1}{2} e^{x_0}(x_1^2 + 2x_2)$$

$$A_3 = \tfrac{1}{6} e^{x_0}(x_1^3 + 6x_1 x_2 + 6x_3)$$

$$\vdots$$

If $f(x) = e^{kx}$, $h_n = k^n e^{kx}$ and

$$A_0 = e^{kx_0}$$

$$A_1 = kx_1 e^{kx_0}$$

$$A_2 = \tfrac{1}{2}e^{kx_0}(k^2 x_1^2 + 2kx_2)$$

$$A_3 = \tfrac{1}{6}e^{kx_0}(k^3 x_1^3 + 6k^2 x_1 x_2 + 6kx_3)$$

$$\vdots$$

Consider, as an example, the equation $x = k + e^{-x}$, $k > 0$. The solution is

$$x = k + \sum_{n=1}^{\infty} (-1)^{n-1} \frac{n^{n-1}}{n!} e^{-nk}$$

If we write $x = \sum_{n=0}^{\infty} x_n$ and $Nx = \sum_{n=0}^{\infty} A_n$, we have

$$\sum_{n=0}^{\infty} x_n = k + \sum_{n=0}^{\infty} A_n$$

$$x_0 = k$$

$$x_1 = A_0 = e^{-x_0}$$

$$x_2 = A_1 = e^{-x_0}(-x_1)$$

$$x_3 = A_2 = e^{-x_0}(-x_2 + \tfrac{1}{2}x_1^2)$$

$$x_4 = A_3 = e^{-x_0}(-x_3 + x_1 x_2 - \tfrac{1}{6}x_1^3)$$

$$x_5 = A_4 = e^{-x_0}(-x_4 + \tfrac{1}{2}x_2^2 + x_1 x_3 - \tfrac{1}{2}x_1^2 x_2 + \tfrac{1}{24}x_1^4)$$

$$x_6 = A_5 = e^{-x_0}(-x_5 + x_2 x_3 + x_1 x_4 - \tfrac{1}{2}x_1 x_2^2 - \tfrac{1}{2}x_1^2 x_3 + \tfrac{1}{6}x_1^3 x_2 - \tfrac{1}{120}x_1^5)$$

$$x_7 = A_6 = e^{-x_0}(-x_6 + \tfrac{1}{2}x_3^2 + x_2 x_4 + x_1 x_5 - \tfrac{1}{6}x_2^3 - x_1 x_2 x_3 - \tfrac{1}{2}x_1^2 x_4 + \tfrac{1}{4}x_1^2 x_2^2 + \tfrac{1}{6}x_1^3 x_3 - \tfrac{1}{24}x_1^4 x_2 + \tfrac{1}{720}x_1^6)$$

$$x_8 = A_7 = e^{-x_0}(-x_7 + x_3 x_4 + x_2 x_5 + x_1 x_6 - \tfrac{1}{2}x_2^2 x_3 - \tfrac{1}{2}x_1 x_3^2 - x_1 x_2 x_4 - \tfrac{1}{2}x_1^2 x_5 + \tfrac{1}{6}x_1 x_2^3 + \tfrac{1}{2}x_1^2 x_2 x_3 + \tfrac{1}{6}x_1^3 x_4 - \tfrac{1}{12}x_1^3 x_2^2 - \tfrac{1}{24}x_1^4 x_3 + \tfrac{1}{120}x_1^5 x_2 - \tfrac{1}{5040}x_1^7)$$

$$\vdots$$

Each term is successively calculated:

$$x_0 = k$$

$$x_1 = e^{-k}$$

$$x_2 = -e^{-2k}$$

$$x_3 = \tfrac{3}{2}e^{-3k}$$

$$x_4 = -\tfrac{8}{3}e^{-4k}$$

$$x_5 = \tfrac{125}{24}e^{-5k}$$

$$x_6 = -\frac{6^5}{6!}e^{-6k}$$

$$\vdots$$

We notice that the signs alternate for the x_n—positive for $x_1, x_3, x_5, \ldots$ and negative for $x_2, x_4, x_6, \ldots$ Thus, for x_n we have a coefficient $(-1)^{n+1}$. The corresponding exponential is e^{-nk}. The numerical coefficient [other than $(-1)^{n+1}$] for e^{-nk} is given as

$n = 1$	1	or	$1^0/1$
$n = 2$	1	or	$2^1/1 \cdot 2$
$n = 3$	$\tfrac{3}{2}$	or	$3 \cdot 3/2 \cdot 3 = 3^2/3!$
$n = 3$	$\tfrac{8}{3}$	or	$8 \cdot 2 \cdot 4/2 \cdot 3 \cdot 4 = 4^3/4!$
$n = 5$	$\tfrac{125}{24}$	or	$125 \cdot 5/24 \cdot 5 = 5^4/5!$
$n = 6$	$\tfrac{1296}{120}$	or	$1296 \cdot 6/120 \cdot 6 = 7776/720 = 6^5/6!$

Thus $x_n = (-1)^{n+1} (n^{n-1}/n!)e^{-nk}$, and we have an algorithm making unnecessary computation of more A_n polynomials for this specific problem.

We can evidently get a graphical solution by plotting e^{-x} versus x, raising the values by k (we choose $k = 2$) and looking for the intersection of the resulting curve with the line $y = x$. For $k = 2$, we find the solution $x = 2.120028239$.

Our solution by decomposition is

$$x = k + \sum_{n=1}^{\infty} (-1)^{n+1}\left(\frac{n^{n-1}}{n!}\right)e^{-nk}$$

$$x_0 = k = 2$$

$$x_1 = e^{-2} = 1.3533528 \times 10^{-1}$$

$$x_2 = -e^{-4} = -1.8315639 \times 10^{-2}$$

The corresponding values of the exponential are

$$e^{-2} = 1.3533528 \times 10^{-1}$$

$$e^{-4} = 1.8315639 \times 10^{-2}$$

$$e^{-6} = 2.4787522 \times 10^{-3}$$

$$e^{-8} = 3.3546263 \times 10^{-4}$$

$$e^{-10} = 4.539993 \times 10^{-5}$$

$$e^{-12} = 6.1442124 \times 10^{-6}$$

The results for the x_n are given in the accompanying tabulation.

n	x_n	n	x_n
0	2.0	4	$-8.9456701 \times 10^{-4}$
1	1.3533528×10^{-1}	5	2.3645797×10^{-4}
2	$-1.8315639 \times 10^{-2}$	6	$-6.6357493 \times 10^{-5}$
3	3.7181283×10^{-3}		

The n term approximation $\phi_n = x_0 + x_1 + \cdots + x_{n-1}$. Values of ϕ_n are given in Table 2. The accuracy is such that a seven-term approximation has an error of 0.0007%. The small amplitude oscillating (and rapidly damped) convergence is interesting to note and a subject of further study. If we plot ψ_n versus n, we see oscillations of decreasing amplitude. The envelope of the oscillations decreases asymptotically to zero. The calculated value of $\psi_8 = 0.00021091328\%$; $\psi_9 = -0.0001392257\%$. Thus with a nine-term approximation the error is approximately $(1/10000)\%$. The oscillating convergence means the solution is between ϕ_8 and ϕ_9. Thus, $\phi_8 < x < \phi_9$ or

$$2.1200327 < x < 2.1200269$$

where the true solution is $x = 2.120028239$.

TABLE 2

n	ϕ_n	% error $\psi_n = [(\phi_n - x)/x]100$
1	2.00	-5.6
2	2.13533528	$+0.722$
3	2.117019641	-0.142
4	2.1207378	$+0.0330$
5	2.1198432	-0.00873
6	2.1200797	$+0.00243$
7	2.1200133	-0.000705

Finally, it is interesting to consider the following. For the equation $x = k + e^{-x}$, $k > 0$, we determined x as

$$x = k + \sum_{n=1}^{\infty} (-1)^{n+1} \frac{n^{n-1}}{n!} e^{-nk}$$

Substituting this into the original equation, we must have

$$\exp - \left[k + \sum_{n=1}^{\infty} (-1)^{n+1} \frac{n^{n-1}}{n!} e^{-nk} \right] = \sum_{n=1}^{\infty} (-1)^{n+1} \frac{n^{n-1}}{n!} e^{-nk}$$

or

$$e^{-k} e^{-\Sigma(-1)^{n+1}(n^{n-1}/n!)e^{-nk}} = \sum_{n=1}^{\infty} (-1)^{n+1}(n^{n-1}/n!)e^{-nk}$$

which says

$$e^{-k} e^{-[e^{-k} - e^{-2k} + \cdots]} = e^{-k} - e^{-2k} + \cdots$$

Multiply by e^k to get

$$e^{-[\ \ ]} = 1 - [\ \ ]$$

or

$$e^{-x} = 1 - x + \cdots$$

where $x = \sum_{n=1}^{\infty} (-1)^{n+1} e^{-nk}$.

10.11. LOGARITHMIC EQUATION: PURELY NONLINEAR EQUATIONS

It has been shown that the decomposition method solves equations of the form $Fy = Ly + Ny = x$. In the previous volume we suggested that an equation of the form $Fy = Ny = x$, i.e., a purely nonlinear equation, could be solved by adding linear terms to both sides. Let us consider a simple but interesting example with $Ny = e^y$ or the equation $e^y = x$. Adding linear terms as suggested, we get

$$Ly + e^y = x + Ly \tag{10.11.1}$$

Since L is a linear and, in this case, algebraic operator, we choose $Ly = \beta y + \gamma$

$$\beta y + \gamma + e^y = x + \beta y + \gamma$$

Solving for y from the βy on the left, we find

$$y = (x - \gamma)/\beta + y + (\gamma/\beta) - (1/\beta)e^y$$

Replacing y by the decomposition and $Ny = e^y$ by $\sum_{n=0}^{\infty} A_n$, i.e., $\sum_{n=0}^{\infty} A_n(e^y)$, and parametrizing, we get

$$y = \sum_{n=0}^{\infty} \lambda^n y_n = \frac{(x - \gamma)}{\beta} + \lambda \sum_{n=0}^{\infty} \lambda^n y_n + \frac{\lambda\gamma}{\beta} - \lambda\left(\frac{1}{\beta}\right) \sum_{n=0}^{\infty} \lambda^n A_n$$

Now we can write

$$y_0 = (x - \gamma)/\beta$$
$$y_1 = y_0 + (\gamma/\beta) - (1/\beta)A_0$$
$$y_2 = y_1 - (1/\beta)A_1 \tag{10.11.2}$$
$$\vdots$$
$$y_{n+1} = y_n - (1/\beta)A_n \qquad \text{for} \quad n \geq 2$$

The $A_n(e^y)$ are given by

$$A_0 = e^{y_0}$$
$$A_1 = y_1 e^{y_0}$$
$$A_2 = \tfrac{1}{2}e^{y_0}(y_1^2 + 2y_2)$$
$$A_3 = \tfrac{1}{6}e^{y_0}(y_1^3 + 6y_1 y_2 + 6y_3)$$
$$\vdots$$

Consequently,

$$y_0 = (x - \gamma)/\beta$$
$$y_1 = y_0 + (\gamma/\beta) - (1/\beta)e^{y_0}$$
$$\vdots$$
$$y_{n+1} = y_n - (1/\beta)A_n \tag{10.11.3}$$

To find y specifically now and show $y = \ln x$ (we will get a series involving x which is equivalent to $\ln x$), let us choose a specific x, say $x = 2$, and verify that we get $y = \ln 2 = 0.693$ for reasonable n. The remaining question then is what values to use for the slope and intercept β and γ in Ly. We try $\beta = 2.5$ and $\gamma = 0.5$. Then

$$y_0 = 1.5/2.5 = 0.60$$

$$y_1 = -(1/2.5)e^{0.60} + (2/2.5) = 0.071$$

$$y_2 = (1/6.25)e^{1.2} + \left(\frac{2}{6.25} + \frac{1}{2.5}\right)e^{0.60} + (2/2.5) = 0.019$$

$$y_3 = -(1-5)e^{0.60}(y_1^2 + 2y_2) + y_2 = 0.003$$

$$\vdots$$

Approximations ϕ_n are given for $n = 1, 2, \ldots$ by

$$\phi_1 = 0.60$$

$$\phi_2 = 0.671$$

$$\phi_3 = 0.690$$

$$\phi_4 = 0.693$$

$$\phi_5 = 0.693$$

and we need go no further, i.e., the approximation is now accurate to 3 decimals in comparison to the value we specified for ln 2.

The question arises whether we can find an optimal Ly. We note that if e^y is to be approximated with the single term y_0, or $e^{y_0} = x$ then $y_0 = \ln x$. Since we chose $x = 2$, $y_0 = 0.693 = (x - \gamma)/\beta = (2 - \gamma)/\beta$. With the choice $\gamma = 0.5$ that we made, β should be 2.16, and we had chosen 2.5. Thus choosing β and γ to satisfy $\ln x = (x - \gamma)/\beta$ appears to be the right choice. However, the series soon converges as we saw for other choices. Adomian and Rach have also considered (in unpublished work) the addition of an $Fy = Ly + y^2$ term and obtained convergence, but the present results appear preferable because of simplicity.

EXERCISE

We could approximate y_0 with only the first term y. Then $e^{y_0} \approx 1 + y_0 = 2$ and $(2 - \gamma)/\beta = 1$ or $\gamma + \beta = 2$ is a condition on our choice of β and γ. If we write $e^{y_0} \approx 1 + y_0 + y_0^2/2$, we get $\gamma + 0.7\beta = 2$; or we can approximate y with $y_0 + y_1$ or approximate e^y with a few terms for a condition on our choices of γ and β. (As a further exercise, try to find a better choice of constants and check the convergence.) (Note: if we use $\gamma + 0.7\beta = 2$ and choose, for example, $\beta = 1$, we should get the correct answer in *one* term!)

10.12. PRODUCTS OF NONLINEAR FUNCTIONS

Examples—whether algebraic or differential equations—which involve complicated nonlinearities sometimes are made more easily calculable by considering the nonlinearity to consist of products of simpler nonlinearities. Consider a simple example:

$$x = k + e^{-x} \sin(x/2) \qquad (10.12.1)$$

which is in our usual general form with the nonlinear function $N(x) = e^{-x} \sin(x/2)$. We will consider $N(x)$ to be the product of $N_1(x)N_2(x)$, where $N_1(x) = e^{-x}$ and $N_2(x) = \sin(x/2)$. We expand $N_1(x)$ in the A_n polynomials and similarly expand $N_2(x)$ using B_n for the second set simply to distinguish the two. With the usual decomposition, (10.12.1) becomes

$$\sum_{n=0}^{\infty} x^n = k + \left(\sum_{n=0}^{\infty} A_n \right) \left(\sum_{n=0}^{\infty} B_n \right) \qquad (10.12.2)$$

We will solve (10.12.2) for $k = 1$ in more detail than necessary to learn as much as possible about its behaviour. To the nearest 1×10^{-10} the solution is $x = 1.1713285129$. (The last digit can be verified by writing $x = A + B$, where $A = 1$ and $B = 0.1713285129$. Then $e^{-A-B} = e^{-A}e^{-B}$ and $\sin[A/2) + (B/2)] = \sin(A/2)\cos(B/2) + \cos(A/2)\sin(B/2)$ and the right-hand side of (10.12.2) is given by $\tilde{x} = 1 + e^{-A}e^{-B}[\sin(A/2)\cos(B/2) + \cos(A/2)\sin(B/2)]$ which yields $\tilde{x} = x$.)

First, let us examine the results of computation by the decomposition method before considering the detailed calculation. Our approximations ϕ_n are given by $\phi_n = \sum_{i=0}^{n-1} x_i$. The error $\psi_n = 100(x - \phi_n)/x$. (See Table 3.) Note that by ϕ_7, the error is less than 0.0004% and is less than 0.5% with ϕ_2 which required computing only the *single* term x_1. If we did not know the correct solution, we could stop the calculation since the results had clearly stabilized to the desired accuracy. Thus, if accuracy to 10^{-2} is sufficient, we would stop

TABLE 3

n	x_n	ϕ_n	ψ_n
0	1.000...		
1	0.1763707992	1.000...	14.63%
2	−0.0026364803	1.1763707992	−0.43%
3	−0.0029245319	1.1737344319	−0.21%
4	0.0004979183	1.170809787	0.044%
5	0.0000511587	1.171307705	0.0018%
6	−0.0000345495	1.171358864	−0.00259%
7	−	1.171324315	0.00036%

at ϕ_3, which requires computing only x_1 and x_2 and verifying the solution by substitution. The procedure is so easy that it is not much trouble to go further as desired. Now let us look at the calculation.

We can see quickly how the computation is done for a few terms (which are usually quite sufficient) after which we will take a deeper look. Since $e^{-x} = \sum_{n=0}^{\infty} A_n$ and $\sin(x/2) = \sum_{n=0}^{\infty} B_n$ we calculate the A_n, and B_n as in Chapter 3

$$A_0 = e^{-x_0}$$

$$A_1 = e^{-x_0}(-x_1)$$

$$A_2 = e^{-x_0}(-x_2 + \tfrac{1}{2}x_1^2)$$

$$\vdots$$

$$B_0 = \sin(x_0/2)$$

$$B_1 = (x_1/2)\cos(x_0/2)$$

$$B_2 = (x_2/2)\cos(x_0/2) - (x_1^2/8)\sin(x_0/2)$$

$$\vdots$$

We have now $x = 1 + (A_0 + A_1 + \cdots)(B_0 + B_1 + \cdots) = 1 + A_0 B_0 + \cdots$ where we employ our simple rule discussed in [1] that each x_i involves terms of lower index, thus $x_0 = 1$ and

$$x_1 = A_0 B_0$$

$$x_2 = A_0 B_1 + A_1 B_0$$

$$x_3 = A_1 B_1 + A_0 B_2 + A_2 B_0$$

$$\vdots$$

$$x_n = \sum_{i+j=n-1} A_i B_j$$

and using the above A_i and B_i,

$$x_1 = e^{-1} \sin \tfrac{1}{2} = 0.1763708$$

$$x_2 = -0.00263648$$

$$x_3 = -0.0029245319$$

$$x_4 = 0.0004979183$$

$$x_5 = 0.0000511587$$

$$x_6 = -0.0000345495$$

and ϕ_n, our approximation to n terms is given by $\phi_n = \sum_{i=0}^{n-1} x_i$. Here ϕ_1, of course, is 1.0; ϕ_2, which required computing only x_1, is equal to 1.176, which is already a good approximation (under 0.5 %). Increasing n yields better and better approximation ϕ_n. The correct solution satisfying the equation is $x = 1.713285129$. If we calculate $\psi_n = [(x - \phi_n)/x](100)$ to determine percentage error, then ψ_2 is already less than 0.4 %, ψ_4 is less than 0.04 %, and by ψ_7 the error is less than 0.0004 %. If the correct solution is not available for comparison, how do we know where to stop the computation?

By the time we get to ϕ_4 or ϕ_5, it is clear the solution has stabilized to a certain number of decimals and we need go on only if we require a more exact solution. We can also calculate the right side with a given ϕ_n i.e., $1 + e^{-\phi_n} \sin(\phi_n/2)$, call this $\tilde{\phi}_n$, and see how closely $\tilde{\phi}_n = \phi_n$, since ϕ_n is the approximation to x on the left side. Thus $\tilde{\phi}_2 - \phi_2 = -0.00525661$.

Detailed Computation: As we learned in Chapter 3, we can write for a nonlinear function $Ny = f(y) = \sum_{n=0}^{\infty} A_n = \sum_{n=0}^{\infty} h_n(y_0)C(v, n)$. In this problem the nonlinearity is $Nx = e^{-x} \sin(x/2)$, and we will consider it to be the product $N_1(x)N_2(x)$, where $N_1(x) = e^{-x}$ and $N_2(x) = \sin(x/2)$.
Evaluating the $N_1(x)$ term, we have

$$f(x) = e^{-x} \text{ and } G_n(x_0) = (d^n/dx^n)f(x)|_{\lambda=0}$$

thus

$$G_n(x_0) = (-1)^n e^{-x_0} = (-1)^n e^{-1} = (-1)^n [0.3678794412].$$

Evaluating $N_2(x)$, $f(x) = \sin(x/2)$ we have (since $x_0 = 1$, $\sin \frac{1}{2} = 0.4794255386$, $\cos \frac{1}{2} = 0.8775825619$, and $H_n(x_0) = (d^n/dx^n)h(x)|_{\lambda=0}$

$$H_0(x_0) = \sin(x_0/2) = 0.4794255386$$

$$H_1(x_0) = \tfrac{1}{2} \cos(x_0/2) = 0.4387912809$$

$$H_2(x_0) = -\tfrac{1}{4} \sin(x_0/2) = -0.1198563847$$

$$H_3(x_0) = -\tfrac{1}{8} \cos(x_0/2) = -0.1096978202$$

$$H_4(x_0) = \tfrac{1}{16} \sin(x_0/2) = 0.0299640962$$

$$H_5(x_0) = \tfrac{1}{32} \cos(x_0/2) = 0.0274244551$$

Since we see the H_n are cyclic with a period of four terms, we can write for $n \geq 0$

$$H_{4n}(x_0) = (\tfrac{1}{2})^{4n} \sin(x_0/2)$$

$$H_{4n+1}(x_0) = (\tfrac{1}{2})^{4n+1} \cos(x_0/2)$$

$$H_{4n+2}(x_0) = (\tfrac{1}{2})^{4n+2}(-1) \sin(x_0/2)$$

$$H_{4n+3}(x_0) = (\tfrac{1}{2})^{4n+3}(-1) \cos(x_0/2)$$

Now we can write

$$F_0 = G_0 H_0$$

$$F_1 = G_0 H_1 + G_1 H_0$$

$$F_2 = G_0 H_2 + 2G_1 H_1 + G_2 H_0$$

$$F_3 = G_0 H_3 + 3G_1 H_2 + 3G_2 H_1 + G_3 H_0$$

$$F_4 = G_0 H_4 + 4G_1 H_3 + 6G_2 H_2 + 4G_3 H_1 + G_4 H_0$$

$$F_5 = G_0 H_5 + 5G_1 H_4 + 10G_2 H_3 + 10G_3 H_2 + 5G_4 H_1 + G_5 H_0$$

$$\vdots$$

where

$$G_0(x_0) = e^{-x_0} = e^{-1} = 0.3678794412$$

$$G_1(x_0) = -e^{-x_0} = -e^{-1} = -0.3678794412$$

$$G_2(x_0) = e^{-x_0} = e^{-1} = 0.3678794412$$

$$G_3(x_0) = -e^{-x_0} = -e^{-1} = -0.3678794412$$

$$\vdots$$

$$H_0(x_0) = \sin \tfrac{1}{2} = 0.4794255386$$

$$H_1(x_0) = \tfrac{1}{2} \cos \tfrac{1}{2} = 0.4387912809$$

$$H_2(x_0) = -\tfrac{1}{4} \sin \tfrac{1}{2} = -0.1198563847$$

$$H_3(x_0) = -\tfrac{1}{8} \cos \tfrac{1}{2} = -0.1096978202$$

$$H_4(x_0) = \tfrac{1}{16} \sin \tfrac{1}{2} = 0.0299640962$$

$$H_5(x_0) = \tfrac{1}{32} \cos \tfrac{1}{2} = 0.0274244551$$

Now

$$F_0 = 0.1763707992$$

$$F_1 = -0.014948508$$

$$F_2 = -0.190566483$$

$$F_3 = 0.3998186012$$

$$F_4 = -0.5614290984$$

$$F_5 = 0.623849452$$

$$\vdots$$

Finally,

$$x_0 = 1.0$$

$$x_1 = F_0 = 0.1763707992$$

$$x_2 = F_1 x_1 = -0.0026364803$$

$$x_3 = F_1 x_2 + F_2(\tfrac{1}{2})x_1^2 = -0.0029245319$$

$$x_4 = F_1 x_3 + F_2 x_1 x_2 + F_3(\tfrac{1}{6})x_1^3 = 0.0004979183$$

$$x_5 = F_1 x_4 + F_2(\tfrac{1}{2}x_2^2 + x_1 x_3) + F_3(\tfrac{1}{2})(x_1^2 x_2) + F_4(\tfrac{1}{24})x_1^4 = 0.0000511587$$

$$x_6 = F_1 x_5 + F_2(x_2 x_3 + x_1 x_4) + F_3(\tfrac{1}{2})(x_1 x_2^2 + x_1^2 x_3) + F_4(\tfrac{1}{6})x_1^3 x_2$$
$$\quad + F_5(\tfrac{1}{120})x_1^5$$
$$\quad = -0.0000345495$$

$$\vdots$$

which yields the previous solution.

Some similar examples are given by $x = 1 + x^2 x^{-2}$ and $x = k + (e^{-x})(e^x)$, which, though trivial, are useful for verification of the methodology since we can write for either $\sum_{n=0}^{\infty} x^n = 1 + (\sum_{n=0}^{\infty} A_n)(\sum_{n=0}^{\infty} B_n)$. We could write the Nx term as one term, but it is generally simpler this way in a nontrivial case, expanding each factor in the A_n polynomials using B_n for the second set simply to avoid confusion. The first case has the obvious solution $x = 2$ and the second case has the solution $x = k + 1$. The A_n have been given for these nonlinear terms so it becomes an easy exercise to verify the solutions.

As another example, consider

$$x = 2 + e^{-x}$$

for which the solution is 2.120028239. By decomposition,

$$x_0 = 2$$

$$x_1 = e^{-2}$$

$$x_2 = -e^{-4}$$

$$x_3 = 1.5e^{-6}$$

$$x_4 = -\tfrac{8}{3}e^{-8}$$

$$x_5 = \tfrac{125}{24}e^{-10}$$

$$\vdots$$

$$x_n = (-1)^{n+1} \frac{n^{n-2}}{(n-1)!} e^{-nk} \qquad n \geq 1.$$

We obtain $\phi_5 = 2.120$, which is correct to three decimal places. The sixth term $x_5 = 2.37 \times 10^{-4}$ and further terms are even smaller.

10.13. HYPERBOLIC SINE NONLINEARITY

Consider the equation $x = k + \mu \sinh vx$, where Nx involves a hyperbolic sine nonlinearity. We previously solved a partial differential equation with such a nonlinearity. In both cases we find the A_n identically. We choose the constants $k = \mu = 1$ and $v = \frac{1}{2}$. Then

$$x = 1 + \sinh(x/2)$$

$$= 1 + \sum_{n=0}^{\infty} A_n \qquad x_0 = 1$$

Evaluating the A_n

$x_1 = A_0 = \sinh(x_0/2) = \sinh \frac{1}{2} = 0.5210953$

$x_2 = A_1 = \frac{1}{2}x_1 \cosh(x_0/2) = \frac{1}{2}(0.5210953)(1.1276259) = 0.2938003$

$x_3 = A_2 = \frac{1}{2}x_2 \cosh(x_0/2) + \frac{1}{2}x_1^2(\frac{1}{2})^2 \sinh(x_0/2)$

$x_4 = A_3 = \frac{1}{2}x_3 \cosh(x_0/2) + (\frac{1}{2})^2 x_1 x_2 \sinh(x_0/2) + \frac{1}{6}x_1^3(\frac{1}{2})^3 \cosh(x_0/2)$

$x_5 = A_4 = \frac{1}{2}x_4 \cosh(x_0/2) + [\frac{1}{2}x_2^2 + x_1 x_3](\frac{1}{2})^2 \sinh(x_0/2)$
$\qquad + \frac{1}{2}x_1^2 x_2(\frac{1}{2})^3 \cosh(x_0/2) + \frac{1}{24}(\frac{1}{2})^4 x_1^4 \sinh(x_0/2)$

$x_6 = A_5 = \cdots$

Numerical results are tabulated as follows:

$$x_0 = 1, \qquad\qquad \phi_1 = 1$$
$$x_1 = 0.5210953, \qquad \phi_2 = 1.5210953$$
$$x_2 = 0.2938003, \qquad \phi_3 = 1.8148956$$
$$x_3 = 0.1833357, \qquad \phi_4 = 1.9982313$$
$$x_4 = 0.1266358, \qquad \phi_5 = 2.1248671$$
$$x_5 = 0.0951898, \qquad \phi_6 = 2.2200569$$

If we calculate $\tilde{\phi}_m = 1 + \sinh(\phi_m/2)$ to see if the approximate solution will satisfy the original equation we have

$$\tilde{\phi}_1 = 1.5210953$$
$$\tilde{\phi}_2 = 1.8360186$$
$$\tilde{\phi}_3 = 2.0372186$$

$$\tilde{\phi}_4 = 2.1738371$$
$$\tilde{\phi}_5 = 2.2738949$$
$$\tilde{\phi}_6 = 2.3524476$$

and the percentage difference $\psi_m = [(\phi_m - \tilde{\phi}_m)/\tilde{\phi}_m]100$ is

$$\psi_1 = -52.11\%$$
$$\psi_2 = -20.70\%$$
$$\psi_3 = -12.25\%$$
$$\psi_4 = -8.79\%$$
$$\psi_5 = -7.01\%$$
$$\psi_6 = -5.94\%$$

i.e., we are approaching the solution nicely.

10.14.   COMPOSITE NONLINEARITIES

Extending now to composite nonlinear terms, consider

$$x = k + e^{-x^2}$$

with k real and the nonlinear function represented by $N_0(x) = N_1(N_2(x)) = N_1 \cdot N_2(x) = e^{-x^2}$. To get the A_n polynomials for the composite nonlinearity e^{-x^2}, let $u = u(x) = x^2$, then let

$$x = k + e^{-u}, \qquad \sum_{n=0}^{\infty} x_n = k + \sum_{n=0}^{\infty} A_n$$

where the A_n are generated for the exponential term $Nu = e^{-u}$. Thus

$$A_0(u_0) = e^{-u_0}$$
$$A_1(u_0, u_1) = -u_1 e^{-u_0}$$
$$A_2(u_0, u_1, u_2) = \tfrac{1}{2} e^{-u_0}[u_1^2 - 2u_2]$$
$$\vdots$$

Now let $x^2 = \sum_{n=0}^{\infty} B_n = \sum_{n=}^{\infty} u_n$ then

$$u_0 = B_0(x_0) = x_0^2$$
$$u_1 = B_1(x_0, x_1) = 2x_0 x_1$$
$$u_2 = B_2(x_0, x_1, x_2) = x_1^2 + 2x_0 x_2$$
$$\vdots$$

Substituting

$$A_0(x_0) = A_0[B_0(x_0)]$$
$$A_1(x_0, x_1) = A_1[B_0(x_0), B_1(x_0, x_1)]$$
$$A_2(x_0, x_1, x_2) = A_2[B_0(x_0), B_1(x_0, x_1), B_2(x_0, x_1 x_2)]$$
$$\vdots$$

implying

$$A_0 = e^{-x_0^2}$$
$$A_1 = -2x_0 x_1 e^{-x_0^2}$$
$$A_2 = \{2x_0^2 x_1^2 - x_1^2 - 2x_0 x_2\}e^{-x_0^2}$$
$$\vdots$$

The example $x = k + e^{-x^2}$ is now solved with

$$x_0 = k$$
$$x_1 = e^{-k^2}$$
$$x_2 = -2ke^{-2k^2}$$
$$x_3 = (6k^2 - 1)e^{-3k^2}$$

If $k = 2$, then

$$x_0 = 2$$
$$x_1 = 0.0183156$$
$$x_2 = -0.0013419$$
$$x_3 = 0.0001413$$

Thus $\phi_4 = 2.017115$ and $\tilde{\phi}_4 = 2 + e^{-\phi_4^2} = 2.0170989$. The difference between $\tilde{\phi}_4$ and ϕ_4 is less than $\frac{1}{1000}$ of 1 %. The error in a three-term approximation $\phi_3 = \sum_{i=0}^{2} x_i$ is approximately 1 % and decreases rapidly with more terms.

We have considered here a simple composite operation but we can generalize to cases such as

(1) $x = k + e^{(\alpha x^3 - \beta x^2 + \gamma x - \delta)}$
(2) $x = k + e^{-\sin(\nu x)}$
(3) $x = k + \alpha \sinh(\beta) \cdot \sin(\gamma x)$

In general let

$$x = k + N_0(x)$$
$$N_0(x) = N_1(N_2(...(N_m(x)))) = N_1 \cdot N_2 \cdots N_m(x)$$

Now

$$N_1(u^{(1)}) = \sum_{n=0}^{\infty} A_n^{(1)}(u_0^{(1)}, \ldots, u_{n-1}^{(1)}) = \sum_{n=0}^{\infty} u_n^{(0)}$$

$$N_2(u^{(2)}) = \sum_{n=0}^{\infty} A_n^{(2)}(u_0^{(2)}, \ldots, u_{n-1}^{(2)}) = \sum_{n=0}^{\infty} u_n^{(1)}$$

$$N_3(u^{(3)}) = \sum_{n=0}^{\infty} A_n^{(3)}(u_0^{(3)}, \ldots, u_{n-1}^{(3)}) = \sum_{n=0}^{\infty} u_n^{(2)}$$

$$\vdots$$

$$N_m(u^m) = \sum_{n=0}^{\infty} A_n^m(u_0^m, \ldots, u_{n-1}^m) = \sum_{n=0}^{\infty} u_n^{m-1} = \sum_{n=0}^{\infty} x_n$$

and $N_0(x) = \sum_{n=0}^{\infty} u_n^{(0)}(x_0, \ldots, x_{n-1})$, therefore $\sum_{n=0}^{\infty} A_n^{(1)} = \sum_{n=0}^{\infty} u_n^{(0)}$. Explicitly now

$$N_0(x) = \sum_{n=0}^{\infty} u_n^{(0)}(x_0, \ldots, x_{n-1})$$

$$= \sum_{n=0}^{\infty} A_n^{(1)}(A_0^{(2)}(A_0^{(3)}(\ldots(A_0^m(x_0))\ldots))), \ldots,$$

$$A_{n-1}^{(2)}(A_0^{(3)}(\ldots(A_0^m(x_0))\ldots)), \ldots,$$

$$A_{n-1}^{(3)}(\ldots(A_0^m(x_0), \ldots, A_{n-1}^m(x_0, \ldots, x_{n-1})\ldots))$$

with $x_0 = k$ and $x_n = u_{n-1}^{(0)}$ for $n \geq 1$ which provides the specific A_n and evaluation of the x_n.

We now consider an equation using the first-order example of Section 3.6 with $\tilde{N}_1 x = e^{-\sin(x/2)}$. Thus consider the equation

$$x = (\pi/2) + e^{-\sin(x/2)}$$

Letting $x = \sum_{n=0}^{\infty} x_n$ we have

$$\sum_{n=0}^{\infty} x_n = \frac{\pi}{2} + \tilde{N}_1 x$$

where

$$x_0 = \pi/2 = 1.570796327$$

$$x_1 = e^{-\sin(x_0/2)} = e^{-\sin(\pi/4)} = 0.4930686914$$

$$x_2 = e^{-\sin(x_0/2)}(-1)\left(\frac{x_1}{2}\cos\frac{x_0}{2}\right) = -0.0859547458$$

$$x_3 = 0.0480557892$$

$$x_4 = -0.0293847366$$

$$\vdots$$

The sum ϕ_5 of only five terms x_0 to x_4 is 1.99658132 which is correct within about $\frac{1}{4}$ of 1%. (We can see that the next term should add about 0.01. If we guess $x = 2$ and calculate the right-hand side, we have $1.570796327 + 0.431075951 = 2.00187228$.)

Now consider the second-order example of Section 3.6 with $x = k + \tilde{N}_2 x$, where $k = \pi/2$ and $\tilde{N}_2 x = e^{-\sin^2(x/2)} = N_0 N_1 N_2 x$. Using the A_n we have already written, we now have

$$A_0^0 = e^{-u_0^0} = e^{-A_0^1} = e^{-(u_0^0)^2} = e^{-(A_0^2)^2} = e^{-\sin^2(x_0/2)}$$

$$A_1^0 = e^{-u_0^0}(-u_1^0) = e^{-\sin^2(x_0/2)}(-u_1^0)$$

$$\text{where}\quad u_1^0 = A_1^1 = 2u_0^1 u_1^1 = 2A_0^2 A_1^2$$

$$= 2\sin(x_0/2)(x_1/2)\cos(x_0/2)$$

$$A_1^0 = -x_1 \sin(x_0/2)\cos(x_0/2)e^{-\sin^2(x_0/2)}$$

$$A_2^0 = e^{-u_0^0}(-u_2^0 + \tfrac{1}{2}(u_1^0)^2)$$

$$\text{where}\quad u_2^0 = A_2^1 = (u_1^1)^2 + 2u_0^1 u_2^1$$

$$u_1^0 = A_1^1 = 2u_0^1 u_1^1$$

$$u_1^1 = A_1^2 = (x_1/2)\cos(x_0/2)$$

$$u_0^1 = A_0^2 \sin(x_0/2)$$

$$A_2^0 = e^{-u_0^0}(-\{(u_1^1)^2 + 2u_0^1 u_2^1\} + \tfrac{1}{2}(2u_0^1 u_1^1)^2)$$

$$= e^{-u_0^0}(-(u_1^1)^2 - 2u_0^1 u_2^1 + \tfrac{1}{2}(2u_0^1 u_1^1)^2)$$

$$\text{where}\quad u_1^1 = A_1^2 = (x_1/2)\cos(x_0/2)$$

$$u_0^1 = \sin(x_0/2) = A_0^2$$

$$u_2^1 = A_2^2 = (x_2/2)\cos(x_0/2) - (x_1^2/8)\sin(x_0/2)$$

$$A_2^0 = e^{-\sin^2(x_0/2)}\{-(x_1^2/4)\cos^2(x_0/2) - 2(\sin(x_0/2))((x_2/2)\cos(x_0/2)$$

$$- (x_1^2/8)\sin(x_0/2)) + 2(\sin(x_0/2))^2((x_1/2)\cos(x_0/2))^2\}$$

Finally,

$$A_2^0 = e^{-\sin^2(x_0/2)}\{(x_1^2/4)\sin^2(x_0/2) - (x_1^2/4)\cos^2(x_0/2)$$

$$- x_2 \sin(x_0/2)\cos(x_0/2) + (x_1^2/2)\sin^2(x_0/2)\cos^2(x_0/2)\}$$

$$A_3^0 = e^{-u_0^0}(-u_3^0 + u_1^0 u_2^0 - \tfrac{1}{6}(u_1^0)^3)$$

$$= e^{-A_0^1}(-A_3^1 + A_1^1 A_2^1 - \tfrac{1}{6}(A_1^1)^3)$$

$$\vdots$$

so that $x = \sum_{n=0}^{\infty} x_n$ where

$$x_0 = \pi/2 = 1.570796327$$

$$x_1 = e^{-\sin^2(x_0/2)} = 0.999812126$$

$$x_2 = -x_1 \sin(x_0/2)\cos(x_0/2)e^{-\sin^2(x_0/2)} = -0.0137009172$$

etc., using the above A_n and it does not appear worthwhile to go farther; a three-term approximation $\phi_3 \approx 2.58430937$. Checking with $x = \phi_3$, $e^{-\sin^2(\phi_3/2)} = 0.999491607$ so the right-hand side is 2.57028793.

EXAMPLE: Consider $\tilde{N}_1(x) = e^{-e^{-x}} = N_0 N_1 x$, where $N_0(u^0) = e^{-u_0} = \sum A_n^0$, where A_n^0 is given by

$$A_0^0 = e^{-u_0^0}$$

$$A_1^0 = e^{-u_0^0}(-u_1^0)$$

$$A_2^0 = e^{-u_0^0}(-u_2^0 + \tfrac{1}{2}(u_1^0)^2)$$

$$A_3^0 = e^{-u_0^0}(-u_3^0 + u_1^0 u_2^0 - \tfrac{1}{6}(u_1^0)^3)$$

$$\vdots$$

$N_1(x) = e^{-x} = \sum_{n=0}^{\infty} A_n^1 = \sum_{n=0}^{\infty} u_n^0$, where A_n^1 is given by

$$A_0^1 = e^{-x_0}$$

$$A_1^1 = e^{-x_0}(-x_1)$$

$$A_2^1 = e^{-x_0}(-x_2 + \tfrac{1}{2}x_1^2)$$

$$A_3^1 = e^{-x_0}(-x_3 + x_1 x_2 - \tfrac{1}{6}x_1^3)$$

$$\vdots$$

Now for $\sum_{n=0}^{\infty} A_n^0 = e^{-e^{-x}}$

$$A_0^0 = e^{-u_0^0} = e^{-A_0^1} = e^{-e^{-x_0}}$$

$$A_1^0 = e^{-u_0^0}(-u_1^0) = e^{-A_0^1}(-A_1^1)$$

$$= e^{-e^{-x_0}}(-1)(e^{-x_0}(-x_1))$$

$$= x_1 e^{-e^{-x_0}}$$

$$A_2^0 = e^{-u_0^0}(-u_2^0 + \tfrac{1}{2}(u_1^0)^2)$$

$$= e^{-e^{x_0}}\{-e^{-x_0}[-x_2 + \tfrac{1}{2}x_1^2] + (1/2)(x_1^2 e^{-2x_0})\}$$

$$= e^{-e^{-x_0}}(x_2 e^{-x_0} + \tfrac{1}{2}x_1^2 e^{-x_0} + \tfrac{1}{2}x_1^2 e^{-2x_0})$$

$$\vdots$$

Thus in an algebraic equation $x = k + \tilde{N}_1(x)$ or a differential equation $Ly + \tilde{N}_1(x) = g(x)$, where L is a linear differential operator and $\tilde{N}_1(x)$ is specified above, there is no difficulty in obtaining a solution by the decomposition method.

EXAMPLE: Consider the equation $x = k + e^{-x^2}$. Using the normal decomposition rather than treating e^{-x^2} as a composite nonlinearity, the above equation is written as $\sum_{n=0}^{\infty} x_n = x = x_0 + Nx$ with the nonlinear term $Nx = e^{-x^2}$ decomposed into $\sum_{n=0}^{\infty} A_n$. Thus

$$x_0 = k$$
$$x_1 = A_0 = e^{-k^2}$$
$$x_2 = A_1 = -2ke^{-2k^2}$$
$$x_3 = A_2 = (6k^2 - 1)e^{-3k^2}$$
$$\vdots$$

If we choose $k = 2$ we have

$$x_0 = 2$$
$$x_1 = e^{-4} = 0.0183$$
$$x_2 = -4e^{-8} = -0.0013$$
$$x_3 =$$
$$\vdots$$

A three-term approximation $\phi_3 = \sum_{j=0}^{2} x_i = 2.0170$. The error in this result is only (approximately) 1% and decreases very rapidly with more terms.

Now let us use composite nonlinearity idea to calculate the result. We write e^{-x^2} as e^{-u} with the $u = x^2$ (first writing $Nu = e^{-u}$ in the A_n polynomials, then $u = Nx = x^2$ in the appropriate A_n). To avoid confusion, we will call the polynomials B_n

$$A_0 = e^{-u_0} = A_0(u_0)$$
$$A_1 = -u_1 e^{-u_0} = A_1(u_0, u_1)$$
$$A_2 = \tfrac{1}{2}e^{-u_0}[u_1^2 - 2u_2] = A_2(u_0, u_1, u_2)$$
$$\vdots$$
$$B_0 = x_0^2 = B_0(x_0)$$
$$B_1 = 2x_0 x_1 = B_1(x_0, x_1)$$
$$B_2 = x_1^2 + 2x_0 x_2 = B_2(x_0, x_1, x_2)$$
$$\vdots$$

Hence

$$A_0(x_0) = A_0(B_0(x_0)) = e^{-u_0} = e^{-x_0^2}$$

$$A_1(x_0, x_1) = -u_1 e^{-u_0} = -(2x_0 x_1)e^{-x_0^2}$$

$$A_2(x_0, x_1, x_2) = \tfrac{1}{2}e^{-x_0^2}\{(2x_0 x_1)^2 - 2(x_1^2 + 2x_0 x_2)\}$$

$$\vdots$$

and therefore

$$x = k + e^{-k^2} - 2ke^{-2k^2} + (6k^2 - 1)e^{-3k^2} - \cdots$$

which yields the same result as the direct decomposition but can be very useful when the A_n are difficult to calculate directly for a composite nonlinearity.

EXAMPLE: Consider $\tilde{N}_1(x) = e^{-e^{-x}} = N_0 N_1 x$, where $N_0(u^0) = e^{-u_0} = \sum_{n=0}^{\infty} A_n^0$, where A_n^0 is given by

$$A_0^0 = e^{-u_0^0}$$

$$A_1^0 = e^{-u_0^0}(-u_1^0)$$

$$A_2^0 = e^{-u_0^0}(-u_2^0 + \tfrac{1}{2}(u_1^0)^2)$$

$$A_3^0 = e^{-u_0^0}(-u_3^0 + u_1^0 u_2^0 - \tfrac{1}{6}(u_1^0)^3)$$

$$\vdots$$

$N_1(x) = e^{-x} = \sum_{n=0}^{\infty} A_n^1 = \sum_{n=0}^{\infty} u_n^0$ where A_n^1 is given by

$$A_0^1 = e^{-x_0}$$

$$A_1^1 = e^{-x_0}(-x_1)$$

$$A_2^1 = e^{-x_0}(-x_2 + \tfrac{1}{2}x_1^2)$$

$$A_3^1 = e^{-x_0}(-x_3 + x_1 x_2 - \tfrac{1}{6}x_1^3)$$

$$\vdots$$

Now for $\sum_{n=0}^{\infty} A_n^0 = e^{-e^{-x}}$

$$A_0^0 = e^{-u_0^0} = e^{-A_0^1} = e^{-e^{-x_0}}$$

$$A_1^0 = e^{-u_0^0}(-u_1^0) = e^{-A_0^1}(-A_1^1)$$

$$\quad = e^{-e^{-x_0}}(-1)(e^{-x_0}(-x_1))$$

$$\quad = x_1 e^{-x_0} e^{-e^{-x_0}}$$

$$A_2^0 = e^{-u_0^0}(-u_2^0 + \tfrac{1}{2}(u_1^0)^2)$$

$$\quad = e^{-e^{-x_0}}\{-e^{-x_0}[-x_2 + \tfrac{1}{2}x_1^2] + \tfrac{1}{2}(x_1^2 e^{-2x_0})\}$$

$$\quad = e^{-e^{-x_0}}(x_2 e^{-x_0} + \tfrac{1}{2}x_1^2 e^{-x_0} + \tfrac{1}{2}x_1^2 e^{-2x_0})$$

$$\vdots$$

Thus, in an algebraic equation $x = k + \tilde{N}_1(x)$ or differential equation $Ly + \tilde{N}_1(x) = g(x)$, where L is a linear differential operator, there is no difficulty in obtaining a solution by the decomposition method.

Composite Nonlinearities Involving Radicals: As a specific example, consider the (composite) nonlinear term $\tilde{N}x = (\alpha x^2 + \beta)^{1/2}$ appearing in an equation which may be algebraic or differential. We will consider now an algebraic equation

$$mx = k - (\alpha x^2 + \beta)^{1/2}$$

or

$$x = x_0 - (1/m)(\alpha x^2 + \beta)^{1/2}$$

where $x_0 = k/m$ and $x = \sum_{n=0}^{\infty} x_n$. We treat the term $(\alpha x^2 + \beta)^{1/2}$ as a composite nonlinearity with $N_0 u^0 = (u^0)^{1/2}$ and $u^0 = \alpha N_1 u^1 + \beta$. Decomposing u^0 into $\sum_{n=0}^{\infty} u_n^0$ and $N_1 u^1 = \sum_{n=0}^{\infty} A_n^1$, we have

$$\sum_{n=0}^{\infty} u_n^0 = \alpha \sum_{n=0}^{\infty} A_n^1 + \beta$$

$$u_0^0 = \beta + \alpha A_0^1$$

$$u_{n \geq 1}^0 = \alpha A_n^1$$

$$\sum_{n=0}^{\infty} A_n^1 = x^2$$

Hence

$$x_0 = k/m$$

$$x_1 = -(1/m)(\beta + \alpha x_0^2)^{1/2}$$

$$x_2 = -(\alpha/m)(x_0 x_1)(\beta + \alpha x_0^2)^{-1/2}$$

$$x_3 = -(\alpha/2m)[(x_1^2 + 2x_0 x_2)(\beta + \alpha x_0^2)^{-1/2} - (x_0^2 x_1^2)(\beta + \alpha x_0^2)^{-3/2}]$$

$$\vdots$$

Calculating the A_n^0 we obtain

$$A_0^0 = (u_0^0)^{1/2}$$

$$A_1^0 = \tfrac{1}{2}(u_0^0)^{-1/2}(u_1^0)$$

$$A_2^0 = \tfrac{1}{2}(u_0^0)^{-1/2}(u_2^0) - \tfrac{1}{8}(u_0^0)^{-3/2}(u_1^0)^2$$

$$A_3^0 = \tfrac{1}{2}(u_0^0)^{-1/2}(u_3^0) - \tfrac{1}{4}(u_0^0)^{-3/2}(u_1^0)(u_2^0) + \tfrac{1}{16}(u_0^0)^{-5/2}(u_1^0)^3$$

$$A_4^0 = \tfrac{1}{2}(u_0^0)^{-1/2}(u_4^0) - \tfrac{1}{4}(u_0^0)^{-3/2}\{(u_2^0)^2/2$$
$$+ (u_1^0)(u_3^0)\} + \tfrac{3}{16}(u_0^0)^{-5/2}(u_1^0)^2(u_2^0) - \tfrac{5}{128}(u_0^0)^{-7/2}(u_1^0)^4$$

$$A_5^0 = \tfrac{1}{2}(u_0^0)^{-1/2}(u_5^0) - \tfrac{1}{4}(u_0^0)^{-3/2}\{u_2^0 u_3^0 + u_1^0 u_4^0\}$$
$$+ \tfrac{3}{16}(u_0^0)^{-5/2}\{(u_1^0)(u_2^0)^2 + (u_1^0)^2(u_3^0)\}$$
$$- \tfrac{5}{32}(u_0^0)^{-7/2}(u_1^0)^3(u_2^0) + \tfrac{7}{256}(u_0^0)^{-9/2}(u_1^0)^5$$

$$\vdots$$

Since $x^2 = \sum_{n=0}^{\infty} A_n^1$, we calculate

$$A_0^1 = x_0^2$$

$$A_1^1 = 2x_0 x_1$$

$$A_2^1 = x_1^2 + 2x_0 x_2$$

$$A_3^1 = 2x_1 x_2 + 2x_0 x_3$$

$$A_4^1 = x_2^2 + 2x_1 x_3 + 2x_0 x_4$$

$$A_5^1 = 2x_2 x_3 + 2x_1 x_4 + 2x_0 x_5$$

$$\vdots$$

$$x_0 = (k/m)$$

$$x_1 = -(1/m)(\beta + \alpha k^2/m^2)^{1/2}$$

$$x_2 = -(\alpha/m)(k/m)\{(-1/m)(\beta + (\alpha k^2/m^2))^{1/2}(\beta + \alpha x_0^2)^{-1/2}\} = \alpha k/m^3$$

$$x_3 = (-\alpha/2m^3)[(\beta + \alpha x_0^2)^{1/2} + (2\alpha - 1)(k^2/m^2)(\beta + \alpha x_0^2)^{-1/2}]$$

Choose for the constants $\alpha = \tfrac{1}{4}$, $\beta = 1$, $m = 10$, and $k = 5$ to get

$$x_0 = 0.5000000000 \qquad \phi_1 = 0.5000000000$$

$$x_1 = -0.1030776406 \qquad \phi_2 = 0.3969223594$$

$$x_2 = 0.00125 \qquad \phi_3 = 0.3981723594$$

$$x_3 = -0.0001136886 \qquad \phi_4 = 0.3980586708$$

$$\vdots \qquad\qquad \vdots$$

Taking ϕ_4 as the solution (we could of course go to more terms if needed), let us examine the accuracy of the result with so few terms. The original equation can be written as

$$(mx - k)^2 = [-(\alpha x^2 + \beta)^{1/2}]^2$$

or

$$(m^2 - \alpha)x^2 - 2kmx + (k^2 + \beta) = 0$$

Substituting the given values of the constants and solving by the quadratic formula, the smaller root is 0.4000000; thus, the error is 0.00485 or less than 0.5%.

Another check is to use the value of ϕ_4 and substitute in the quadratic to define $\tilde{\phi}_4$

$$\tilde{\phi}_4 = (k/m) - (1/m)[\alpha\phi_4^2 + \beta]^{1/2} = 0.3960387$$

Then $((\phi_4 - \tilde{\phi}_4)/\phi_4) \times 100 = 0.5\%$ error.

It may be of some interest to point out that solving the quadratic by decomposition in this case is undesirable because in this example the roots are close together which slows up convergence. We get

$$x = \frac{k^2 - \beta}{2km} + \frac{m^2 - \alpha}{2km}x^2$$

$$x_0 = (k^2 - \beta)/2km$$

$$x_1 = [(m^2 - \alpha)/2km]x_0^2$$

$$x_2 = [(m^2 - \alpha)/2km](2x_0x_1) = 2\left(\frac{m^2 - \alpha}{2km}\right)^2\left(\frac{k^2 - \beta}{2km}\right)^3$$

$$\vdots$$

or

$$x_0 = \mu$$

$$x_1 = v\mu^2$$

$$x_2 = 2v^2\mu^3$$

$$x_3 = 5v^3\mu^4$$

$$x_4 = 14v^4\mu^5$$

$$\vdots$$

$$x_n = k_n v^n \mu^{n+1} \qquad k_0 = 1$$

with $\mu = 0.24$, $v = 0.9975$ i.e., $x = \sum_{n=0}^{\infty} k_n v^n \mu^{n+1}$ (where the k_n for the quadratic case are given in Section 10.1). Calculation of the x_n will verify that the composite nonlinearity approach with its very rapid convergence is far superior.

It is easy to see now that these results apply not only to algebraic equations but also to differential equations in the form $Ly + Ny = g(x)$, where Ny is a composite nonlinearity since we get $L^{-1}Ly = L^{-1}g(x) - L^{-1}Ny = L^{-1}g(x) - L^{-1}\sum_{n=0}^{\infty} A_n$. If $Ly = dy/dx$ and $y(0) = k$ for example, $y = \sum_{n=0}^{\infty} y_n = k + L^{-1}g - L^{-1}\sum_{n=0}^{\infty} A_n$, where $y_0 = k + L^{-1}g$, and $y_{n+1} = -L^{-1}A_n$ for $n \geq 0$ and the A_n are calculated by the methods discussed. Now, of course, L^{-1} is the integral operator; otherwise, results follow in a straightforward way.

EXERCISES

1. Show the solution of $y' = (y - x)^{1/2}$ with $y(0) = 1$ by the Picard method becomes very difficult. Show the solution by decomposition to two-term approximation is $\phi_2 = \frac{5}{3} - \frac{2}{3}(1 - x)^{3/2}$, i.e., $y_0 = 1$ and $y_1 = -\frac{2}{3}(1 - x)^{3/2} + \frac{2}{3}$. [Hint: $A_0^0 = (u_0^0)^{1/2} = (y_0 - x)^{1/2}$ and $A_1^0 = \frac{1}{2}(u_0^0)^{-1/2}u_1^0 = \frac{1}{2}(y_0 - x)^{1/2}(y_1 - x)$.]

2. Show the solution of $y' = (y^2 + 1)^{1/2}$ with $y(0) = 1$ is given by $y = 1 - \sqrt{2}x + x^2/2 - x^3/6 + \cdots$ and verify the solution by substituting the approximation into the differential equation. (*Hint:* The substitution for y' must use all three terms if the substitution for y uses the first two terms.)

3. Calculate the A_n for the nonlinear term $(yy')^4$. Solution: Let $u = yy'$ and consider

$$Nu = u^4 = \sum_{n=0}^{\infty} A_n,$$

where $A_0 = u_0^4$, $A_1 = 4u_0^3 u_1$, $A_2 = 4u_0^3 u_2 + 6u_0^2 u_1^2$, $A_3 = 4u_0^3 u_3 + 4u_1^3 u_0 + 12u_0^2 u_1 u_2$, $A_4 = u_1^4 + 4u_0^3 u_4 + 6u_0^2 u_2^2 + 12u_0^2 u_1 u_3 + 12u_1^2 u_0 u_2, \ldots$ Then

$$u = \sum_{n=0}^{\infty} u_n = \left(\sum_{n=0}^{\infty} y_n\right)\left(\sum_{n=0}^{\infty} y_n'\right) = \sum_{n=0}^{\infty} B_n$$

with $u_0 = y_0 y_0'$, $u_1 = y_0 y_1' + y_0' y_1$, $u_2 = y_1 y_1' + y_0 y_2' + y_0' y_2$, $u_3 = y_1 y_2' + y_1' y_2 + y_0 y_3' + y_0' y_3, \ldots$ Then $A_n = A_n(u_0, u_1, \ldots, u_{n-1})$, where the u components are given above so we can write the A_n explicitly as functions of the $y_0, y_1, \ldots$, i.e.,

$$A_0 = u_0^4 = (y_0 y_0')^4$$

$$A_1 = 4(y_0 y_0')^3(y_0 y_1' + y_0' y_1)$$

$$\vdots$$

PART III: INVERSION OF MATRICES

10.15. DISCUSSION: INVERSION BY DECOMPOSITION

We begin with the matrix equation $A\psi = x$. We assume A is given and we decompose A into $\Lambda + \Lambda_r$ in a convenient way. If A is a matrix whose elements are numbers we can let the elements of Λ be the matrix of nearest integers. If A is stochastic, Λ can be an invertible deterministic matrix and Λ_r would contain the remainder. We then have $(\Lambda + \Lambda_r)\psi = x$ where ψ and x are column vectors. We assume that Λ and Λ_r are matrices such that matrix products are defined. Formally then

$$\psi = (\Lambda + \Lambda_r)^{-1}x$$

However, our previous work on the linear case shows we can write for $|\Lambda| \neq 0$

$$(\Lambda + \Lambda_r)^{-1} = \sum_{n=0}^{\infty} (-1)^n (\Lambda^{-1}\Lambda_r)^n \Lambda^{-1}$$

THEOREM: $(\Lambda + \Lambda_r)^{-1}(\Lambda + \Lambda_r) = I$ if $(\Lambda + \Lambda_r)^{-1}$ is defined as $\sum_{i=0}^{\infty} (-1)^i (\Lambda^{-1}\Lambda_r)^i \Lambda^{-1}$.

Proof.

$$\sum_{i=0}^{\infty} (-1)^i (\Lambda^{-1}\Lambda_r)^i \Lambda^{-1}(\Lambda + \Lambda_r)$$

$$= \sum_{i=0}^{\infty} (-1)^i (\Lambda^{-1}\Lambda_r)^i \Lambda^{-1}\Lambda + \sum_{i=0}^{\infty} (-1)^i (\Lambda^{-1}\Lambda_r)^i \Lambda^{-1}\Lambda_r$$

$$= \sum_{i=0}^{\infty} (-1)^i (\Lambda^{-1}\Lambda_r)^i I + \sum_{i=0}^{\infty} (-1)^i (\Lambda^{-1}\Lambda_r)^{i+1}$$

$$= \sum_{i=0}^{\infty} (-1)^i (\Lambda^{-1}\Lambda_r)^i I - \sum_{i=0}^{\infty} (-1)^{i+1} (\Lambda^{-1}\Lambda_r)^{i+1}$$

$$= I$$

It is reasonable from the same work to expect that

$$(\Lambda + \Lambda_r)^{-1} \simeq \sum_{n=0}^{N \lll \infty} (-1)^n (\Lambda^{-1}\Lambda_r)^n \Lambda^{-1}$$

i.e., we expect a good approximation in a reasonable number of terms. Thus to invert a matrix such as

$$\begin{pmatrix} \frac{3}{2} & \frac{5}{2} \\ \frac{4}{3} & \frac{11}{3} \end{pmatrix} \cong \begin{pmatrix} 1.50 & 2.50 \\ 1.33 & 3.66 \end{pmatrix}$$

we decompose it into $\Lambda + \Lambda_r$ where

$$\Lambda = \begin{pmatrix} 1 & 2 \\ 1 & 4 \end{pmatrix}, \qquad \Lambda^{-1} = \begin{pmatrix} 2 & -1 \\ -\frac{1}{2} & \frac{1}{2} \end{pmatrix}$$

$$\Lambda_r = \begin{pmatrix} 0.50 & 0.50 \\ 0.33 & -0.34 \end{pmatrix}, \qquad \Lambda^{-1}\Lambda_r = \begin{pmatrix} \frac{2}{3} & \frac{4}{3} \\ -\frac{1}{12} & -\frac{5}{12} \end{pmatrix}$$

$$\det[\Lambda^{-1}] = \tfrac{1}{2}, \qquad \det[\Lambda^{-1}\Lambda_r] = -\tfrac{1}{6}$$

Then

$$[\Lambda + \Lambda_r]^{-1} = \sum_{n=0}^{\infty} (-1)^n (\Lambda^{-1}\Lambda_r)^n \Lambda^{-1}$$

so the first approximant $\phi_1 = \Lambda^{-1}$. All other terms depend on $\Lambda^{-1}\Lambda_r$; hence we calculate this matrix product and the quantity $(\Lambda^{-1}\Lambda_r)\Lambda^{-1}$ and finally

$\phi_2 = \Lambda^{-1} - \Lambda^{-1}\Lambda_r\Lambda^{-1}$. For the third approximant, we calculate $(\Lambda^{-1}\Lambda_r)^2\Lambda^{-1}$ or $(\Lambda^{-1}\Lambda_r)[(\Lambda^{-1}\Lambda_r)\Lambda^{-1}]$ and then $\phi_3 = \phi_2 + (\Lambda^{-1}\Lambda_r)^2\Lambda^{-1}$, $\phi_4 = \phi_3 - (\Lambda^{-1}\Lambda_r)^3\Lambda^{-1}$, etc.

If we use the same notation for matrices as we did for operators, we write $\mathscr{L}$ as the matrix to be inverted, $\mathscr{L}^{-1}$ as the desired inverse, L as the easily invertible matrix of nearest integers, and R the matrix of the difference elements of $\mathscr{L} - R$.

EXERCISES

1. Calculate the inverse of the matrix discussed above. Here ϕ_{10} is sufficient for approximation to three decimal places.

2. Let $A = \mathscr{L}$, $B = \mathscr{L}^{-1}$, $C = L^{-1}$, $D = -L^{-1}R$, $C(m) = \mathscr{L}_m^{-1} = -(L^{-1}R)^m L^{-1} = D * (C(m-1))$, $F(m) = \phi_m = \sum_{n=0}^{m-1} \mathscr{L}^{-1} = \phi_{m-1} + \mathscr{L}_{m-1}^{-1}$ and compute ten-digit precision results to ϕ_{21} or $F21$.

SOLUTION: $(F1(1,1))$ will mean the 1,1 element of ϕ_1 or $F1$, etc.)

F1(1,1) = 2   F2(1,1) = 1.333 333 333

F1(1,1) = 2	F2(1,1) = 1.333 333 333
F1(1,2) = -1	F2(1,2) = -1
F1(2,1) = -0.5	F2(2,1) = 0.541 666 666 7
F1(2,2) = 0.5	F2(2,2) = 0.625
F3(1,1) = 1.833 333 333	F4(1,1) = 1.597 222 222
F3(1,2) = $-1.166 666 667$	F4(1,2) = -1.125
F3(2,1) = $-0.614 583 333 3$	F4(2,1) = $-0.603 298 611 1$
F3(2,2) = 0.677 083 333 3	F4(2,2) = 0.684 895 833 3
F5(1,1) = 1.739 583 333	F6(1,1) = 1.664 641 204
F5(1,2) = $-1.163 194 444$	F6(1,2) = $-1.146 701 389$
F5(2,1) = $-0.618 272 569 4$	F6(2,1) = $-0.612 648 292 8$
F5(2,2) = 0.691 623 263 9	F6(2,2) = 0.691 243 489 6
F7(1,1) = 1.707 103 588	F8(1,1) = 1.683 997 637
F7(1,2) = $-1.157 190 394$	F8(1,2) = $-1.151 819 3$
F7(2,1) = $-0.616 550 021 7$	F8(2,1) = 0.614 637 211 1
F7(2,2) = 0.692 459 671 6	F8(2,2) = 0.692 092 330 4
F9(1,1) = 1.696 851 189	F10(1,1) = 1.689 786 809
F9(1,2) = $-1.154 910 241$	F10(1,2) = $-1.153 242 323$
F9(2,1) = $-0.615 765 701 1$	F10(2,1) = $-0.615 164 776 4$
F9(2,2) = 0.692 386 862 7	F10(2,2) = 0.692 252 006 1
F11(1,1) = 1.693 695 163	F12(1,1) = 1.691 540 678
F11(1,2) = $-1.154 174 459$	F12(1,2) = 1.153 663 439
F11(2,1) = 0.615 503 089 4	F12(2,1) = 0.615 318 357
F11(2,2) = 0.692 334 808 9	F12(2,2) = 0.692 291 632 1

F13(1,1) = 1.692 730 691   F14(1,1) = 1.692 074 107
F13(1,2) = −1.153 946 555   F14(1,2) = −1.153 790 602
F13(2,1) = −0.615 420 925 6   F14(2,1) = −0.615 364 494 8
F13(2,2) = 0.692 316 226 8   F14(2,2) = 0.692 302 882 2

F15(1,1) = 1.692 436 588   F16(1,1) = 1.692 236 537
F15(1,2) = −1.153 876 774   F16(1,2) = −1.153 829 244
F15(2,1) = −0.615 395 697 3   F16(2,1) = −0.615 378 491 5
F15(2,2) = 0.692 310 317 3   F16(2,2) = 0.692 306 234 3

F17(1,1) = 1.692 346 964   F18(1,1) = 1.692 286 015
F17(1,2) = −1.153 855 486   F18(1,2) = −1.153 841 002
F17(2,1) = −0.615 387 993 3   F18(2,1) = −0.615 382 750 2
F17(2,2) = 0.692 308 494 3   F18(2,2) = 0.692 307 248 8

F19(1,1) = 1.692 319 657   F20(1,1) = 1.692 301 088
F19(1,2) = −1.153 848 997   F20(1,2) = −1.153 844 584
F19(2,1) = −0.615 385 644 7   F20(2,1) = −0.615 384 047 2
F19(2,2) = 0.692 307 936 8   F20(2,2) = 0.692 307 557 3

F21(1,1) = 1.692 311 337
F21(1,2) = −1.153 847 022
F21(2,1) = −0.615 384 929
F21(2,2) = 0.692 307 766 8

The error at this stage for the worst or 1,1 element is $2.13 \times 10^{-4}\%$. The error for the 1,2 element is $7.80 \times 10^{1-5}\%$. The error for the 2,1 element is $4.87 \times 10^{-5}\%$. The error for the 2,2 element is $1.44 \times 10^{-5}\%$. We can stop when we see the numbers stabilized to the number of decimal places required.

3. In the same examples, suppose we had chosen $\lambda_{12} = 3$ instead of the nearest integer 4. Calculate the inverse. For the reader's convenience, we have listed the calculations for comparison as follows:

$$[\Lambda + \Lambda_r] = \begin{pmatrix} 1.50 & 2.50 \\ 1.33 & 3.66 \end{pmatrix}$$

$$\Lambda = \begin{pmatrix} 1 & 2 \\ 1 & 3 \end{pmatrix}, \qquad \Lambda_r = \begin{pmatrix} 0.50 & 0.50 \\ 0.33 & 0.66 \end{pmatrix}$$

$$[\Lambda + \Lambda_r]^{-1} = \sum_{n=0}^{\infty} (-1)^n (\Lambda^{-1}\Lambda_r)^n \Lambda^{-1}$$

$$= \Lambda^{-1} - \Lambda^{-1}\Lambda_r\Lambda^{-1} + (\Lambda^{-1}\Lambda_r\Lambda^{-1}\Lambda_r)\Lambda^{-1} - \cdots$$

The first approximation (the approximant $\phi_m = \sum_{n=0}^{m-1} \Lambda_n^{-1}$)

$$\phi_1 = \Lambda^{-1} = \begin{pmatrix} 3 & -2 \\ -1 & 1 \end{pmatrix}$$

All other terms depend on $\Lambda^{-1}\Lambda_r$; hence we calculate

$$\Lambda^{-1}\Lambda_r = \begin{pmatrix} 3 & -2 \\ -1 & 1 \end{pmatrix}\begin{pmatrix} 0.50 & 0.50 \\ 0.33 & 0.66 \end{pmatrix} = \begin{pmatrix} \frac{5}{6} & \frac{1}{6} \\ -\frac{1}{6} & \frac{1}{6} \end{pmatrix}$$

For the second approximation ϕ_2 we will need

$$(\Lambda^{-1}\Lambda_r)\Lambda^{-1} = \begin{pmatrix} \frac{5}{6} & \frac{1}{6} \\ -\frac{1}{6} & \frac{1}{6} \end{pmatrix}\begin{pmatrix} 3 & -2 \\ -1 & 1 \end{pmatrix} = \begin{pmatrix} 2.33 & -1.5 \\ -0.66 & 0.50 \end{pmatrix}$$

Consequently,

$$\phi_2 = \Lambda^{-1} - \Lambda^{-1}\Lambda_r\Lambda^{-1}$$

$$= \begin{pmatrix} 3 & -2 \\ -1 & 1 \end{pmatrix} - \begin{pmatrix} 2.33 & -1.5 \\ -0.66 & 0.50 \end{pmatrix} = \begin{pmatrix} 0.67 & -0.50 \\ -0.34 & 0.50 \end{pmatrix}$$

To compute the third approximation we need

$$(\Lambda^{-1}\Lambda_r)^2\Lambda^{-1} = \Lambda^{-1}\Lambda_r((\Lambda^{-1}\Lambda_r)\Lambda^{-1})$$

$$= \begin{pmatrix} \frac{5}{6} & \frac{1}{6} \\ -\frac{1}{6} & \frac{1}{6} \end{pmatrix}\begin{pmatrix} 2.33 & -1.5 \\ -0.66 & 0.50 \end{pmatrix} = \begin{pmatrix} 1.8317 & -1.1667 \\ -0.4983 & 0.333 \end{pmatrix}$$

Now

$$\phi_3 = \Lambda^{-1} - \Lambda^{-1}\Lambda_r\Lambda^{-1} + (\Lambda^{-1}\Lambda_r)^2\Lambda^{-1} = \phi_2 + (\Lambda^{-1}\Lambda_r)^2\Lambda^{-1}$$

$$= \begin{pmatrix} 0.67 & -0.50 \\ -0.34 & 0.50 \end{pmatrix} + \begin{pmatrix} 1.8317 & -1.667 \\ -0.49833 & 0.3333 \end{pmatrix} = \begin{pmatrix} 2.5 & -1.6667 \\ -0.83833 & 0.8333 \end{pmatrix}$$

$$\phi_4 = \phi_3 - (\Lambda^{-1}\Lambda_r)^3\Lambda^{-1}$$

$$= \begin{pmatrix} 2.5 & -1.667 \\ -0.83833 & 0.8333 \end{pmatrix} - \begin{pmatrix} 1.44334 & -0.91668 \\ -0.3883433 & 0.250 \end{pmatrix}$$

$$= \begin{pmatrix} 1.05668 & -0.75002 \\ -0.4499867 & 0.58333 \end{pmatrix}$$

Continuing in this manner, we list results

$$\phi_1 = \begin{pmatrix} 3 & -2 \\ -1 & 1 \end{pmatrix} \qquad \phi_2 = \begin{pmatrix} 0.67 & -0.50 \\ -0.34 & 0.50 \end{pmatrix}$$

$$\phi_3 = \begin{pmatrix} 2.5 & -1.667 \\ -0.83833 & 0.8333 \end{pmatrix} \qquad \phi_4 = \begin{pmatrix} 1.05666 & -0.75002 \\ -0.4499867 & 0.58333 \end{pmatrix}$$

$$\phi_5 = \begin{pmatrix} 2.1917 & -1.47222 \\ -0.75571 & 0.74028 \end{pmatrix} \qquad \phi_6 = \begin{pmatrix} 1.314 & -0.8964 \\ -0.516 & 0.5940 \end{pmatrix}$$

$$\phi_7 = \begin{pmatrix} 2.01 & -1.35 \\ -0.7523 & 0.7143 \end{pmatrix} \qquad \phi_8 = \begin{pmatrix} 1.464 & -0.99 \\ -0.556 & 0.6183 \end{pmatrix}$$

$$\phi_9 = \begin{pmatrix} 1.895 & -1.274 \\ -0.6714 & 0.6943 \end{pmatrix} \qquad \phi_{10} = \begin{pmatrix} 1.555 & -1.05 \\ -0.5804 & 0.6343 \end{pmatrix}$$

$$\phi_{11} = \begin{pmatrix} 1.82 & -1.23 \\ -0.653 & 0.682 \end{pmatrix} \qquad \phi_{12} = \begin{pmatrix} 1.609 & -1.090 \\ -0.5964 & 0.6446 \end{pmatrix}$$

$$\phi_{13} = \begin{pmatrix} 1.7757 & -1.20 \\ -0.641 & 0.6741 \end{pmatrix} \qquad \phi_{14} = \begin{pmatrix} 1.644 & -1.113 \\ -0.6058 & 0.6508 \end{pmatrix}$$

$$\phi_{15} = \begin{pmatrix} 1.7476 & -1.18 \\ -0.6336 & 0.6691 \end{pmatrix} \qquad \phi_{16} = \begin{pmatrix} 1.6659 & -1.126 \\ -0.6117 & 0.6546 \end{pmatrix}$$

$$\phi_{17} = \begin{pmatrix} 1.730 & -1.1686 \\ -0.62896 & 0.6660 \end{pmatrix} \qquad \phi_{18} = \begin{pmatrix} 1.6792 & -1.135 \\ -0.61535 & 0.6570 \end{pmatrix}$$

$$\phi_{19} = \begin{pmatrix} 1.7192 & -1.1615 \\ -0.62608 & 0.6641 \end{pmatrix} \qquad \phi_{20} = \begin{pmatrix} 1.6877 & -1.14058 \\ -0.617628 & 0.65850 \end{pmatrix}$$

$$\phi_{21} = \begin{pmatrix} 1.713 & -1.157 \\ -0.62429 & 0.66292 \end{pmatrix}$$

Note that the correct solution is still obtained but with slower convergence. The approximate solution to four terms, ϕ_4, has the 1,1 element 1.05668 (when $\lambda_{12} = 3$) and 1.57222 (when $\lambda_{12} = 4$ as in the first example). The correct result, which we can call ϕ_∞, is 1.69 to two places. Thus, the correct choice decreases the error at this point from about 37% to about 7%. By ϕ_{21}, the 1,1 element (the worst case) is within 1% with the $\lambda_{12} = 3$ choice and within 2×10^{-4}% with the $\lambda_{12} = 4$ choice. Considering that two elements were "worst-case" choices between integers, we see that normally accuracy would be still greater. The convergence of each matrix element is not the same because of initial percentage error from Λ and because of interactions due to matrix multiplications.

   4. Compute the inverse for the matrix

$$[\Lambda + \Lambda_r] = \begin{pmatrix} 1.2 & 2.40 \\ 1.33 & 3.66 \end{pmatrix}$$

using

$$\Lambda = \begin{pmatrix} 1 & 2 \\ 1 & 4 \end{pmatrix}$$

and verify the result.

   5. Calculate

$$\begin{pmatrix} 1.13 & 2.09 \\ 4.15 & 3.99 \end{pmatrix}^{-1}$$

and verify.

The method can be used for stochastic matrices as well, letting Λ be deterministic and invertible with Λ_r representing random terms. The appropriate statistics are obtained with no statistical separability problems [1].

10.16.   CONVERGENCE

Our first example was deliberately chosen to converge slowly by the inclusion of two elements midway between integers. (The problem can be done so long as $L^{-1}R$ is less than one.) The Λ should be chosen *with the nearest integers* to the given $\Lambda = (\Lambda + \Lambda_r)$ matrix so the element of Λ_r may be quite small and the convergence will be faster. Each term of ϕ_n involves an additional multiplication by $\Lambda^{-1}\Lambda_r$. Note that if we factor out the Λ^{-1} to the right, each multiplication by $\Lambda^{-1}\Lambda_r$ reduces the magnitude since the elements of Λ_r are always less than one because we take nearest integers for elements of Λ. We have, consequently, an alternating series with terms of decreasing magnitude. We have shown earlier that the series does indeed represent the inverse operator.

We can also examine convergence of the determinant of the inverse. Since

$$\Lambda^{-1} = \sum_{n=0}^{\infty} (-1)^n (L^{-1}R)^n L^{-1}$$

where $\Lambda = L + R$, the determinant is given by

$$|\Lambda^{-1}| = \sum_{n=0}^{\infty} (-1)^n |(L^{-1}R)^n L^{-1}|$$

$$= \sum_{n=0}^{\infty} (-1)^n \{|L^{-1}| \cdot |R|\}^n \cdot |L^{-1}|$$

implying $|L^{-1}| \cdot |R| < 1$ or $|L| > |R|$.

10.17.   DECOMPOSITION INTO DIAGONAL MATRICES

Consider (Case I)

$$\Lambda = \begin{pmatrix} \lambda_{11} & \lambda_{12} \\ \lambda_{21} & \lambda_{22} \end{pmatrix} = L + R$$

where

$$L = \begin{pmatrix} \lambda_{11} & 0 \\ 0 & \lambda_{22} \end{pmatrix}, \qquad R = \begin{pmatrix} 0 & \lambda_{12} \\ \lambda_{21} & 0 \end{pmatrix}$$

Although this will yield slower convergence (because this choice of L is farther from Λ than the nearest integers choice of Section 10.15, the terms Λ_n^{-1} are much easier to compute in analogy to our approach for differential operators. We could alternatively (Case II) decompose Λ into

$$
L = \begin{pmatrix} 0 & \lambda_{12} \\ \lambda_{21} & 0 \end{pmatrix}, \qquad R = \begin{pmatrix} \lambda_{11} & 0 \\ 0 & \lambda_{22} \end{pmatrix}
$$

Returning to Case I,

$$
L^{-1} = \begin{pmatrix} 1/\lambda_{11} & 0 \\ 0 & 1/\lambda_{22} \end{pmatrix} \equiv \Lambda_0^{-1}
$$

$$
\begin{aligned}
\Lambda_1^{-1} &= (-1)(L^{-1}R)L^{-1} \\
&= -\begin{pmatrix} 1/\lambda_{11} & 0 \\ 0 & 1/\lambda_{22} \end{pmatrix}\begin{pmatrix} 0 & \lambda_{12} \\ \lambda_{21} & 0 \end{pmatrix}\begin{pmatrix} 1/\lambda_{11} & 0 \\ 0 & 1/\lambda_{22} \end{pmatrix} \\
&= -\begin{pmatrix} 0 & \lambda_{12}/\lambda_{11} \\ \lambda_{21}/\lambda_{22} & 0 \end{pmatrix}\begin{pmatrix} 1/\lambda_{11} & 0 \\ 0 & 1/\lambda_{22} \end{pmatrix} \\
&= \begin{pmatrix} 0 & -\lambda_{12}/\lambda_{11}\lambda_{22} \\ -\lambda_{21}/\lambda_{11}\lambda_{22} & 0 \end{pmatrix}
\end{aligned}
$$

$$
\begin{aligned}
\Lambda_2^{-1} &= (-1)^2(L^{-1}R)(L^{-1}R)L^{-1} \\
&= \begin{pmatrix} 0 & \lambda_{12}/\lambda_{11} \\ \lambda_{21}/\lambda_{22} & 0 \end{pmatrix}\begin{pmatrix} 0 & \lambda_{12}/\lambda_{11}\lambda_{22} \\ \lambda_{21}/\lambda_{11}\lambda_{22} & 0 \end{pmatrix} \\
&= \begin{pmatrix} \lambda_{12}\lambda_{21}/\lambda_{11}^2\lambda_{22} & 0 \\ 0 & \lambda_{12}\lambda_{21}/\lambda_{11}\lambda_{22}^2 \end{pmatrix}
\end{aligned}
$$

$$
\begin{aligned}
\Lambda_3^{-1} &= (-1)^3(L^{-1}R)(L^{-1}R)^2L^{-1} \\
&= -\begin{pmatrix} 0 & \lambda_{12}/\lambda_{11} \\ \lambda_{21}/\lambda_{22} & 0 \end{pmatrix}\begin{pmatrix} \lambda_{12}\lambda_{21} & 0 \\ 0 & \lambda_{12}\lambda_{21}/\lambda_{11}\lambda_{22}^2 \end{pmatrix} \\
&= \begin{pmatrix} 0 & -\lambda_{12}^2\lambda_{21}/\lambda_{11}^2\lambda_{22}^2 \\ -\lambda_{12}\lambda_{21}^2/\lambda_{11}^2\lambda_{22}^2 & 0 \end{pmatrix}
\end{aligned}
$$

$$
\begin{aligned}
\Lambda_4^{-1} &= (-1)^4(L^{-1}R)(L^{-1}R)^3L^{-1} \\
&= \begin{pmatrix} 0 & \lambda_{12}/\lambda_{11} \\ \lambda_{21}/\lambda_{22} & 0 \end{pmatrix}\begin{pmatrix} 0 & \lambda_{12}^2\lambda_{21}/\lambda_{11}^2\lambda_{22}^2 \\ \lambda_{12}\lambda_{21}^2/\lambda_{11}^2\lambda_{22}^2 & 0 \end{pmatrix} \\
&= \begin{pmatrix} \lambda_{12}^2\lambda_{21}^2/\lambda_{11}^3\lambda_{22}^2 & 0 \\ 0 & \lambda_{12}^2\lambda_{21}^2/\lambda_{11}^2\lambda_{22}^3 \end{pmatrix}
\end{aligned}
$$

$$
\vdots
$$

Inspection of the Λ_n^{-1} terms shows alternating terms are zero and the nonzero terms are successively multiplied by the multiplier $r = \lambda_{12}\lambda_{21}/\lambda_{11}\lambda_{22}$ so we have a geometric progression. The smaller this term is, the faster the convergence becomes. We must have $\lambda_{12}\lambda_{21} < \lambda_{11}\lambda_{22}$. We cannot have equality, which would imply nonexistence of the inverse. If $\lambda_{12}\lambda_{21} > \lambda_{11}\lambda_{22}$ we simply choose L and R as in Case II (the zero elements of L should be on the smallest diagonal).

EXAMPLE: Consider

$$\Lambda = \begin{pmatrix} 2 & 1 \\ 1 & -3 \end{pmatrix}$$

Choose

$$L = \begin{pmatrix} 2 & 0 \\ 0 & 3 \end{pmatrix}, \qquad R = \begin{pmatrix} 0 & 1 \\ 1 & 0 \end{pmatrix}$$

then,

$$\Lambda_0^{-1} = L^{-1} = \begin{pmatrix} \frac{1}{2} & 0 \\ 0 & \frac{1}{3} \end{pmatrix}$$

$$\Lambda_1^{-1} = (-1)(L^{-1}R)L^{-1}$$

$$= -\begin{pmatrix} \frac{1}{2} & 0 \\ 0 & \frac{1}{3} \end{pmatrix}\begin{pmatrix} 0 & 1 \\ 1 & 0 \end{pmatrix}\begin{pmatrix} \frac{1}{2} & 0 \\ 0 & \frac{1}{3} \end{pmatrix}$$

$$= -\begin{pmatrix} 0 & \frac{1}{2} \\ \frac{1}{3} & 0 \end{pmatrix}\begin{pmatrix} \frac{1}{2} & 0 \\ 0 & \frac{1}{3} \end{pmatrix} = \begin{pmatrix} 0 & -\frac{1}{6} \\ -\frac{1}{6} & 0 \end{pmatrix}$$

$$\Lambda_2^{-1} = (-1)^2(L^{-1}R)(L^{-1}R)L^{-1}$$

$$= \begin{pmatrix} 0 & \frac{1}{2} \\ \frac{1}{3} & 0 \end{pmatrix}\begin{pmatrix} 0 & \frac{1}{6} \\ \frac{1}{6} & 0 \end{pmatrix} = \begin{pmatrix} \frac{1}{12} & 0 \\ 0 & \frac{1}{18} \end{pmatrix}$$

$$\Lambda_3^{-1} = (-1)^3(L^{-1}R)(L^{-1}R)^2L^{-1}$$

$$= -\begin{pmatrix} 0 & \frac{1}{2} \\ \frac{1}{3} & 0 \end{pmatrix}\begin{pmatrix} \frac{1}{12} & 0 \\ 0 & \frac{1}{18} \end{pmatrix} = \begin{pmatrix} 0 & -\frac{1}{36} \\ -\frac{1}{36} & 0 \end{pmatrix}$$

$$\Lambda_4^{-1} = (-1)^4(L^{-1}R)(L^{-1}R)^3L^{-1}$$

$$= \begin{pmatrix} 0 & \frac{1}{2} \\ \frac{1}{3} & 0 \end{pmatrix}\begin{pmatrix} 0 & \frac{1}{36} \\ \frac{1}{36} & 0 \end{pmatrix} = \begin{pmatrix} \frac{1}{72} & 0 \\ 0 & \frac{1}{108} \end{pmatrix}$$

$$\Lambda_5^{-1} = (-1)^5(L^{-1}R)(L^{-1}R)^4L^{-1}$$

$$= -\begin{pmatrix} 0 & \frac{1}{2} \\ \frac{1}{3} & 0 \end{pmatrix}\begin{pmatrix} \frac{1}{72} & 0 \\ 0 & \frac{1}{108} \end{pmatrix} = \begin{pmatrix} 0 & -\frac{1}{216} \\ -\frac{1}{216} & 0 \end{pmatrix}$$

$$\Lambda_6^{-1} = (-1)^6 (L^{-1}R)(L^{-1}R)^5 L^{-1}$$

$$= \begin{pmatrix} 0 & \frac{1}{2} \\ \frac{1}{3} & 0 \end{pmatrix} \begin{pmatrix} 0 & \frac{1}{216} \\ \frac{1}{216} & 0 \end{pmatrix} = \begin{pmatrix} \frac{1}{432} & 0 \\ 0 & \frac{1}{648} \end{pmatrix}$$

Since the elements are now only about 0.5% of the elements of L^{-1}, this is sufficient. Adding, we have our approximate inverse $\phi_7 = \sum_{n=0}^6 \Lambda_n^{-1}$ or

$$\begin{pmatrix} 0.599 & -0.198 \\ -0.198 & 0.398 \end{pmatrix} \approx \begin{pmatrix} 0.6 & -0.2 \\ -0.2 & 0.4 \end{pmatrix}$$

which is the *exact* inverse.

Since the multiplier r here was $\frac{1}{6}$, each term of the geometric sequence of corresponding elements of the Λ_n^{-1} is given by λr^{n-1}, where λ is the first element of the sequence. Since $\lambda r^{n-1} = \lambda/200$ corresponds to $\frac{1}{2}\%$ error, and $(\frac{1}{6})^3 = \frac{1}{216}$, $n = 4$ is sufficient[1] starting from Λ_0^{-1}. Because of the alternating zeros, the estimate Λ_6^{-1} is sufficient as we have found. If we began with

$$\Lambda = \begin{pmatrix} 2 & 1 \\ 4 & 3 \end{pmatrix}$$

we have

$$\Lambda_0^{-1} = \begin{pmatrix} \frac{1}{2} & 0 \\ 0 & \frac{1}{3} \end{pmatrix}$$

Since $r = \frac{2}{3}$, $\lambda(\frac{2}{3})^{n-1} = \lambda/200$ requires $n = 14$ for an error of less than 0.5% in the result. Because of the alternating zeros, it means calculation of approximately 26 terms to get a very good approximation to

$$\Lambda^{-1} = \begin{pmatrix} 1.5 & -0.5 \\ -2 & 1 \end{pmatrix}$$

Since $r = \frac{2}{3}$, $\lambda(\frac{2}{3})^{n-1} = \lambda/200$ requires $n = 14$ for an error of less than 0.5% in the result. Because of the alternating zeros, it means calculation of approximately 26 terms to get a very good approximation to

$$\Lambda = \begin{pmatrix} \lambda_{11} & \lambda_{12} \\ \lambda_{21} & \lambda_{22} \end{pmatrix}$$

provided $\lambda_{12}\lambda_{21} \neq \lambda_{11}\lambda_{12}$. Assume the Case I situation then $|\lambda_{12}\lambda_{21}| < |\lambda_{11}\lambda_{22}|$. This is equivalent to saying the absolute value of the determinant of L is greater than the absolute value of the determinant of R. Since $\lambda_{12}\lambda_{21}/\lambda_{11}\lambda_{22}$ is a multiplier r for the nonzero terms we write

$$\Lambda^{-1} = \begin{pmatrix} \sigma/\lambda_{11} & -\lambda_{12}\sigma/\lambda_{11}\lambda_{22} \\ -\lambda_{21}\sigma/\lambda_{11}\lambda_{22} & \sigma/\lambda_{22} \end{pmatrix}$$

---

[1] If error in percent is $(100/p)$, then $\lambda r^{n-1} = \lambda/p$ or $n = (-\ln p/\ln r) + 1$.

since the first nonzero terms are multiplied by r successively. Now σ is given by

$$\sigma = \sum_{n=0}^{\infty} r^n = \sum_{n=0}^{\infty} \left(\frac{\lambda_{12}\lambda_{21}}{\lambda_{11}\lambda_{22}}\right)^n$$

$$= \frac{1}{[1 - (\lambda_{12}\lambda_{21})/(\lambda_{11}\lambda_{22})]}$$

For Case II where $|\lambda_{11}\lambda_{22}| < |\lambda_{12}\lambda_{21}|$

$$\Lambda^{-1} = \begin{pmatrix} -\lambda_{22}\sigma/\lambda_{12}\lambda_{21} & \sigma/\lambda_{21} \\ \sigma/\lambda_{12} & -\lambda_{11}\sigma/\lambda_{12}\lambda_{21} \end{pmatrix}$$

where

$$\sigma = \sum_{n=0}^{\infty} \left(\frac{\lambda_{11}\lambda_{22}}{\lambda_{12}\lambda_{21}}\right)^n$$

$$= \frac{1}{[1 - (\lambda_{11}\lambda_{22})/(\lambda_{12}\lambda_{21})]}$$

THEOREM: *The inverse of the matrix Λ given by*

$$\Lambda = \begin{pmatrix} \lambda_{11} & \lambda_{12} \\ \lambda_{21} & \lambda_{22} \end{pmatrix}$$

is given by

$$\Lambda^{-1} = \begin{pmatrix} \sigma/\lambda_{11} & -\lambda_{12}\sigma/\lambda_{11}\lambda_{22} \\ -\lambda_{21}\sigma/\lambda_{11}\lambda_{22} & \sigma/\lambda_{22} \end{pmatrix}$$

where

$$\sigma = \frac{1}{1 - (\lambda_{12}\lambda_{21}/\lambda_{11}\lambda_{22})} = \frac{\lambda_{11}\lambda_{22}}{|\Lambda|}$$

if $|\lambda_{12}\lambda_{21}| < |\lambda_{11}\lambda_{22}|$ and by

$$\Lambda^{-1} = \begin{pmatrix} -\lambda_{22}\sigma/\lambda_{12}\lambda_{21} & \sigma/\lambda_{21} \\ \sigma/\lambda_{12} & -\lambda_{11}\sigma/\lambda_{12}\lambda_{21} \end{pmatrix}$$

where

$$\sigma = \frac{1}{1 - (\lambda_{11}\lambda_{22}/\lambda_{12}\lambda_{21})}$$

if $|\lambda_{11}\lambda_{22}| < |\lambda_{12}\lambda_{21}|$.

Substitution of the appropriate value of σ for both Case 1 and Case 2 yields the inverse directly for a 2×2 matrix; or, of course, we can simply calculate sufficient terms of the series.

EXAMPLE: (CASE I) Consider

$$\Lambda_I = \begin{pmatrix} 2 & 1 \\ 4 & 3 \end{pmatrix}$$

$$\Lambda_I^{-1} = \begin{pmatrix} \sigma/2 & -\sigma/6 \\ -4\sigma/6 & \sigma/3 \end{pmatrix} = \begin{pmatrix} \frac{3}{2} & -\frac{1}{2} \\ -2 & 1 \end{pmatrix}$$

since $r = \frac{2}{3}$ and σ consequently equals $1/[1 - (\frac{2}{3})] = 3$.

EXAMPLE: (CASE II) Consider

$$\Lambda_{II} = \begin{pmatrix} 1 & 2 \\ 3 & 4 \end{pmatrix}$$

$$\Lambda_{II}^{-1} = \begin{pmatrix} -4/6\sigma & \sigma/3 \\ \sigma/2 & -\sigma/6 \end{pmatrix} = \begin{pmatrix} -2 & 1 \\ \frac{3}{2} & -\frac{1}{2} \end{pmatrix}$$

since $\sigma = 3$ again.

Verification:

$$\Lambda_I^{-1}\Lambda_I = \begin{pmatrix} 2 & 1 \\ 4 & 3 \end{pmatrix}\begin{pmatrix} \frac{3}{2} & -\frac{1}{2} \\ -2 & 1 \end{pmatrix} = \begin{pmatrix} 1 & 0 \\ 0 & 1 \end{pmatrix}$$

$$\Lambda_{II}^{-1}\Lambda_{II} = \begin{pmatrix} 1 & 2 \\ 3 & 4 \end{pmatrix}\begin{pmatrix} -2 & 1 \\ \frac{3}{2} & -\frac{1}{2} \end{pmatrix} = \begin{pmatrix} 1 & 0 \\ 0 & 1 \end{pmatrix}$$

Extension to $n \times n$ matrices will appear elsewhere.

If we wish to invert

$$\Lambda = \begin{pmatrix} 2 & 1 \\ 4 & 3 \end{pmatrix}$$

using the method of Part II, (this is Case I),

$$\Lambda^{-1} = \begin{pmatrix} \sigma/2 & -\sigma/6 \\ -4\sigma/6 & \sigma/3 \end{pmatrix}$$

and since $\sigma = 1/(1 - \frac{2}{3}) = 3$

$$\Lambda^{-1} = \begin{pmatrix} \frac{3}{2} & -\frac{1}{2} \\ -2 & 1 \end{pmatrix}$$

which is the correct inverse as easily verified. Of course, we can proceed also by writing for

$$\Lambda = \begin{pmatrix} 2 & 1 \\ 4 & 3 \end{pmatrix}$$

(which is Case I)

$$L = \begin{pmatrix} 2 & 0 \\ 0 & 3 \end{pmatrix}$$

$$L^{-1} = \begin{pmatrix} \frac{1}{2} & 0 \\ 0 & \frac{1}{3} \end{pmatrix} = \Lambda_0^{-1}$$

$$\Lambda_1^{-1} = (-1) \begin{pmatrix} \frac{1}{2} & 0 \\ 0 & \frac{1}{3} \end{pmatrix} \begin{pmatrix} 0 & 1 \\ 4 & 0 \end{pmatrix} \begin{pmatrix} \frac{1}{2} & 0 \\ 0 & \frac{1}{3} \end{pmatrix}$$

$$= \begin{pmatrix} 0 & -\frac{1}{6} \\ -\frac{2}{3} & 0 \end{pmatrix}$$

$$\Lambda_2^{-1} = (-1)^2 (L^{-1}R)^2 L^{-1} = \begin{pmatrix} \frac{1}{3} & 0 \\ 0 & \frac{2}{9} \end{pmatrix}$$

$$\Lambda_3^{-1} = (-1)^3 (L^{-1}R)^3 L^{-1} = \begin{pmatrix} 0 & -\frac{1}{9} \\ \frac{4}{9} & 0 \end{pmatrix}$$

$$\vdots$$

then $\Phi_m = \sum_{n=0}^{m-1} \Lambda_n^{-1}$. We stop when the terms of Λ_n^{-1} are sufficiently small.

EXAMPLE: (CASE II) Consider

$$\Lambda = \begin{pmatrix} 5 & 10 \\ 10 & 5 \end{pmatrix}$$

$$\sigma = \sum_{n=0}^{\infty} \left(\frac{25}{100} \right)^n = \frac{1}{1 - (1/4)} = \frac{4}{3}$$

$$\Lambda^{-1} = \begin{pmatrix} \dfrac{-5(4/3)}{100} & \dfrac{(4/3)}{10} \\ \dfrac{(4/3)}{10} & \dfrac{-5(4/3)}{100} \end{pmatrix}$$

$$= \begin{pmatrix} -\dfrac{1}{15} & \dfrac{2}{15} \\ \dfrac{2}{15} & -\dfrac{1}{15} \end{pmatrix}$$

$$\begin{pmatrix} 5 & 10 \\ 10 & 5 \end{pmatrix} \begin{pmatrix} -\dfrac{1}{15} & \dfrac{2}{15} \\ \dfrac{2}{15} & -\dfrac{1}{15} \end{pmatrix} = \begin{pmatrix} 1 & 0 \\ 0 & 1 \end{pmatrix}$$

The case given by

$$\Lambda = \begin{pmatrix} 10 & 1 \\ 1 & 10 \end{pmatrix}$$

should be rapidly convergent. We see that

$$\sigma = 1 + 0.01 + 0.0001 + \cdots = 100/99 = 1.010101 \ldots$$

$$\Lambda^{-1} \simeq \begin{pmatrix} 1.01/10 & -1.01/100 \\ -1.01/100 & 1.01/10 \end{pmatrix} = \begin{pmatrix} 0.101 & -0.0101 \\ -0.0101 & 0.101 \end{pmatrix}$$

and could be done quickly as well by summing Λ_n^{-1} for a few terms.

EXAMPLE: $(3 \times 3$ matrix$)$

$$\Lambda = \begin{pmatrix} 2 & 0 & 1 \\ 1 & 3 & 0 \\ 0 & 1 & 2 \end{pmatrix}, \qquad L = \begin{pmatrix} 2 & 0 & 0 \\ 0 & 3 & 0 \\ 0 & 0 & 2 \end{pmatrix}$$

$$R = \begin{pmatrix} 0 & 0 & 1 \\ 1 & 0 & 0 \\ 0 & 1 & 0 \end{pmatrix}, \qquad L^{-1} = \begin{pmatrix} \frac{1}{2} & 0 & 0 \\ 0 & \frac{1}{3} & 0 \\ 0 & 0 & \frac{1}{2} \end{pmatrix} = \Lambda_0^{-1}$$

$$L^{-1}R = (-1)\begin{pmatrix} \frac{1}{2} & 0 & 0 \\ 0 & \frac{1}{3} & 0 \\ 0 & 0 & \frac{1}{2} \end{pmatrix}\begin{pmatrix} 0 & 0 & 1 \\ 1 & 0 & 0 \\ 0 & 1 & 0 \end{pmatrix} = \begin{pmatrix} 0 & 0 & -\frac{1}{2} \\ -\frac{1}{3} & 0 & 0 \\ 0 & -\frac{1}{2} & 0 \end{pmatrix}$$

$$\Lambda_1^{-1} = -[L^{-1}R] \cdot \begin{pmatrix} \frac{1}{2} & 0 & 0 \\ 0 & \frac{1}{3} & 0 \\ 0 & 0 & \frac{1}{2} \end{pmatrix}$$

$$= \begin{pmatrix} 0 & 0 & -\frac{1}{2} \\ -\frac{1}{3} & 0 & 0 \\ 0 & -\frac{1}{2} & 0 \end{pmatrix}\begin{pmatrix} \frac{1}{2} & 0 & 0 \\ 0 & \frac{1}{3} & 0 \\ 0 & 0 & \frac{1}{2} \end{pmatrix}$$

$$= \begin{pmatrix} 0 & 0 & -\frac{1}{4} \\ -\frac{1}{6} & 0 & 0 \\ 0 & -\frac{1}{6} & 0 \end{pmatrix}$$

$$\Lambda_2^{-1} = \begin{pmatrix} 0 & 0 & -\frac{1}{2} \\ -\frac{1}{3} & 0 & 0 \\ 0 & -\frac{1}{2} & 0 \end{pmatrix}\begin{pmatrix} 0 & 0 & -\frac{1}{4} \\ -\frac{1}{6} & 0 & 0 \\ 0 & -\frac{1}{6} & 0 \end{pmatrix}$$

$$= \begin{pmatrix} 0 & \frac{1}{12} & 0 \\ 0 & 0 & \frac{1}{12} \\ \frac{1}{12} & 0 & 0 \end{pmatrix}$$

The approximation $\Phi_3 = \Lambda_0^{-1} + \Lambda_1^{-1} + \Lambda_2^{-1}$ is

$$\Phi_3 = \begin{pmatrix} \frac{1}{2} & \frac{1}{12} & -\frac{1}{4} \\ -\frac{1}{6} & \frac{1}{3} & \frac{1}{12} \\ \frac{1}{12} & -\frac{1}{6} & -\frac{1}{12} \end{pmatrix} = \begin{pmatrix} 0.50 & 0.08 & -0.25 \\ -0.17 & 0.33 & 0.08 \\ 0.08 & -0.17 & 0.58 \end{pmatrix}$$

The correct inverse is

$$\Lambda^{-1} = \begin{pmatrix} \frac{6}{13} & \frac{1}{13} & -\frac{3}{13} \\ -\frac{2}{13} & \frac{4}{13} & \frac{1}{13} \\ \frac{1}{13} & -\frac{2}{13} & \frac{6}{13} \end{pmatrix} = \begin{pmatrix} 0.46 & 0.08 & -0.23 \\ -0.15 & 0.31 & 0.08 \\ 0.08 & -0.15 & 0.46 \end{pmatrix}$$

which we are approaching rapidly, i.e., with only a three-term approximation. If we calculate further, we have

$$\Lambda_3^{-1} = \begin{pmatrix} -\frac{1}{24} & 0 & 0 \\ 0 & -\frac{1}{36} & 0 \\ 0 & 0 & -\frac{1}{24} \end{pmatrix}$$

$$\Lambda_4^{-1} = \begin{pmatrix} 0 & 0 & \frac{1}{48} \\ \frac{1}{72} & 0 & 0 \\ 0 & \frac{1}{72} & 0 \end{pmatrix}$$

$$\Lambda_5^{-1} = \begin{pmatrix} 0 & -\frac{1}{144} & 0 \\ 0 & 0 & -\frac{1}{144} \\ -\frac{1}{144} & 0 & 0 \end{pmatrix}$$

It is not necessary for most purposes to go further but continuing

$$\Lambda_6^{-1} = \begin{pmatrix} \frac{1}{288} & 0 & 0 \\ 0 & \frac{1}{432} & 0 \\ 0 & 0 & \frac{1}{288} \end{pmatrix}$$

$$\Lambda_7^{-1} = \begin{pmatrix} 0 & 0 & -\frac{1}{576} \\ -\frac{1}{864} & 0 & 0 \\ 0 & -\frac{1}{864} & 0 \end{pmatrix}$$

$$\Lambda_8^{-1} = \begin{pmatrix} 0 & \frac{1}{1728} & 0 \\ 0 & 0 & \frac{1}{1728} \\ \frac{1}{1728} & 0 & 0 \end{pmatrix}$$

$$\Lambda_9^{-1} = \begin{pmatrix} -\frac{1}{3456} & 0 & 0 \\ 0 & -\frac{1}{5184} & 0 \\ 0 & 0 & -\frac{1}{3456} \end{pmatrix}$$

$$\Lambda_{10}^{-1} = \begin{pmatrix} 0 & 0 & \frac{1}{6912} \\ \frac{1}{10,368} & 0 & 0 \\ 0 & \frac{1}{10,368} & 0 \end{pmatrix}$$

Hence the approximations are

$$\Phi_1 = \begin{pmatrix} \frac{1}{2} & 0 & 0 \\ 0 & \frac{1}{3} & 0 \\ 0 & 0 & \frac{1}{2} \end{pmatrix}$$

$$\Phi_2 = \begin{pmatrix} \frac{1}{2} & 0 & -\frac{1}{4} \\ -\frac{1}{6} & \frac{1}{3} & 0 \\ 0 & -\frac{1}{6} & \frac{1}{2} \end{pmatrix}$$

$$\Phi_3 = \begin{pmatrix} \frac{1}{2} & \frac{1}{12} & -\frac{1}{4} \\ -\frac{1}{6} & \frac{1}{3} & \frac{1}{12} \\ \frac{1}{12} & -\frac{1}{6} & \frac{1}{2} \end{pmatrix}$$

$$\Phi_4 = \begin{pmatrix} \frac{11}{24} & \frac{1}{12} & -\frac{1}{4} \\ -\frac{1}{6} & \frac{11}{36} & \frac{1}{12} \\ \frac{1}{12} & -\frac{1}{6} & \frac{11}{24} \end{pmatrix}$$

$$\Phi_5 = \begin{pmatrix} \frac{11}{24} & \frac{1}{12} & -\frac{11}{48} \\ -\frac{11}{72} & \frac{11}{76} & \frac{1}{12} \\ \frac{1}{12} & -\frac{11}{72} & \frac{11}{24} \end{pmatrix}$$

(Note the error $< 1\%$; now, e.g., the 1,1 element is in error by 0.69%.)

$$\Phi_6 = \begin{pmatrix} \frac{11}{24} & \frac{11}{144} & -\frac{11}{48} \\ -\frac{11}{72} & \frac{11}{36} & \frac{11}{144} \\ \frac{11}{144} & -\frac{11}{72} & \frac{11}{24} \end{pmatrix}$$

$$\Phi_7 = \begin{pmatrix} \frac{133}{288} & \frac{11}{144} & -\frac{11}{48} \\ -\frac{11}{72} & \frac{133}{432} & \frac{11}{144} \\ \frac{11}{144} & -\frac{11}{72} & \frac{133}{288} \end{pmatrix}$$

$$\Phi_8 = \begin{pmatrix} \frac{133}{288} & \frac{11}{144} & -\frac{133}{576} \\ -\frac{133}{864} & \frac{133}{432} & \frac{11}{144} \\ \frac{11}{144} & -\frac{133}{864} & \frac{133}{288} \end{pmatrix}$$

$$\Phi_9 = \begin{pmatrix} \frac{133}{288} & \frac{133}{1728} & -\frac{133}{576} \\ -\frac{133}{864} & \frac{133}{432} & \frac{133}{1728} \\ \frac{133}{1728} & -\frac{133}{864} & \frac{133}{288} \end{pmatrix}$$

$$\Phi_{10} = \begin{pmatrix} \frac{1595}{3456} & \frac{133}{1728} & -\frac{133}{576} \\ -\frac{133}{864} & \frac{1595}{5184} & \frac{133}{1728} \\ \frac{133}{1728} & -\frac{133}{864} & \frac{1595}{3456} \end{pmatrix}$$

or in decimal form

$$\Phi_{10} = \begin{pmatrix} 0.4615162 & 0.0769676 & -0.2309028 \\ -0.1539352 & 0.3076775 & 0.0769676 \\ 0.0769676 & -0.1539352 & 0.4615162 \end{pmatrix}$$

Note the convergence particularly. The elements of Λ_{19}^{-1} for example (to calculate Φ_{20}) are all less than 1×10^{-7}. Calculation of Φ_{21} yields the elements of the correct inverse within $3 \times 10^{-6}\%$. Calculation of Φ_{30}, not shown here, yields Λ^{-1} to ten decimal place accuracy ($1.6 \times 10^{-9}\%$ error). The approximate inverse Φ_{21} and the actual inverse Λ^{-1} are:

$$\Phi_{21} = \begin{pmatrix} \frac{2756293}{5971968} & \frac{2756293}{35831808} & -\frac{2756293}{11943936} \\ -\frac{2756293}{17915904} & \frac{2756293}{8957952} & \frac{2756293}{35831808} \\ \frac{2756293}{35831808} & -\frac{2756293}{17915904} & \frac{2756293}{5971968} \end{pmatrix}$$

$$\Lambda^{-1} = \begin{pmatrix} \frac{6}{13} & \frac{1}{13} & -\frac{3}{13} \\ -\frac{2}{13} & \frac{4}{13} & \frac{1}{13} \\ \frac{1}{13} & -\frac{2}{13} & \frac{6}{13} \end{pmatrix}$$

for 3×3 matrices:

$$\Lambda = \begin{pmatrix} \lambda_{11} & \lambda_{12} & \lambda_{13} \\ \lambda_{21} & \lambda_{22} & \lambda_{23} \\ \lambda_{31} & \lambda_{32} & \lambda_{33} \end{pmatrix}$$

$$L = \begin{pmatrix} \lambda_{11} & 0 & 0 \\ 0 & \lambda_{22} & 0 \\ 0 & 0 & \lambda_{33} \end{pmatrix}$$

$$R = \begin{pmatrix} 0 & \lambda_{12} & \lambda_{13} \\ \lambda^{21} & 0 & \lambda_{23} \\ \lambda_{31} & \lambda_{32} & 0 \end{pmatrix}$$

$$\Lambda_0^{-1} = L^{-1} = \begin{pmatrix} \dfrac{1}{\lambda_{11}} & 0 & 0 \\ 0 & \dfrac{1}{\lambda_{32}} & 0 \\ 0 & 0 & \dfrac{1}{\lambda_{33}} \end{pmatrix}$$

Assume $|\lambda_{11}\lambda_{22}\lambda_{33}| > |-\lambda_{12}(\lambda_{23}\lambda_{31}) + \lambda_{13}(\lambda_{21}\lambda_{32})|$ (Case I), i.e., $|\det L| > |\det R|$.

$$\Lambda_1^{-1} = (-L^{-1}R)L^{-1}$$

$$= (-1)\begin{pmatrix} \dfrac{1}{\lambda_{11}} & 0 & 0 \\ 0 & \dfrac{1}{\lambda_{22}} & 0 \\ 0 & 0 & \dfrac{1}{\lambda_{33}} \end{pmatrix}\begin{pmatrix} 0 & \lambda_{12} & \lambda_{13} \\ \lambda_{21} & 0 & \lambda_{23} \\ \lambda_{31} & \lambda_{32} & 0 \end{pmatrix}\begin{pmatrix} \dfrac{1}{\lambda_{11}} & 0 & 0 \\ 0 & \dfrac{1}{\lambda_{22}} & 0 \\ 0 & 0 & \dfrac{1}{\lambda_{33}} \end{pmatrix}$$

The product $-L^{-1}R$ is given by

$$\begin{pmatrix} 0 & -\dfrac{\lambda_{12}}{\lambda_{11}} & -\dfrac{\lambda_{13}}{\lambda_{11}} \\ -\dfrac{\lambda_{21}}{\lambda_{22}} & 0 & -\dfrac{\lambda_{23}}{\lambda_{22}} \\ -\dfrac{\lambda_{31}}{\lambda_{33}} & -\dfrac{\lambda_{22}}{\lambda_{33}} & 0 \end{pmatrix}$$

The $-(L^{-1}R)$ matrix multiplies L^{-1} to yield λ_1^{-1}. The same matrix multiplies Λ_1^{-1} to yield Λ_2^{-1}, etc.

10.18. SYSTEMS OF MATRIX EQUATIONS

Consider the matrix equations

$$Ax + By = f$$

$$Cx + Dy = g$$

where A, B, C, and D are matrices, and x, y, f, and g are vectors

$$\begin{pmatrix} A & B \\ C & D \end{pmatrix}\begin{pmatrix} x \\ y \end{pmatrix} = \begin{pmatrix} f \\ g \end{pmatrix}$$

If

$$\begin{pmatrix} x \\ y \end{pmatrix} = \xi \quad \text{and} \quad \begin{pmatrix} f \\ g \end{pmatrix} = \eta$$

and finally

$$\begin{pmatrix} A & B \\ C & D \end{pmatrix} = \Gamma$$

then

$$\Gamma\xi = \eta \quad \text{or} \quad \xi = \Gamma^{-1}\eta$$

is in our general form. Generalizing consider the equations

$$A_{11}x + A_{12}y + A_{13}z = G_1$$
$$A_{21}x + A_{22}y + A_{23}z = G_2$$
$$A_{31}x + A_{32}y + A_{33}z = G_3$$

which can be written in matrix form where x, y, z, G_1, G_2, and G_3 are 3×1 matrices (vectors) and the A_{ij} are 3×3 matrices.

Let $A_{ij} = a_{ij} + \alpha_{ij}$, where a_{ij} are deterministic and α_{ij} are stochastic. Similarly $G_i = g_i + \gamma_i$. Now

$$\begin{pmatrix} A_{11} & A_{12} & A_{13} \\ A_{21} & A_{22} & A_{23} \\ A_{31} & A_{32} & A_{33} \end{pmatrix} \begin{pmatrix} x \\ y \\ z \end{pmatrix} = \begin{pmatrix} G_1 \\ G_2 \\ G_3 \end{pmatrix}$$

Denoting the 9×9 matrix of A_{ij}'s by A and $\begin{pmatrix} x \\ y \\ z \end{pmatrix}$ by x, we can write

$$Ax = G$$
$$x = A^{-1}G$$

The matrix inverse A^{-1} is computed by the technique of Section 10.20.

10.19.   INVERSION OF RANDOM MATRICES

Consider

$$\Lambda = \begin{pmatrix} \lambda_{11} & \lambda_{12} \\ \lambda_{21} & \lambda_{22} \end{pmatrix} = L + R$$

$$L = \begin{pmatrix} a_{11} & a_{12} \\ a_{21} & a_{22} \end{pmatrix}$$

$$R = \begin{pmatrix} \alpha_{11} & \alpha_{12} \\ \alpha_{21} & \alpha_{22} \end{pmatrix}$$

Choose $\|L\| > \|R\|$ a.s. (where the notation indicates absolute value of the determinants). Furthermore, let $L = L_1 + L_2$ where

$$L_1 = \begin{pmatrix} a_{11} & 0 \\ 0 & a_{22} \end{pmatrix}$$

$$L_2 = \begin{pmatrix} 0 & a_{12} \\ a_{21} & 0 \end{pmatrix}$$

If $\|L_1\| > \|L_2\|$ then $L^{-1} = \sum_{n=0}^{\infty} (-1)^n (L_1^{-1} L_2)^n L_1^{-1}$ where

$$L_1^{-1} = \begin{pmatrix} \dfrac{1}{a_{11}} & 0 \\ 0 & \dfrac{1}{a_{22}} \end{pmatrix}$$

hence

$$L^{-1} = \sum_{n=0}^{\infty} (-1)^n \left\{ \begin{pmatrix} \dfrac{1}{a_{11}} & 0 \\ 0 & \dfrac{1}{a_{22}} \end{pmatrix} \begin{pmatrix} 0 & a_{12} \\ a_{21} & 0 \end{pmatrix} \right\}^n \begin{pmatrix} \dfrac{1}{a_{11}} & 0 \\ 0 & \dfrac{1}{a_{22}} \end{pmatrix}$$

Depending on the elements of Λ (i.e., whether Λ falls into Case I or Case II), we can sum and write the inverse as a single matrix for L^{-1}. Then

$$\Lambda^{-1} = \sum_{n=0}^{\infty} (-1)^n (L^{-1} R)^n L^{-1}$$

where R contains the random elements which require averaging. It is a straightforward step to compute the various statistical measures defined in [1], such as the expected inverse $\langle \Lambda^{-1} \rangle$ or the correlation $\langle \Lambda^{-1} \Lambda^{-1} \rangle$ of the inverse matrix.

We can also consider convergence of the determinant of the inverse. Since the determinant of a product of matrices is equal to the product of the determinants,

$$|\Lambda^{-1}| = \sum_{n=0}^{\infty} (-1)^n (|L^{-1}|\cdot|R|)^n |L^{-1}|$$

therefore $|L^{-1}|\cdot|R| < 1$ for convergence implying $|L| > |R|$ or $|L^{-1}|\cdot|R| < |I|$. If, for example,

$$L = \begin{bmatrix} 2 & 0 \\ 0 & 2 \end{bmatrix}, \qquad L^{-1}\begin{bmatrix} \frac{1}{2} & 0 \\ 0 & \frac{1}{2} \end{bmatrix}, \qquad |L| = 4$$

Choose

$$R = \begin{bmatrix} \sqrt{2} & 0 \\ 0 & \sqrt{2} \end{bmatrix}$$

so $|R| = 2$. Then $|L^{-1}R| < \frac{1}{2}$.

10.20. INVERSION OF VERY LARGE MATRICES

We now show that the inversion algorithms can be applied to the inversion of very large matrices, providing easily programmed and computable and accurate inverses.

Case 1: $n \times n$ **Matrix with Even** n: Let us begin with a 4×4 example:

$$\Lambda = \begin{pmatrix} \lambda_{11} & \lambda_{12} & \lambda_{13} & \lambda_{14} \\ \lambda_{21} & \lambda_{22} & \lambda_{23} & \lambda_{24} \\ \lambda_{31} & \lambda_{32} & \lambda_{33} & \lambda_{34} \\ \lambda_{41} & \lambda_{42} & \lambda_{43} & \lambda_{44} \end{pmatrix}$$

and partition it into 2×2 matrices, thus

$$\Lambda = \begin{pmatrix} A & B \\ C & D \end{pmatrix}$$

Now using the inversion method discussed in [4], write

$$\Lambda = L + R$$

where

$$L = \begin{pmatrix} A & 0 \\ 0 & D \end{pmatrix}, \qquad L^{-1} = \begin{pmatrix} A^{-1} & 0 \\ 0 & D^{-1} \end{pmatrix}$$

$$R = \begin{pmatrix} 0 & B \\ C & 0 \end{pmatrix}, \qquad L^{-1}R = \begin{pmatrix} 0 & A^{-1}B \\ D^{-1}C & 0 \end{pmatrix}$$

Consequently

$$\Lambda = \sum_{n=0}^{\infty} (-1)^n (L^{-1}R)^n L^{-1}$$

$$= \sum_{n=0}^{\infty} (-1)^n \begin{pmatrix} 0 & A^{-1}B \\ D^{-1}C & 0 \end{pmatrix}^n \cdot \begin{pmatrix} A^{-1} & 0 \\ 0 & D^{-1} \end{pmatrix}$$

where the inverses A^{-1} and D^{-1} can be written without computation (last section). To go to larger matrices, we realize that this process can be continued if the λ_{ij} themselves are matrices. Thus a $(2n) \times (2n)$ matrix can be partitioned into n^2 (2×2) matrices and then subjected to the decomposition method of inversion. The procedure can be applied to very large even matrices. Now write

$$\Lambda = \begin{pmatrix} A_1 & A_2 \\ A_3 & A_4 \end{pmatrix}$$

where A_1, A_2, A_3, and A_4 are *matrices* given by

$$A_1 = \begin{pmatrix} A_{11} & A_{12} \\ A_{13} & A_{14} \end{pmatrix}$$

$$A_2 = \begin{pmatrix} A_{21} & A_{22} \\ A_{23} & A_{24} \end{pmatrix}$$

$$A_3 = \begin{pmatrix} A_{31} & A_{32} \\ A_{33} & A_{34} \end{pmatrix}$$

$$A_4 = \begin{pmatrix} A_{41} & A_{42} \\ A_{43} & A_{44} \end{pmatrix}$$

i.e.,

$$\Lambda = \left(\begin{array}{cc|cc} A_{11} & A_{12} & A_{21} & A_{22} \\ A_{13} & A_{14} & A_{23} & A_{24} \\ \hline A_{31} & A_{32} & A_{41} & A_{42} \\ A_{33} & A_{34} & A_{43} & A_{44} \end{array} \right)$$

The notation on subscripts is unusual but convenient; the first subscript identifies the submatrix A_1, A_2, A_3, or A_4 and the second identifies the element.

However, the elements A_{11}, A_{12},... are themselves matrices and we write

$$A_{11} = \begin{pmatrix} A_{111} & A_{112} \\ A_{113} & A_{114} \end{pmatrix}$$

$$A_{12} = \begin{pmatrix} A_{121} & A_{122} \\ A_{123} & A_{124} \end{pmatrix}$$

$$\vdots$$

until the elements, e.g., $A_{111\cdots1}$, become scalars. Then

$$\Lambda^{-1} = \sum_{n=0}^{\infty} (-1)^n \begin{pmatrix} 0 & A_1^{-1}A_2 \\ A_4^{-1}A_3 & 0 \end{pmatrix} \begin{pmatrix} A_1^{-1} & 0 \\ 0 & A_4^{-1} \end{pmatrix}$$

where

$$A_1^{-1} = \sum_{n=0}^{\infty} (-1)^n \begin{pmatrix} 0 & A_{11}^{-1}A_{12} \\ A_{14}^{-1}A_{13} & 0 \end{pmatrix} \begin{pmatrix} A_{11}^{-1} & 0 \\ 0 & A_{14}^{-1} \end{pmatrix}$$

Similarly to get A_{11}^{-1}

$$A_{11}^{-1} = \sum_{n=0}^{\infty} (-1)^n \begin{pmatrix} 0 & A_{111}^{-1}A_{12} \\ A_{114}^{-1}A_{113} & 0 \end{pmatrix} \begin{pmatrix} A_{111}^{-1} & 0 \\ 0 & A_{114}^{-1} \end{pmatrix}$$

etc. Finally, $A_{111\cdots1}^{-1}$ will be a scalar $\equiv 1/a_1$.

Case 2: $n \times n$ **Matrix for Odd** n: We begin with a 3×3 example. (We can, for example, have a 6×6 matrix and partition it into a 3×3 matrix whose elements are 2×2 matrices.)

$$A = \begin{pmatrix} a_{11} & a_{12} & a_{13} \\ a_{21} & a_{22} & a_{23} \\ a_{31} & a_{32} & a_{33} \end{pmatrix}$$

which we partition as shown rewriting it as

$$A = \begin{pmatrix} A_{11} & A_{12} \\ A_{21} & A_{22} \end{pmatrix}$$

In the 2×2 form, we use the decomposition taking the matrix of diagonal elements as L and the remainder as R. Then

$$A^{-1} = \sum_{n=0}^{\infty} (-1)^n (L^{-1}R)^n L^{-1}$$

$$A^{-1} = \sum_{n=0}^{\infty} (-1)^n \left\{ \begin{pmatrix} A_{11}^{-1} & 0 \\ 0 & A_{22}^{-1} \end{pmatrix} \cdot \begin{pmatrix} 0 & A_{12} \\ A_{21} & 0 \end{pmatrix} \right\}^n \cdot \begin{pmatrix} A_{11}^{-1} & 0 \\ 0 & A_{22}^{-1} \end{pmatrix}$$

where the A_{11}^{-1} is simply a_{11}^{-1} and A_{22}^{-1} is given as in the preceding discussion for 2×2 matrices as

$$A_{22}^{-1} = \sum_{n=0}^{\infty} (-1)^n \left\{ \begin{pmatrix} a_{22}^{-1} & 0 \\ 0 & a_{33}^{-1} \end{pmatrix} \cdot \begin{pmatrix} 0 & a_{23} \\ a_{32} & 0 \end{pmatrix} \right\}^n \cdot \begin{pmatrix} a_{22}^{-1} & 0 \\ 0 & a_{33}^{-1} \end{pmatrix}$$

Since $A^{-1} = \sum_{n=0}^{\infty} A_n^{-1}$

$$A_0^{-1} = \begin{pmatrix} A_{11}^{-1} & 0 \\ 0 & A_{22}^{-1} \end{pmatrix} = \begin{pmatrix} a_{11}^{-1} & 0 & 0 \\ 0 & a_{22}^{-1} & 0 \\ 0 & 0 & a_{33}^{-1} \end{pmatrix}$$

which we get also if we simply start with the diagonal elements of the 3×3 unpartitioned A matrix, calling it L. If we had done that we should have

$$R = \begin{pmatrix} 0 & a_{12} & a_{13} \\ a_{21} & 0 & a_{23} \\ a_{31} & a_{32} & 0 \end{pmatrix}$$

The next term would be $-(L^{-1}R)L^{-1}$ etc.

EXAMPLE: Consider the 3×3 matrix A partitioned as indicated

$$A = \begin{pmatrix} 5 & \vdots & 0 & 1 \\ \text{-}\text{-}\text{-} & \vdots & \text{-}\text{-}\text{-}\text{-} \\ 0 & \vdots & 2 & 1 \\ 1 & \vdots & 1 & 3 \end{pmatrix}$$

Now we can write A as a 2×2 matrix

$$A = \begin{pmatrix} a_{11} & a_{12} \\ a_{21} & a_{22} \end{pmatrix}$$

which is invertible by the methods we have discussed, thus

$$A^{-1} = \sum_{n=0}^{\infty} (-1)^n \left(\begin{pmatrix} a_{11}^{-1} & 0 \\ 0 & a_{22}^{-1} \end{pmatrix} \cdot \begin{pmatrix} 0 & a_{12} \\ a_{21} & 0 \end{pmatrix} \right)^n \cdot \begin{pmatrix} a_{11}^{-1} & 0 \\ 0 & a_{22}^{-1} \end{pmatrix}$$

Here a_{11} is the single element 5; $a_{11}^{-1} = \frac{1}{5}$, and a_{22} is the 2×2 matrix. The latter is immediately invertible by the methods already discussed:

$$a_{22}^{-1} = \sum_{n=0}^{\infty} (-1)^n \left(\begin{pmatrix} \frac{1}{2} & 0 \\ 0 & \frac{1}{3} \end{pmatrix} \cdot \begin{pmatrix} 0 & 1 \\ 1 & 0 \end{pmatrix} \right)^n \cdot \begin{pmatrix} \frac{1}{2} & 0 \\ 0 & \frac{1}{3} \end{pmatrix}$$

$$= \begin{pmatrix} \frac{3}{5} & -\frac{1}{5} \\ -\frac{1}{5} & \frac{2}{5} \end{pmatrix}$$

(Calculation of only three terms of the above gives $\begin{pmatrix} 0.58 & 0.16 \\ -0.16 & 0.39 \end{pmatrix}$ which is already quite close, but we can sum exactly as we have discussed for the 2×2.) Now we write the terms of $A^{-1} = \sum_{n=0}^{\infty} A_n^{-1}$.

$$A_0^{-1} = \begin{pmatrix} a_{11}^{-1} & 0 \\ 0 & a_{22}^{-1} \end{pmatrix}$$

$$= \begin{pmatrix} \frac{1}{5} & 0 & 0 \\ 0 & \frac{3}{5} & -\frac{1}{5} \\ 0 & -\frac{1}{5} & \frac{2}{5} \end{pmatrix} \equiv L^{-1}$$

$$A_1^{-1} = (-1) \begin{pmatrix} \frac{1}{5} & 0 & 0 \\ 0 & \frac{3}{5} & -\frac{1}{5} \\ 0 & -\frac{1}{5} & \frac{2}{5} \end{pmatrix} \cdot \begin{pmatrix} 0 & \vdots & 0 & 1 \\ \hdashline 0 & \vdots & 0 & 0 \\ 1 & \vdots & 0 & 0 \end{pmatrix} \cdot A_0^{-1}$$

$$A_1^{-1} = \begin{pmatrix} 0 & 0 & -\frac{1}{5} \\ \frac{1}{5} & 0 & 0 \\ -\frac{2}{5} & 0 & 0 \end{pmatrix} \cdot A_0^{-1} = \begin{pmatrix} 0 & \frac{1}{25} & -\frac{2}{25} \\ \frac{1}{25} & 0 & 0 \\ -\frac{2}{25} & 0 & 0 \end{pmatrix}$$

$$A_2^{-1} = -(L^{-1}R)A_1^{-1} = \begin{pmatrix} \frac{2}{125} & 0 & 0 \\ 0 & \frac{1}{125} & -\frac{2}{125} \\ 0 & -\frac{2}{125} & \frac{4}{125} \end{pmatrix}$$

$$\vdots$$

each successive term being multiplied by $-L^{-1}R$. The approximation to the desired inverse is $\Phi_n = A_0^{-1} + A_1^{-1} + A_2^{-1} + \cdots + A_{n-1}^{-1}$. Our results are

$$\Phi_1 = \begin{pmatrix} \frac{1}{5} & 0 & 0 \\ 0 & \frac{3}{5} & -\frac{1}{5} \\ 0 & -\frac{1}{5} & \frac{2}{5} \end{pmatrix}$$

$$\Phi_2 = \begin{pmatrix} \frac{1}{5} & \frac{1}{25} & -\frac{2}{25} \\ \frac{1}{25} & \frac{3}{5} & -\frac{1}{5} \\ -\frac{2}{25} & -\frac{1}{5} & \frac{2}{5} \end{pmatrix}$$

$$\Phi_3 = \begin{pmatrix} \frac{27}{125} & \frac{1}{25} & -\frac{2}{25} \\ \frac{1}{25} & \frac{76}{125} & -\frac{27}{125} \\ -\frac{2}{25} & -\frac{27}{125} & \frac{54}{125} \end{pmatrix}$$

In decimal form

$$\Phi_3 = \begin{pmatrix} 0.216 & 0.04 & -0.08 \\ 0.04 & 0.608 & -0.216 \\ -0.08 & -0.216 & -0.432 \end{pmatrix}$$

We emphasize that this is only a *three-term* approximation which can easily be carried much further, but let us see now if $\Phi_3 A \approx I$ (i.e., is $\Phi_3 \approx A^{-1}$?) We have

$$\begin{pmatrix} 0.216 & 0.04 & -0.08 \\ 0.04 & 0.608 & -0.216 \\ -0.08 & -0.216 & 0.432 \end{pmatrix} \cdot \begin{pmatrix} 5 & 0 & 1 \\ 0 & 2 & 1 \\ 1 & 1 & 3 \end{pmatrix}$$

$$= \begin{pmatrix} 1 & 0 & 0.01 \\ -0.01 & 1 & 0 \\ 0.03 & 0 & 1 \end{pmatrix} \simeq \begin{pmatrix} 1 & 0 & 0 \\ 0 & 1 & 0 \\ 0 & 0 & 1 \end{pmatrix}$$

EXERCISES

1. Calculate Φ_5.

2. Solve by decomposition using the matrix of diagonal elements of A as L and R as the matrix of the off-diagonal elements of A. Convergence will be slower. Verify.

3. Choose a 6×6 matrix. Make it a 3×3 matrix of elements which are 2×2 matrices.

REFERENCES

1. G. Adomian, Solution of algebraic equations, *Math and Comp in Simulation*, **28**, 1–3, 1986.

SUGGESTED FURTHER READING

G. Birkhoff and S. MacLane, "A Survey of Modern Algebra." MacMillan, New York, 1965.
R. Bellman, "Introduction to Matrix Analysis," 2nd ed., McGraw-Hill, New York, 1970.
V. I. Smirnov, in "Linear Algebra and Group Theory" (R. A. Silverman, ed.), McGraw-Hill, New York, 1961.
G. Adomian and R. Roch, A new computational approach for inversion of very large matrices, *Math. Modelling*, in press.

CHAPTER 11

Convergence

11.1. THE CONVERGENCE QUESTION FOR THE NONLINEAR CASE

We have previously shown in Adomian [1] that for the linear stochastic equation $Ly = x$ with zero initial conditions, our derived series for the "inverse" $\mathscr{L}^{-1}$ does indeed satisfy $\mathscr{L}^{-1}\mathscr{L} = I$, where I is the identity and is, therefore, the true inverse. A similar general proof for a nonlinear operator is much more difficult[1] although we can show easily the validity of particular solutions. Let us examine the general problem. Since the difficulty lies in the nonlinearity rather than the stochasticity, we will let $N(y)$ represent a nonlinear (deterministic) operation resulting in the function $f(y)$. We assume that $\{x(t) - Ny\}$ is continuous with respect to t and y in a convex region and that $\partial(Ny)/\partial y$ exists and is bounded. Consider the equation $Fy = x$, which we write as $Ly + Ny = x$, where L is a linear operator giving the linear portion of the left-hand side. We write

$$Ly = x - Ny$$

$$y = y_0 - L^{-1}Ny = y_0 - L^{-1}\sum_{n=0}^{\infty} A_n$$

where the A_n are generated for $f(y)$. We have after y_0,

$$y_1 = -L^{-1}A_0, \qquad y_2 = -L^{-1}A_1, \text{ etc.}$$

Hence,

$$y = F^{-1}x = y_0 - L^{-1}A_0 - L^{-1}A_1 - \cdots$$

[1] Such a mathematical proof has now been made as the book goes to press. See Section 11.4.

223

Operating with F, we have

$$Fy = F(F^{-1}x) = F\left[y_0 - L^{-1} \sum_{n=0}^{\infty} A_n \right]$$

$$= L\left[y_0 - L^{-1} \sum_{n=0}^{\infty} A_n \right] + N\left[y_0 - L^{-1} \sum_{n=0}^{\infty} A_n \right]$$

$$= L[y_0] - \sum_{n=0}^{\infty} A_n + \sum_{n=0}^{\infty} B_n$$

where the B_n are the polynomials for the nonlinear operation represented by N on the function $\{ y_0 - L^{-1} \sum_{n=0}^{\infty} A_n \}$ rather than just y as before. These are, of course, a sum of polynomials where each term after y_0 represents an integration L^{-1} of one of the original A_n polynomials. (If initial conditions are zero, then y_0 is simply $L^{-1}x$. Thus, we must show that the sum of the last two sums vanishes if B_n are the polynomials for $N[L^{-1}x - L^{-1} \sum_{n=0}^{\infty} A_n] = f(L^{-1}x - L^{-1} \sum_{n=0}^{\infty} A_n)$. Thus, if $f(y)$ represents, for example, y^2, then

$$f\left(L^{-1}x - L^{-1} \sum_{n=0}^{\infty} A_n \right) = \left(L^{-1}x - L^{-1} \sum_{n=0}^{\infty} A_n \right)\left(L^{-1}x - L^{-1} \sum_{n=0}^{\infty} A_n \right)$$

$$= L^{-1}xL^{-1}x - L^{-1}xL^{-1} \sum_{n=0}^{\infty} A_n - L^{-1}A_nL^{-1}x$$

$$+ L^{-1} \sum_{n=0}^{\infty} A_nL^{-1} \sum_{n=0}^{\infty} A_n$$

We could take a half dozen terms of the A_n as an approximation and consider the entire resulting sum above as a function $g(u)$ for which we evaluate the polynomials (now designated by B_n).

Clearly, a simpler method would be to substitute ϕ_n for some relatively small n and verify that as $n \to \infty$, the solution does indeed satisfy the original equation.

Let us try another approach. Consider the (deterministic) nonlinear equation $Ly + Ny = x$. Then $Ly = x - Ny$ or $y = L^{-1}x - L^{-1}Ny = L^{-1}x - L^{-1} \sum_{n=0}^{\infty} A_n = \sum_{n=0}^{\infty} y_n$, where

$$A_0 = f(y_0) = h_0(y_0)$$

$$A_1 = C(1, 1)h_1 = y_1h_1(y_0)$$

$$A_2 = C(1, 2)h_1 + C(2, 2)h_2$$

$$= y_2h_1(y_0) + (1/2!)y_1^2h_2(y_0)$$

$$\vdots$$

which are finite polynomials in y_0 since $y_1, y_2, \ldots$ can be given in terms of y_0, i.e.,

$$y_0 = L^{-1}x = \int_0^t l(t, \tau)x(\tau)\, d\tau$$

assuming $|x(t)| < M_1$ for $t \in T$ and $|l(t, \tau)| < M_2$ for $t, \tau \in T$. Hence,

$$|y_0| = M_2 M_1 \int_0^t d\tau = M_2 M_1 t$$

$$y_1 = -L^{-1}A_0 = -\int_0^t l(t, \tau)h_0(y_0)\, d\tau$$

$$y_2 = -L^{-1}A_1 = -\int_0^t l(t, \tau)y_1 h_1(y_0)\, d\tau$$

$$\vdots$$

We will consider y^m-type nonlinearities, and for simplicity we consider y^2 specifically. Now

$$y_1 = -\int_0^t l(t, \tau)y_0^2\, d\tau$$

$$|y_1| = -M_2 \int_0^t |L^{-1}x L^{-1}x|\, d\tau$$

$$= -\frac{M_2^3 M_1^2 t^3}{3!}$$

$$y_2 = -L^{-1}(2y_0 y_1) = -2L^{-1}L^{-1}x L^{-1}L^{-1}x L^{-1}x$$

$$|y_2| = \frac{2M_2^5 M_1^3 t^5}{5!}$$

We can absorb the $1/n!$ into the coefficients and write

$$A_n = \sum_{v=1}^{n} C(v, n)h_v(y_0)$$

Then, for example,

$$A_3 = C(1, 3)h_1 + C(2, 3)h_2 + C(3, 3)h_3$$

or

$$A_5 = C(1, 5)h_1 + C(2, 5)h_2 + \cdots + C(5, 5)h_5$$

etc. The n-term approximation ϕ_n is given by

$$\phi_n = y_0 - L^{-1} \sum_{i=0}^{n-1} A_i$$

$$\phi_{n+1} = y_0 - L^{-1} \sum_{i=0}^{n} A_i = y_0 - L^{-1} \sum_{i=0}^{n-1} - L^{-1} A_n$$

$$|\phi_{n+1} - \phi_n| = -|L^{-1} A_n = -|y_{n+1}| \to 0$$

Term by term examination of the components y_n shows convergent terms for any term y^m[2]. Let us consider $m = 2$ as an example. Let $l(t, \tau)$ be bounded by M_l and $x(t)$ be bounded by M_x (in the almost-everywhere sense if x is stochastic). The first term of $y = \sum_{n=0}^{\infty} y_n$ is $y_0 = L^{-1} x = \int_0^t l(t, \tau) x(\tau) \, d\tau$, which is $M_l M_x t$. The second is $y_1 = L^{-1} y_0^2 = L^{-1} L^{-1} x L^{-1} x = M_x^2 M_l^3 t^3/3!$. Multiply and divide the second term by M_x to write $(M_x^3 M_l^3 t^3/3!)/M_x$. The third term is $2 M_x^3 M_l^5 t^5/5!$, which can be written as $(M_x^5 M_l^5 t^5/5!)/(M_x^2/2)$. The next term is $M_x^4 M_l^7 t^7/7! + 4 M_x^4 M_l^7 t^7/7!$ or $\{(M_x^7 M_l^7/7!)/M_x^3\} + \{(M_x^7 M_l^7 t^7/7!)/(M_x^3/4)\}$. Each term is in the form $(M_x^n M_l^n t^n/n!)$ divided by increasing powers of M_x, i.e., the series is bounded by $e^{M_x M_l t}/M_x^\alpha$, where α is a positive exponent. The series converges for all finite t. For y_n we have $\{(M_x M_l t)^{2n+1}/(2n + 1)!\}/M_x^n$ and $y_n \to 0$ as $n \to \infty$ for any finite t. A series behaving like $t^n/n!$ would have the $(n + 1)$th term divided by the nth term equal to $(t^{n+1}/(n + 1)!)/(n!/t^n) = t/n$ and would approach zero for finite t as $n \to \infty$. This series converges much faster as illustrated by many examples often yielding stable, accurate results in a few to a dozen terms.

It has been shown that nonlinear terms can be expanded in the A_n polynomials which approach zero for high n, and consequently the decomposition method yields an accurate solution.

In solving the equation $Ly + Ny = x$ with the approximation $\phi_n = \sum_{i=0}^{n-1} y_i$ we have $\phi_n = L^{-1} x - L^{-1} \sum_{i=0}^{n-2} A_i$, but $\lim_{n \to \infty} \phi_n = y$ and $\lim_{n \to \infty} \sum_{i=0}^{n} A_i = Ny$, so the equation is satisfied. Existence and uniqueness are guaranteed by the previously stated continuity and differentiability properties.

EXAMPLE: The following (anharmonic oscillator) equation clearly shows the expected behavior. Consider

$$d^2\theta/dt^2 + k^2 \sin \theta = 0, \qquad \theta(0) = \gamma = \text{const}, \qquad \theta'(0) = 0$$

The solution is

$$\theta(t) = \gamma - |(kt)^2/2!| \cdot |\sin \gamma| + |(kt)^4/4!| \cdot |\sin \gamma \cos \gamma|$$
$$- |(kt)^6/6!| \cdot |\sin \gamma \cos^2 \gamma - 3 \sin^3 \gamma| + \cdots$$

If γ is small this reduces to

$$\theta(t) = \gamma \cos kt$$

i.e., the result for the linear harmonic oscillator.

To verify solutions with $\theta_n = \sum_{i=0}^{n-1} y_i$, substitute into $Ly + Ny = x(t)$

$$L\phi_{n+1} + \sum_{i=0}^{n-1} A_i = x(t)$$

For example, by writing $\phi_2 = y_0 + y_1$, the $\sum_{n=0}^{\infty} A_i$ would include only A_0 since $y_1 = -L^{-1}A_0$ and depends only on A_0.

11.2. ESTIMATING THE RADIUS OF CONVERGENCE

With rapidly converging solutions, we can examine radii of convergence very simply. As an example, consider the equation

$$y' = y^2 - y(x), \qquad y(0) = 2$$

The solution is $2/(2 - e^x)$, which is singular at $x = \ln 2$. By decomposition we write

$$y = y(0) - L^{-1}y + L^{-1} \sum_{n=0}^{\infty} A_n$$

$$y_0 = 2$$

$$y_1 = -L^{-1}y_0 + L^{-1}A_0$$

$$y_2 = -L^{-1}y_1 + L^{-1}A_1$$

$$\vdots$$

$$y_{n+1} = -L^{-1}y_n + L^{-1}A_n$$

The $A_n(y^2)$ are given by

$$A_0 = y_0^2$$

$$A_1 = 2y_0y_1$$

$$A_2 = y_1^2 + 2y_0y_2$$

$$A_3 = 2y_1y_2 + 2y_0y_3$$

$$\vdots$$

Thus $y_0 = 2$, $y_1 = 2x$, $y_2 = 3x^2$, etc., so that

$$y = 2 + 2x + 3x^2 + \cdots$$

To verify the solution, taking only two terms $y_0 + y_1 = 2 + 2x$, $y^2 = (2 + 2x)^2 \cong 4 + 8x$ and $y' = (y_0 + y_1 + y_2)' = 2 + 6x$, which gives us $y' = y^2 - y$. Verifying with three terms, we get $y = 2 + 2x + 3x^2$, $y' = 2 + 6x + 13x^2$, $y^2 = 4 + 8x + 16x^2 + \cdots$ or $2 + 6x + 13x^3 = 4 + 8x + 16x^2 - 2 - 2x - 3x^2$, which checks.

If we take $|y_2/y_1|$ we have $\frac{3}{2}|x| < 1$ for convergence so $|x| < 0.67$ as an approximation. We can carry this a little further by finding more terms, i.e., a better approximation

$$
\begin{aligned}
y_3 &= -L^{-1}y_2 + L^{-1}A_2 \\
&= -L^{-1}[3x^2] + L^{-1}[y_1^2 + 2y_0 y_2] \\
&= -x^3 + L^{-1}[4x^2 + 2 \cdot 2 \cdot 3x^2] \\
&= -x^3 + \tfrac{4}{3}x^3 + 4x^3 = 13x^3/3
\end{aligned}
$$

or $y = 2 + 2x + 3x^2 + (13x^3/3) + \cdots$.

We note that $|y_3/y_2| = |\frac{13}{3}x^3/3x^2| < 1$, so that $x < 0.69$. Computing y_4, we have

$$
\begin{aligned}
y_4 &= -L^{-1}y_3 + L^{-1}A_3 \\
&= -L^{-1}\left(\frac{13x^3}{3}\right) + L^{-1}[2y_1 y_2 + 2y_0 y_3] \\
&= -L^{-1}\left(\frac{13x^3}{3}\right) + L^{-1}\left(2 \cdot 2x \cdot 3x^2 + 2 \cdot 2 \cdot \frac{13x^3}{3}\right) \\
&= -\frac{13x^4}{12} + 3x^4 + \frac{13x^4}{3} = \frac{75x^4}{12}
\end{aligned}
$$

Now $y = 2 + 2x + 3x^2 + (13x^3/3) + (75x^4/12)$ and $|\frac{75}{12}x^4/\frac{13}{3}x^3| < 1$ or $x < 0.693$ (or ln 2). Thus, we obtain the decomposition series for $x < \ln 2$. If we take a value in the convergent region, say $x = 0.1$, $y = 2 + 0.2 + 0.03 + 0.0039 + \cdots$, which is computed to the accuracy needed.

If we consider the equation $dy/dx = x^2 + y^2$; $y(0) = 1$, decomposition solution yields $y = y_0 + L^{-1}\sum_{n=0}^{\infty} A_n$ with

$$
y_0 = y(0) + L^{-1}x^2
$$

$$
y_1 = L^{-1}A_0
$$

$$
y_2 = L^{-1}A_1
$$

$$
\vdots
$$

with $A_0 = y_0^2$, $A_1 = 2y_0 y_1$, $A_2 = y_1^2 + 2y_0 y_2$, etc. so

$$
y = 1 + x + x^2 + \tfrac{4}{3}x^3 + \cdots
$$

$|y_3/y_2| < 1$ means $x < \frac{3}{4}$. We would get a better value with a few more terms. Taking a value in this region, say 0.4, we get

$$y = 1 + 0.4 + 0.16 + 0.048 + \cdots \simeq 1.608$$

11.3. ON THE CALCULUS

The calculus is that of L_p spaces. The integral operator $\mathcal{H}$ in $y = \mathcal{H}x$ is an a.s. bounded linear stochastic operator from an abstract set χ into itself, mapping $x(t, \omega)$ to $y(t, \omega)$ such that $\mathcal{L}y(t, \omega) = x(t, \omega)$ a.s. The a.s. boundedness of $\mathcal{H}$ follows from the conditions

(i) $F(t, \omega) = \displaystyle\int_0^t l(t, \tau)x(\tau, \omega)\, d\tau$ is bounded a.s.

(ii) $\alpha_v(t, \omega) = a_v(t, \omega) - \langle a_v(t, \omega)\rangle$ are bounded a.s. for all

v from   0   to $n - 1$

The $\langle a_v \rangle$ are continuous on T; the derivatives of α_v are bounded a.s. to appropriate orders; and $l(t, \tau)$ and its kth derivatives for $0 \le k \le n - 1$ are jointly continuous in t and τ over $T \times T$. The set χ consists of all real stochastic processes on T. If $\chi_1 \subset \chi$ consists of all real stochastic processes $x(t, \omega)$ with $\omega \in \Omega$ in the probability space (Ω, B, μ), it follows that $\mathcal{H}: \chi_1 \to \chi_1$ with $\mathcal{H}x(t, \omega) = y(t, \omega)$ a.s.

The expectation $\langle x(t, \omega)\rangle$ of $x(t, \omega)$ on χ_1 is given as the almost sure Lebesgue integral over Ω for each $t \in T$ if the integral exists, i.e.,

$$\langle x_t(\omega)\rangle = \int_\Omega x_t(\omega)\, d\mu(\omega) \qquad \text{a.s.}$$

and we denote by $L_1(\chi_1)$ the set of all equivalence classes of real valued random variables x_t whose expectations $\langle x_t(\omega)\rangle$ exist. Hence, $x_t(\omega) \in L_1(\chi_1)$ if $\langle x_t(\omega)\rangle < \infty$ a.s.

The expectations of x_t^k and $|x_t|^k$ for all k are called the kth moment and the kth absolute moment of the r.v. $x_t(\omega)$ for each $t \in T$. Then $L_p(\chi_1)$ for $1 \le p \le \infty$ denotes equivalence classes of real-valued random variables $x_t(\omega) \in \chi_1$ such that $\langle |x_t|^p\rangle < \infty$ a.s. for $t \in T$. The set of random variables $x(t_1, \omega), x(t_2, \omega),\ldots$ of the process $x(t, \omega)$ generates a linear vector space $V_{x(t, \omega)}$ on R, and the correlation function $R_x(t_1, t_2)$ defines an inner product over the space $V_{x(t, \omega)}$ given by

$$\begin{aligned} R_x(t_1, t_2) &= \langle x(t_1, \omega)x(t_2, \omega)\rangle \\ &= (x(t_1, \omega), x(t_2, \omega)) \end{aligned}$$

and the norm $\|x(t, \omega)\| = (x(t_1, \omega), \ x(t_2, \omega))^{1/2}$. The metric $\rho(x(t_1, \omega),$ $x(t_2, \omega)) = \|x(t_1, \omega) - x(t_2, \omega)\|$, and we have a Hilbert space $L_2(\Omega, R)$.
Some more general notions are discussed by Adomian and Malakian [3].

11.4. SOME REMARKS ON CONVERGENCE

For the equation $\mathcal{F}u = g$, where $\mathcal{F}$ is a nonlinear stochastic operator, we write a formal solution as $u = \mathcal{F}^{-1}g$. Now remembering that we are solving *real-world* applications (physical systems), we decompose the solution $\mathcal{F}^{-1}g$ into components $\mathcal{F}_i^{-1}g$ to be determined with $\sum_{i=0}^{\infty} \mathcal{F}_i^{-1}g = \mathcal{F}^{-1}g$. We are *not* expanding in a series hoping to sum it to the solution u. We are *decomposing* u into components to be found just as we might decompose a function into impulses to determine a Green's function. (Thus $f(t) = \int f(\tau)\delta(t - \tau)\,d\tau$, and the response to an impulse is the Green's function.) We then integrate to get the response for the actual input. A rigorous argument is quite difficult and requires a number of conditions just as expansion in a Fourier series requires conditions. Our conditions are natural and satisfied in physical applications. The function we are looking for in the deterministic case is smooth; it does not have jump discontinuities. (In the stochastic case we have an equivalent situation with probability one.) In nature, jump discontinuities are rare. We may have a rapid transition and it has been *mathematically convenient* to represent such a transition as a jump discontinuity. Thus, discontinuities in solutions of hyperbolic equations, or shock waves, should be viewed as merely regions of rapid variation. Such physically realistic solutions should be arrived at by the decomposition method, since no linearization is necessary. Real inputs are bounded and real processes do *not* have δ function correlations. Our methods are intended for real problems, and we will proceed with that in mind. For the applications, it is not necessary to include stringent proofs. Those will appear in mathematics journals.[2]

REFERENCES

1. G. Adomian, "Stochastic Systems," Academic, New York, 1983.
2. G. Adomian, Convergent series solution of nonlinear equations, *J. Comput. Appl. Math.* **11**, No. 2, 225–230 (1984).

[2] These proofs were completed after this book went to press: (1) $f(u) = \sum_{n=0}^{\infty} A_n$ is a convergent series for the analytic function $f(u)$. (2) The solution of $Fu = Lu + f(u) = \xi(x, y, z, t)$, where $L = L_x + L_y + L_z + L_t$ denotes a sum of partial differential operators with respect to x, y, z, t respectively, is uniquely given by the solution obtained by decomposition.

CHAPTER 12

Boundary Conditions

"The universe is strange. It is stranger than you think. It may be stranger than you can think..."

Aldous Huxley

We now briefly consider the possible boundary conditions for differential equations. These equations may be stochastic (or deterministic in the limiting case) and nonlinear (or linear in the limiting case).

When randomness is present in boundary conditions, it can be present not only in the inhomogeneous term of the boundary condition but also in coefficients of the boundary operator. In this case, the boundary operator becomes a stochastic operator.

Nonlinear and coupled boundary conditions have received very little attention and there is no intent here to study these matters exhaustively; essentially we introduce these topics as a basis for further intensive study. We will show that the decomposition method can be applied to boundary operator equations as well as differential to operator equations.[1] Let us look at possibilities.

12.1. LINEAR BOUNDARY CONDITIONS

A general boundary condition at $t = \tau$ can be written in the form $Bu(\tau) = b$, where B is a boundary operator defined, e.g., by $B = d/dt + a$. Thus, $Bu(\tau) = \dot{u}(\tau) + au(\tau) = b$.

Clearly there exist interesting possibilities: b may be constant or even stochastic, and the coefficient a may be stochastic, in which case B is a

---

[1] We consider boundary problems in the same way as initial-value problems, although by using invariant imbedding techniques, appropriate choices of time and space variables can convert all problems to initial-value problems.

stochastic (boundary) operator. In general, we could replace a by $\langle a \rangle +$ $\alpha(t, \omega)$ and b by $\langle b \rangle + \beta(t, \omega)$, where α and β represent zero-mean processes.

For a finite interval $[\tau_1, \tau_2]$ we can write boundary conditions

$$B_1 u(\tau_1) = b_1(\tau_1)$$
$$B_2 u(\tau_2) = b_2(\tau_2)$$

(12.1.1)

suppressing ω if present and where B_2 is not necessarily the same as B_1.

For a stochastic differential equation

$$\mathcal{L} u(t, \omega) = g(t, \omega)$$

(12.1.2)

we can have (now specifically showing stochasticity of the boundary operator by using a script letter)

$$\mathcal{B}_1 u(\tau_1, \omega) = \dot{u}(\tau_1, \omega) + a_1(\tau_1, \omega) u(\tau_1, \omega) = \ell_1(\tau_1, \omega)$$
$$\mathcal{B}_2 u(\tau_2, \omega) = \dot{u}(\tau_2, \omega) + a_2(\tau_2, \omega) u(\tau_2, \omega) = \ell_2((\tau_2, \omega)$$

(12.1.3)

where a_1, a_2, ℓ_1, and ℓ_2 can be written in terms of deterministic and fluctuating components.

In the stochastic differential equation [(12.1.2)] we let $\mathcal{L} = L + \mathcal{R}$, where $L = \langle \mathcal{L} \rangle$ or if necessary to ensure invertibility as previously discussed, $\mathcal{L} = L + R + \mathcal{R}$, where L is now invertible. We obtain the solution u by decomposition or more specifically the n-term approximation $\phi_n = \sum_{i=0}^{n-1} u_i$. This solution has in the u_0 term the homogeneous solution (of $Lu = 0$) (which we can indicate by u_h) as well as the $L^{-1}g$ term. If $L = d^2/dt^2$, for example, $u_h = c_1 + c_2 t$. Then $Bu(t) = \dot{u} + au = c_2 + a(c_1 + c_2 t) + Bu_p$.

12.2. TREATMENT OF INHOMOGENEOUS BOUNDARY CONDITIONS

Consider a simple differential equation $Lu = g$ such as $d^2 u/dt^2 = g(t)$ with inhomogeneous boundary conditions $u(0) = a$ and $u(1) = b$. A convenient procedure is to reduce the problem to one with homogeneous boundary conditions in the following manner. Write $u = u_1 + u_2$, where u_1 is the solution of the *inhomogeneous* equation $Lu_1 = g$ with *homogeneous* boundary conditions $u_1(0) = u_1(1) = 0$ and where u_2 is the solution of the *homogeneous* equation $Lu_2 = 0$ with *inhomogeneous* boundary conditions $u_2(0) = a$, and $u_2(1) = b$.

For this problem with $Lu = g$ and general boundary conditions $B_1(u) = b_1$ and $B_2(u) = b_2$, the solution u_1 of $Lu_1 = g$ is given by

$$u_1 = \int_0^1 G(t, \tau) g(\tau)\, d\tau$$
$$B_1(u_1) = B_2(u_1) = 0$$

(12.2.1)

where G is the Green's function and the solution u_2 of $Lu_2 = 0$ is given by:

$$u_2 = c_1 t + c_2$$
$$u_2(0) = b_1, \qquad u_2(1) = b_2 \tag{12.2.2}$$

for $L = d^2/dt^2$. We have referred to u_2 as u_h and u_1 as u_p. Thus, it is clear that u_h is evaluated with the conditions $B_1(u_h) = b_1$ and $B_2(u_h) = b_2$, thus fixing the constants c_1, c_2, and that u_p is evaluated with $B_1(u_p) = 0$ and $B_2(u_p) = 0$. Consider a very elementary example given by

$$d^2u/dx^2 = -\pi^2 \sin \pi x$$

$$u(0) = u(1) = 0$$

$$u = c_1 + c_2 x - \pi^2 L^{-1} \sin \pi x$$

The homogeneous solution satisfies $u(0) = u(1) = 0$, which requires $c_1 = c_2 = 0$. Now

$$u = -\pi^2 L^{-1} \sin \pi x$$

$$u = -\sin \pi x$$

is the solution, and it satisfies the boundary conditions.

EXERCISES

1. Consider $d^2u/dt^2 = e^{-t}$ with $u(0) = 1$ and $u'(0) = -1$. Show that the homogeneous solution satisfies the initial (inhomogeneous) condition, that the particular integral $L^{-1}e^{-t}$ satisfies the inhomogeneous condition, and, of course, that the complete solution satisfies the condition. (Note: the entire solution obtained here is simply our u_0 term in more complicated problems where we add terms $\mathscr{R}u + \mathscr{N}u$ to the left-hand side.)

We can also consider combined boundary conditions: By this we will mean that boundary values at the endpoints b_1 and b_2 of the interval $[b_1, b_2]$ are combined in the same boundary condition equation. Thus, if we have $Ly(t) = x(t)$ on $b_1 \leq t \leq b_2$ and are given the boundary equation

$$k_1 y(b_1) + k_2 y(b_2) = \beta$$

we have combined boundary conditions as opposed to coupled boundary conditions, which means that solutions are coupled in boundary-condition equations such as

$$\dot{u}(b_1) + k_1 u(b_1) + k_2 v(b_1) = \beta_1$$

Caution: The integrals are from 0 to t and must be evaluated at both limits each time.

2. Take $u(t) = f(t)$ using any $f(t)$ and writing the condition $u(0) = f(0)$. Write $u' = df(t)/dt$. Now we have a differential equation

$$du/dt = df(t)/dt$$

i.e., $L = d/dt$. Then $L^{-1} = \int_0^t [\ ]\, dt$. Hence,

$$\int_0^t \frac{du}{dt}\, dt = \int_0^t \frac{df(t)}{dt}\, dt$$

$$u(t) - u(0) = f(t)$$

$$u(t) = u(0) + f(t)$$

Check satisfaction of the conditions written from the original solution. Do the same for u'' and L^{-1} as the appropriate double integral. Add a linear term to u' or u'' and proceed by decomposition. Add a nonlinear term such as u^3 or $\sinh u$ to the left-hand side and repeat.

12.3. GENERAL BOUNDARY OPERATORS AND MATRIX EQUATIONS

Consider now a more general boundary operator given by $B = d/dt + a$ and $L = d^2/dt^2$, we have

$$du_h/dt + au_h = b$$

$$(d/dt)(c_1 + c_2 t) + a(c_1 + c_2 t) = b \tag{12.3.1}$$

As a special case where $B_1 u = u$ and $B_2 u = u$, we consider $u(0) = a$ and $u(1) = b$, and find that $c_1 = a$ and $c_2 = b - a$. Initial conditions or boundary conditions are handled the same way.

For $L = d^2/dt^2$ or $u_h = c_1 + c_2 t$ and $B_1 u(\tau_1) = (d/dt_1)u(\tau_1) + a_1 u(\tau_1) = b_1$ and $B_2 u(\tau_2) = (d/dt_2)u(\tau_2) + a_2 u(\tau_2) = b_2$. We have

$$B_1 u(\tau_1) = c_2 + a_1(c_1 + c_2 \tau_1) = b_1$$

$$B_2 u(\tau_2) = c_2 + a_2(c_1 + c_2 \tau_2) = b_2$$

or

$$\begin{pmatrix} a_1 & 1 + \tau_1 a_1 \\ a_2 & 1 + \tau_2 a_2 \end{pmatrix} \cdot \begin{pmatrix} c_1 \\ c_2 \end{pmatrix} = \begin{pmatrix} b_1 \\ b_2 \end{pmatrix} \tag{12.3.2}$$

REMARK: Regarding the matrix inversion above, if we have the matrix equation

$$AY = X$$

where X and Y are column vectors and A is a matrix such that matrix products are defined and $|A| \neq 0$ then formally $Y = A^{-1}X$. We can always decompose the matrix A into $\Lambda + \Lambda_0$, where $|\Lambda| \neq 0$ and Λ^{-1} is easily found. Then

$$(\Lambda + \Lambda_0)^{-1} \simeq \sum_{n=0}^{v} (-1)^n (\Lambda^{-1}\Lambda_0)^n \Lambda^{-1}$$

where $v \ll \infty$, i.e., a few terms (perhaps three to five or six) can yield an excellent approximation. Here Λ is analogous to the operator L in decomposing differential operators.

12.4. RANDOM BOUNDARY OPERATORS

Suppose we have randomness present. Then

$$\mathscr{B}_1 u(\tau_1) = c_2 + a_1(c_1 + c_2\tau_1) = \ell_1$$
$$\mathscr{B}_2 u(\tau_2) = c_2 + a_2(c_1 + c_2\tau_2) = \ell_2$$

or

$$a_1 c_1 + (1 + \tau_1 a_1)c_2 = \ell_1$$
$$a_2 c_1 + (1 + \tau_2 a_2)c_2 = \ell_2$$

and finally

$$\langle a_1 \rangle c_1 + (1 + \tau_1 \langle a_1 \rangle)c_2 + \alpha_1(c_1 + \tau_1 c_2) = \langle \ell_1 \rangle + \beta_1$$
$$\langle a_2 \rangle c_1 + (1 + \tau_2 \langle a_2 \rangle)c_2 + \alpha_2(c_1 + \tau_2 c_2) = \langle \ell_2 \rangle + \beta_2 \tag{12.4.1}$$

or

$$\begin{pmatrix} \langle a_1 \rangle & 1 + \tau_1\langle a_1 \rangle \\ \langle a_2 \rangle & 1 + \tau_2\langle a_2 \rangle \end{pmatrix} \cdot \begin{pmatrix} c_1 \\ c_2 \end{pmatrix} + \begin{pmatrix} \alpha_1 & \tau_1\alpha_1 \\ \alpha_2 & \tau_2\alpha_2 \end{pmatrix} \cdot \begin{pmatrix} c_1 \\ c_2 \end{pmatrix} = \begin{pmatrix} \langle b_1 \rangle \\ \langle b_2 \rangle \end{pmatrix} + \begin{pmatrix} \beta_1 \\ \beta_2 \end{pmatrix}$$

If the α's and β's are zero, then the second term on both sides vanishes. If not, the processes α_1, α_2, β_1, and β_2 must be specified statistically by giving some statistical measures such as correlation, and variance.

It appears generally preferable to combine the matrices by writing

$$\begin{pmatrix} \langle a_1 \rangle + \alpha_1 & 1 + \tau_1\langle a_1 \rangle + \tau_1\alpha_1 \\ \langle a_2 \rangle + \alpha_2 & 1 + \tau_2\langle a_2 \rangle + \tau_2\alpha_2 \end{pmatrix} \cdot \begin{pmatrix} c_1 \\ c_2 \end{pmatrix} = \begin{pmatrix} \langle b_1 \rangle + \beta_1 \\ \langle b_2 \rangle + \beta_2 \end{pmatrix}$$

since the inversion will be accomplished by making the most convenient decomposition of the matrix by multiplying the column vector of c_1 and c_2. If stochasticity occurs only in the matrix on the right-hand side (i.e., the α's vanish or the a's are constants), the inversion is carried out as before and we have

$$\begin{pmatrix} c_1 \\ c_2 \end{pmatrix} = \begin{pmatrix} a_1 & 1 + \tau_1 a_1 \\ a_2 & 1 + \tau_2 a_2 \end{pmatrix}^{-1} \cdot \begin{pmatrix} b_1 \\ b_2 \end{pmatrix}$$

There, since b_1 and b_2 are stochastic, c_1 and c_2 also are stochastic and therefore in a stochastic problem, these quantities must be specified with appropriate statistics. In the general case with the coefficient a stochastic as well, we have a stochastic operator equation (since the boundary operator is a stochastic operator) and even if we have nonlinear terms, we can solve by decomposition and then average (or multiply the average for correlations). Then, having statistics of the given quantities, we find the needed statistics.

12.5.   RANDOM INHOMOGENEOUS BOUNDARY CONDITIONS

Let us abstract the procedure to the stochastic case. If we solve $Lu = 0$, where L is second-order, $u = c_1 \phi_1(t) + c_2 \phi_2(t)$. The boundary conditions are given by

$$B_1 u(t) = \mathscr{L}_{\tau_1} u(\tau_1) = b_1$$

$$B_2 u(t) = \mathscr{L}_{\tau_2} u(\tau_2) = b_2$$

The operators $\mathscr{L}_{\tau_1}$, and $\mathscr{L}_{\tau_2}$ can be

$$\mathscr{L}_{\tau_1} = L_{\tau_1} + \mathscr{R}_{\tau_1} \qquad \text{or} \qquad L_{\tau_1} + R_{\tau_1}$$

$$\mathscr{L}_{\tau_2} = L_{\tau_2} + \mathscr{R}_{\tau_2} \qquad \text{or} \qquad L_{\tau_2} + R_{\tau_2}$$

i.e., we can have the stochastic $\mathscr{R}$ or the deterministic R,

$$L_{\tau_1} = \frac{d}{d\tau_1, L_{\tau_2}} = d/d\tau_2.$$

The boundary conditions are linear stochastic operator equations, and the solutions can be written immediately. Let us suppose the u_0 terms for L_{τ_1} and L_{τ_2} are zero for simplicity. Then

$$u(\tau_1) = \mathscr{L}_{\tau_1}^{-1} b_1 = (L_{\tau_1} + \mathscr{R}_{\tau_1})^{-1} b_1$$

$$= \sum_{v=0}^{n} (-1)^n (L_{\tau_1}^{-1} \mathscr{R}_{\tau_1})^n L_{\tau_1}^{-1} b_1$$

$$u(\tau_2) = \sum_{v=0}^{n} (-1)^n (L_{\tau_2}^{-1} \mathscr{R}_{\tau_2})^n L_{\tau_2}^{-1} b_2$$

Since we also have

$$u(\tau_1) = c_1\phi_1(\tau_1) + c_2\phi_2(\tau_1)$$

$$u(\tau_2) = c_1\phi_1(\tau_2) + c_2\phi_2(\tau_2)$$

$$\begin{pmatrix} u(\tau_1) \\ u(\tau_2) \end{pmatrix} = \begin{pmatrix} \phi_1(\tau_1) & \phi_2(\tau_1) \\ \phi_1(\tau_2) & \phi_2(\tau_2) \end{pmatrix} \cdot \begin{pmatrix} c_1 \\ c_2 \end{pmatrix} = \begin{pmatrix} \mathscr{L}_{\tau_1}^{-1}b_1 \\ \mathscr{L}_{\tau_1}^{-1}b_2 \end{pmatrix}$$

The matrix multiplying the column vector of c_1, c_2 will be called Λ, and we write

$$U = \Lambda_C \quad \text{or} \quad C = \Lambda^{-1}U$$

if $|\Lambda| \neq 0$. Of course, the nonvanishing of the determinant of the Λ matrix is a necessary condition.

The Λ^{-1} matrix is

$$\begin{pmatrix} \phi_2(\tau_2)/|\Lambda| & -\phi_2(\tau_1)/|\Lambda| \\ -\phi_1(\tau_2)/|\Lambda| & \phi_1(\tau_1)/|\Lambda| \end{pmatrix}$$

and

$$\begin{pmatrix} c_1 \\ c_2 \end{pmatrix} = \begin{pmatrix} \phi_2(\tau_2)/|\Lambda| & -\phi_2(\tau_1)/|\Lambda| \\ -\phi_1(\tau_2)/|\Lambda| & \phi_1(\tau_1)/|\Lambda| \end{pmatrix} \cdot \begin{pmatrix} L_{\tau_1}^{-1}b_1 \\ L_{\tau_2}^{-1}b_2 \end{pmatrix}$$

12.6. LINEAR DIFFERENTIAL EQUATIONS WITH LINEAR BOUNDARY CONDITIONS

Consider the example given by $Lu = 0$, where $L = d^2/dt^2$. Thus, $u = c_1 + c_2t$. The boundary conditions are

$$B_1u(\tau_1) = (d/d\tau_1 + 1)u(\tau_1) + \alpha u(\tau_1) = b_1$$

$$B_2u(\tau_2) = (d/d\tau_2 + 1)u(\tau_2) + \beta u(\tau_2) = b_2$$

Thus

$$\dot{u}(\tau_1) + u(\tau_1) + \alpha u(\tau_1) = b_1$$

$$\dot{u}(\tau_2) + u(\tau_2) + \beta u(\tau_2) = b_2$$

Then

$$B_1u(\tau_1) = B_1(c_1 + c_2\tau_1)$$
$$= c_2 + c_1 + c_2\tau_1 + \alpha(c_1 + c_2\tau_1) = b_1$$

$$B_2u(\tau_2) = B_2(c_1 + c_2\tau_2)$$
$$= c_2 + c_1 + c_2\tau_2 + \beta(c_1 + c_2\tau_2) = b_2$$

and

$$c_1(1 + \alpha) + c_2(1 + \tau_1 + \alpha\tau_1) = b_1$$

$$c_1(1 + \beta) + c_2(1 + \tau_2 + \beta\tau_2) = b_2$$

thus giving us the matrix equation

$$\begin{pmatrix} 1 + \alpha & 1 + \tau_1 + \alpha\tau_1 \\ 1 + \beta & 1 + \tau_2 + \beta\tau_2 \end{pmatrix} \cdot \begin{pmatrix} c_1 \\ c_2 \end{pmatrix} = \begin{pmatrix} b_1 \\ b_2 \end{pmatrix}$$

Consequently,

$$\begin{pmatrix} c_1 \\ c_2 \end{pmatrix} = \begin{pmatrix} 1 + \alpha & 1 + \tau_1 + \alpha\tau_1 \\ 1 + \beta & 1 + \tau_2 + \beta\tau_2 \end{pmatrix}^{-1} \cdot \begin{pmatrix} b_1 \\ b_2 \end{pmatrix}$$

To invert the coefficient matrix, we write it as

$$\begin{pmatrix} 1 & \tau_1 + 1 \\ 1 & \tau_2 + 1 \end{pmatrix} + \begin{pmatrix} \alpha & \alpha\tau_1 \\ \beta & \beta\tau_2 \end{pmatrix}$$

Choose $\alpha = \frac{1}{4}$, $\beta = \frac{1}{6}$, $\tau_1 = 1$, and $\tau_2 = 2$. Now

$$\Lambda = \begin{pmatrix} 1 & 2 \\ 1 & 3 \end{pmatrix}$$

EXERCISE

1. Complete the problem to evaluate

$$\begin{pmatrix} c_1 \\ c_2 \end{pmatrix} = (\Lambda + \Lambda_0)^{-1} \begin{pmatrix} b_1 \\ b_2 \end{pmatrix} = \sum_n (-1)^n (\Lambda^{-1}\Lambda_0)^n \Lambda^{-1} \begin{pmatrix} b_1 \\ b_2 \end{pmatrix}$$

(If $|\Lambda| \neq 0$ the inverse exists.)

EXAMPLE: Consider the equation $Lu = 0$ with $L = d^2/dt^2$. The solution is $u = c_1 + c_2 t$. The conditions are

$$B_1 u(t)|_{t=\tau_1} = \frac{du(t)}{dt}\bigg|_{t=\tau_1} + a_1 u(t)\bigg|_{t=\tau_1} = b_1(t)\bigg|_{t=\tau_2}$$

$$B_2 u(t)|_{t=\tau_2} = \frac{du(t)}{dt}\bigg|_{t=\tau_2} + a_2 u(t)\bigg|_{t=\tau_2} = b_2(t)\bigg|_{t=\tau_2}$$

We can write these as

$$Lu + a_1 u = b_1 \qquad \text{at} \quad t = \tau_1$$

$$Lu + a_2 u = b_2 \qquad \text{at} \quad t = \tau_2$$

where the L operators become $\mathscr{L}$ in the stochastic case, i.e., generally,

$$\mathscr{L}_{\tau_1}u(\tau_1) + a_1 u(\tau_1) = b_1(\tau_1)$$

$$\mathscr{L}_{\tau_2}u(\tau_2) + a_2 u(\tau_2) = b_2(\tau_2)$$

Consider the deterministic case with $L = d/dt$. Since $u = c_1 + c_2 t$, we get

$$c_2 + a_1(c_1 + c_2\tau_1) = b_1$$

$$c_2 + a_2(c_1 + c_2\tau_2) = b_2$$

or

$$\begin{pmatrix} a_1 & 1 + a_1\tau_1 \\ a_2 & 1 + a_2\tau_2 \end{pmatrix} \cdot \begin{pmatrix} c_1 \\ c_2 \end{pmatrix} + \begin{pmatrix} b_1 \\ b_2 \end{pmatrix}$$

Let us write this as $\Lambda C = B$. Then $C = \Lambda^{-1}B$ or

$$\begin{pmatrix} c_1 \\ c_2 \end{pmatrix} = \Lambda^{-1} \begin{pmatrix} b_1 \\ b_2 \end{pmatrix}$$

where

$$\Lambda^{-1} = \begin{pmatrix} (1 + a_2\tau_2)/\det \Lambda & -(1 + a_1\tau_1)/\det \Lambda \\ -a_2/\det \Lambda & a_1/\det \Lambda \end{pmatrix}$$

In solving boundary equations such as

$$du(\tau_1)/d\tau_1 + u(\tau_1) = b_1$$

$$du(\tau_2)/d\tau_2 + u(\tau_2) = b_2$$

it is worth noting that the inverse or asymptotic decomposition technique may be useful at this point, e.g.,

$$u(\tau_1) = b_1 - du(\tau_1)/d\tau_1$$

$$u(\tau_2) = b_2 - du(\tau_2)/d\tau_2$$

If the solution of the operator equation is $u = c_1 + c_2 t$, then

$$c_1 + c_2\tau_1 = b_1 - \frac{d}{d\tau_1}(c_1 + c_2\tau_1) = b_1 - c_2$$

$$c_1 + c_2\tau_2 = b_2 - \frac{d}{d\tau_2}(c_1 + c_2\tau_2) = b_2 - c_2$$

$$c_1 + c_2(1 + \tau_1) = b_1$$

$$c_1 + c_2(1 + \tau_2) = b_2$$

$$\begin{pmatrix} 1 & 1 + \tau_1 \\ 1 & 1 + \tau_2 \end{pmatrix} \cdot \begin{pmatrix} c_1 \\ c_2 \end{pmatrix} = \begin{pmatrix} b_1 \\ b_2 \end{pmatrix}$$

thus evaluating c_1 and c_2.

EXERCISE

1. Consider the linear equation $Lu = 0$, where $L = d^2/dt^2$ and $u = c_1 + c_2 t$. The boundary conditions are given by

$$B_1 u(t)|_{\tau_1} = b_1, \qquad B_2 u(t)|_{\tau_2} = b_2$$

Substitute $u = c_1 + c_2 t$ into the conditions and solve completely for various forms of Bu such as $\dot{u}(t) + au(t) = b$ or simply $u(t) = b$.

EXAMPLE: Consider the second-order linear deterministic homogeneous equation

$$\frac{d^2u}{dt^2} + \alpha_1 \frac{du}{dt} + \alpha_2 u = 0$$

Let us assume first-order linear deterministic boundary operator equations for arbitrary τ_1 and τ_2 (where $\tau_1 \neq \tau_2$)

$$\frac{d}{d\tau_1} u(\tau_1) + \beta_1 u(\tau_1) = b_1$$

$$\frac{d}{d\tau_2} u(\tau_2) + \beta_2 u(\tau_2) = b_2$$

Solve the given differential equation for $d^2u/dt^2 \equiv Lu$. The homogeneous solution is $u = c_1 \phi_1(t) + c_2 \phi_2(t)$. [Assume $L_{\tau_1}^{-1} L_{\tau_1} u(\tau_1) = u(\tau_1)$, i.e., there is no constant, and $L_{\tau_2}^{-1} L_{\tau_2} u(\tau_2) = u(\tau_2)$.] Solve the boundary condition equations for $u(\tau_1)$ and $u(\tau_2)$. Then

$$c_1 \phi_1(\tau_1) + c_2 \phi_2(\tau_1) = u(\tau_1) = L_{\tau_1}^{-1} b_1 - L_{\tau_1}^{-1} \beta_1 (c_1 \phi_1(\tau_1) + c_2 \phi_2(\tau_1))$$

$$c_1 \phi_1(\tau_2) + c_2 \phi_2(\tau_2) = u(\tau_2) = L_{\tau_2}^{-1} b_2 - L_{\tau_2}^{-1} \beta_2 (c_1 \phi_1(\tau_2) + c_2 \phi_2(\tau_2))$$

or

$$\begin{pmatrix} \phi_1(\tau_1) & \phi_2(\tau_1) \\ \phi_1(\tau_2) & \phi_2(\tau_2) \end{pmatrix} \cdot \begin{pmatrix} c_1 \\ c_2 \end{pmatrix} = \begin{pmatrix} u(\tau_1) \\ u(\tau_2) \end{pmatrix}$$

EXAMPLE: Consider the second-order (linear deterministic) differential equation

$$d^2u/dt^2 = 0$$

We write the solution $u(t) = c_1 + c_2 t$ and consider boundary conditions. Suppose these are given by

$$u(\tau_1) = c_1 + c_2\tau_1 = b_1$$
$$u(\tau_2) = c_1 + c_2\tau_2 = b_2.$$

We get

$$\begin{pmatrix} 1 & \tau_1 \\ 1 & \tau_2 \end{pmatrix} \cdot \begin{pmatrix} c_1 \\ c_2 \end{pmatrix} = \begin{pmatrix} b_1 \\ b_2 \end{pmatrix}$$

or

$$\Lambda C = B$$

in matrix notation, hence, $C = \Lambda^{-1} B$ gives us c_1 and c_2.

Suppose the boundary conditions are given by

$$\frac{d}{d\tau_1} u(\tau_1) = b_1, \qquad u(\tau_2) = b_2$$

We have now

$$c_2 = b_1, \qquad c_1 + c_2\tau_2 = b_2$$

or

$$\begin{pmatrix} 0 & 1 \\ 1 & \tau_2 \end{pmatrix} \cdot \begin{pmatrix} c_1 \\ c_2 \end{pmatrix} = \begin{pmatrix} b_1 \\ b_2 \end{pmatrix}$$

again in the form $\Lambda C = B$. Since Λ^{-1} is given by

$$\begin{pmatrix} \tau_2/(-1) & -1/(-1) \\ -1/(-1) & 0/(-1) \end{pmatrix}$$

We arrive at $c_1 = -b_1\tau_2 + b_2$ and $c_2 = b_1$.

Note that if the second condition is $(d/d\tau_2)u(\tau_2) = b_2$, we have an ill-posed problem since $\dot{u}(t) = c_2$, but $b_1 \neq b_2$.

If the conditions are $u(\tau_1) = b_1$ and $(d/d\tau_2)u(\tau_2) = b_2$, we have $c_1 + c_2\tau_1 = b_1$ and $c_2 = b_2$. Then

$$\begin{pmatrix} 1 & \tau_1 \\ 0 & 1 \end{pmatrix} \cdot \begin{pmatrix} c_1 \\ c_2 \end{pmatrix} = \begin{pmatrix} b_1 \\ b_2 \end{pmatrix}$$

and

$$\begin{pmatrix} c_1 \\ c_2 \end{pmatrix} = \begin{pmatrix} 1 & -\tau_1 \\ 0 & 1 \end{pmatrix} \cdot \begin{pmatrix} b_1 \\ b_2 \end{pmatrix}$$

so that $c_1 = b_1 - \tau_1 b_2$, and $c_2 = b_2$.

Returning to the first example

$$\Lambda = \begin{pmatrix} 1 & \tau_1 \\ 1 & \tau_2 \end{pmatrix}$$

the determinant of Λ is given by det Λ or $|\Lambda|$ where

$$|\Lambda| = \tau_2 - \tau_1$$

This determinant (evaluated, of course, for the particular boundary conditions) is of general importance since it is used to get Λ^{-1} and thus evaluate the c's for the possible boundary conditions whether linear, nonlinear, stochastic, etc. For the above case

$$\Lambda^{-1} = \begin{pmatrix} \dfrac{\tau_2}{\tau_2 - \tau_1} & \dfrac{-\tau_1}{\tau_2 - \tau_1} \\ \dfrac{-1}{\tau_2 - \tau_1} & \dfrac{1}{\tau_2 - \tau_1} \end{pmatrix}$$

$$\begin{pmatrix} c_1 \\ c_2 \end{pmatrix} = \Lambda^{-1} \begin{pmatrix} b_1 \\ b_2 \end{pmatrix}$$

and it is easy to see what happens to the c's by letting boundary conditions become homogeneous or changing the interval.

Suppose for the same solution $u(t) = c_1 + c_2 t$ we have

$$\dot{u}(\tau_1) + \alpha_1 u(\tau_1) = b_1, \qquad u(\tau_2) = b_2$$

Then

$$c_2 + \alpha_1 c_1 + \alpha_1 c_2 \tau_1 = b_1$$
$$c_1 + c_2 \tau_2 = b_2$$

or

$$\begin{pmatrix} \alpha_1 & 1 + \alpha_1 \tau_1 \\ 1 & \tau_2 \end{pmatrix} \cdot \begin{pmatrix} c_1 \\ c_2 \end{pmatrix} = \begin{pmatrix} b_1 \\ b_2 \end{pmatrix}$$

The inverse of Λ is

$$\begin{pmatrix} \tau_2/|\Lambda| & (-1 - \alpha_1 \tau_1)/|\Lambda| \\ -1/|\Lambda| & \alpha_1/|\Lambda| \end{pmatrix}$$

and the determinant of Λ is

$$|\Lambda| = \alpha_1\tau_2 - 1 - \alpha_1\tau_1$$
$$= \alpha_1(\tau_2 - \tau_1) - 1$$

EXERCISES

1. Suppose $u(\tau_1) = b_1$ and $\dot{u}(\tau_2) + \alpha_2 u(\tau_2) = b_2$, show that

$$\Lambda^{-1} = \begin{pmatrix} \dfrac{1 + \alpha_2\tau_2}{|\Lambda|} & \dfrac{-\tau_1}{|\Lambda|} \\ \dfrac{-\alpha_2}{|\Lambda|} & \dfrac{1}{|\Lambda|} \end{pmatrix}$$

and

$$|\Lambda| = 1 + \alpha_2\tau_2 - \alpha_2\tau_1 = 1 + \alpha_2(\tau_2 - \tau_1)$$

2. Given $\dot{u}(\tau_1) + \alpha_1 u(\tau_1) = b_1$ and $\dot{u}(\tau_2) + \alpha_2 u(\tau_2) = b_2$ show that

$$\Lambda = \begin{pmatrix} \alpha_1 & 1 + \alpha_1\tau_1 \\ \alpha_2 & 1 + \alpha_2\tau_2 \end{pmatrix}$$

$$\Lambda^{-1} = \begin{pmatrix} \dfrac{1 + \alpha_2\tau_2}{|\Lambda|} & \dfrac{-1 - \alpha_1\tau_1}{|\Lambda|} \\ \dfrac{-\alpha_2}{|\Lambda|} & \dfrac{\alpha_1}{|\Lambda|} \end{pmatrix}$$

EXAMPLE: For $u = c_1 + c_2 t$ let us consider combined boundary conditions

$$u(\tau_1) = \alpha_1 u(\tau_2) = b_1$$
$$u(\tau_2) = \alpha_2 u(\tau_2) = b_2$$

Here values at both boundaries are in both boundary equations. Substitution of $c_1 + c_2 t$ yields

$$c_1 + c_2\tau_1 + \alpha_1 c_1 + \alpha_1 c_2\tau_1 = b_1$$
$$c_1 + c_2\tau_2 + \alpha_2 c_1 + \alpha_2 c_2\tau_2 = b_2$$

or $C = \Lambda B$, where

$$\Lambda = \begin{pmatrix} 1 + \alpha_1 & \tau_1 + \alpha_1\tau_1 \\ 1 + \alpha_2 & \tau_2 + \alpha_2\tau_2 \end{pmatrix}$$

and c_1 and c_2 are now easily calculated.

EXAMPLE: Consider $d^2u/dt^2 + k^2u = 0$ which gives us $u(t) = c_1 \cos kt + (c_2/k) \sin kt$. Suppose the conditions given are simply $u(\tau_1) = b_1$ and $u(\tau_2) = b_2$. Then,

$$c_1 \cos k\tau_1 + (c_2/k) \sin k\tau_1 = b_1$$

$$c_1 \cos k\tau_2 + (c_2/k) \sin k\tau_2 = b_2$$

$$\begin{pmatrix} \cos k\tau_1 & \dfrac{\sin k\tau_1}{k} \\ \cos k\tau_2 & \dfrac{\sin k\tau_2}{k} \end{pmatrix} \cdot \begin{pmatrix} c_1 \\ c_2 \end{pmatrix} = \begin{pmatrix} b_1 \\ b_2 \end{pmatrix}$$

and the c's are found from $C = \Lambda^{-1}B$ where

$$\Lambda^{-1} = \begin{pmatrix} \dfrac{\sin k\tau_2}{\sin k(\tau_2 - \tau_1)} & \dfrac{-\sin k\tau_1}{\sin k(\tau_2 - \tau_1)} \\ \dfrac{-k \cos k\tau_2}{\sin k(\tau_2 - \tau_1)} & \dfrac{k \cos k\tau_1}{\sin k(\tau_2 - \tau_1)} \end{pmatrix}$$

where $\tau_2 \neq \tau_1$ and otherwise τ_1 and τ_2 are arbitrary.

EXERCISE

1. For $d^2y/dt^2 = 5$ write $y(t)$ and using boundary conditions $y(\tau_1) = b_1$ and $y(\tau_2) = b_2$, show that

$$\Lambda = \begin{pmatrix} 1 & \tau_1 \\ 1 & \tau_2 \end{pmatrix}$$

$$\Lambda^{-1} = \begin{pmatrix} \dfrac{\tau_2}{\tau_2 - \tau_1} - 1 & \dfrac{-\tau_1}{\tau_2 - \tau_1} \\ \dfrac{-1}{\tau_2 - \tau_1} & \dfrac{1}{\tau_2 - \tau_1} \end{pmatrix}$$

EXAMPLE: Consider the linear deterministic equation $Lu = 0$ with L specified as a general differential operator (not just the highest-ordered term). Then $Lu = 0$ yields

$$u = c_1\phi_1(t) + c_2\phi_2(t)$$

The boundary conditions are

$$B_1u(t)|_{\tau_1} = \frac{d}{dt}u|_{\tau_1} + a_1u|_{\tau_1} = b_1$$

$$B_2u(t)|_{\tau_2} = \frac{d}{dt}u|_{\tau_2} + a_2u|_{\tau_2} = b_2$$

Therefore,

$$\frac{d}{dt}\{c_1\phi_1(t) + c_2\phi_2(t)\}|_{\tau_1} + a_1\{c_1\phi_1(t) + c_2\phi_2(t)\}|_{\tau_1} = b_1$$

$$\frac{d}{dt}\{c_1\phi_1(t) + c_2\phi_2(t)\}|_{\tau_2} + a_2\{c_1\phi_1(t) + c_2\phi_2(t)\}|_{\tau_2} = b_2$$

or

$$c_1\dot{\phi}_1(\tau_1) + c_2\dot{\phi}_2(\tau_1) + a_1c_1\phi_1(\tau_1) + a_1c_2\phi_2(\tau_1) = b_1$$

$$c_1\dot{\phi}_1(\tau_2) + c_2\dot{\phi}_2(\tau_2) + a_2c_1\phi_1(\tau_2) + a_2c_2\phi_2(\tau_2) = b_2$$

thus yielding

$$\begin{pmatrix} \dot{\phi}_1(\tau_1) + a_1\phi_1(\tau_1) & \dot{\phi}_2(\tau_1) + a_1\phi_2(\tau_1) \\ \dot{\phi}_1(\tau_2) + a_2\phi_1(\tau_2) & \dot{\phi}_2(\tau_2) + a_2\phi_2(\tau_2) \end{pmatrix} \cdot \begin{pmatrix} c_1 \\ c_2 \end{pmatrix} = \begin{pmatrix} b_1 \\ b_2 \end{pmatrix}$$

If we designate by D the determinant of the coefficient (matrix) of the column vector of c_1 and C_2, i.e., the determinant of the matrix we call Λ, then

$$\begin{pmatrix} c_1 \\ c_2 \end{pmatrix} = \Lambda^{-1}\begin{pmatrix} b_1 \\ b_2 \end{pmatrix}$$

where Λ^{-1} is given by

$$\begin{pmatrix} \dfrac{\dot{\phi}_2(\tau_2) + a_2\phi_2(\tau_2)}{D} & \dfrac{-\dot{\phi}_2(\tau_1) - a_1\phi_2(\tau_1)}{D} \\[2ex] \dfrac{-\dot{\phi}_1(\tau_2) - a_2\phi_1(\tau_2)}{D} & \dfrac{\dot{\phi}_1(\tau_1) + a_1\phi_1(\tau_1)}{D} \end{pmatrix}$$

12.7. DETERMINISTIC OPERATOR EQUATIONS WITH RANDOM INPUT AND RANDOM BOUNDARY CONDITIONS

Consider a deterministic operator equation with random input $g(t, \omega)$ given by

$$Lu = g(t, \omega), \qquad L = d^2/dt^2$$

on an interval $[\tau_1, \tau_2]$ with stochastic boundary operator conditions, and random inhomogeneous terms given by

$$B_1u|_{t=\tau_1} = \dot{u}(\tau_1, \omega) + a_1(\tau_1, \omega)u(\tau_1, \omega) = b_1(\tau_1, \omega)$$

$$B_2u|_{t=\tau_2} = \dot{u}(\tau_2, \omega) + a_2(\tau_2, \omega)u(\tau_2, \omega) = b_2(\tau_2, \omega)$$

Written more simply, and suppressing ω, we have

$$B_1u = \dot{u}(\tau_1) + a_1u(\tau_1) = b_1$$
$$B_2u = \dot{u}(\tau_2) + a_2u(\tau_2) = b_2$$

Since $L = d^2/dt^2$, the homogeneous solution (of $Lu = 0$) is $u_h = c_1 + c_2 t$. The particular integral u_p is given by $u_p = L^{-1}g$. Writing

$$B_1 u_h = b_1, \qquad B_2 u_h = b_2$$

we have

$$c_2 + a_1(c_1 + c_2 t_1)|_{\tau_1} = b_1$$

$$c_2 + a_2(c_1 + c_2 t)|_{\tau_1} = b_2$$

or

$$c_2 + a_1(c_1 + c_2 \tau_1) = b_1$$

$$c_2 + a_2(c_1 + c_2 \tau_2) = b_2$$

if a_1 and a_2 are constants. Suppose they are not. Then assuming a_1 and a_2 are stochastic processes in the most general case, we let $a_1 = \langle a_1 \rangle + \alpha_1(t, \omega)$ and $a_2 = \langle a_2 \rangle + \alpha_2(t, \omega)$. Substituting these into the boundary conditions and writing the two equations as a matrix equation,

$$\begin{pmatrix} \langle a_1 \rangle & 1 + \tau_1 \langle a_1 \rangle \\ \langle a_2 \rangle & 1 + \tau_2 \langle a_2 \rangle \end{pmatrix} \cdot \begin{pmatrix} c_1 \\ c_2 \end{pmatrix} + \begin{pmatrix} \alpha_1 & \tau_1 \alpha_1 \\ \alpha_2 & \tau_2 \alpha_2 \end{pmatrix} \cdot \begin{pmatrix} c_1 \\ c_2 \end{pmatrix} = \begin{pmatrix} \langle b_1 \rangle + \beta_1 \\ \langle b_2 \rangle + \beta_2 \end{pmatrix}$$

This is in the matrix form $LC + RC = B$ which can be solved as we do scalar equations by writing

$$LC = B - RC \qquad C = L^{-1}B - L^{-1}RC$$

letting $C = \sum_{n=0}^{\infty} C_n$, i.e., a sum of component vectors, letting $C_0 = L^{-1}B$, and writing

$$\sum_{n=0}^{\infty} C_n = C_0 - L^{-1}R \sum_{n=0}^{\infty} C_n$$

so

$$C_1 = -L^{-1}RC_0$$

$$C_2 = -L^{-1}RC_1$$
$$\vdots$$

The solution for

$$C = \begin{pmatrix} c_1 \\ c_2 \end{pmatrix}$$

is given by

$$C = \sum_{n=0}^{\infty} (-1)^n (L^{-1}R)^n L^{-1}B$$

Consider the C_0 vector or $L^{-1}B$. Let elements of L^{-1} matrix be λ_{ij}; then

$$\begin{pmatrix} c_1 \\ c_2 \end{pmatrix} = \begin{pmatrix} \lambda_{11} & \lambda_{12} \\ \lambda_{21} & \lambda_{12} \end{pmatrix} \cdot \begin{pmatrix} b_1 \\ b_2 \end{pmatrix}$$

Then $(c_1)_0$ or simply $c_{10} = \lambda_{11}b_1 + \lambda_{12}b_2$ and $c_{20} = \lambda_{21}b_1 + \lambda_{22}b_2$. Now

$$\langle c_{10} \rangle = \lambda_{11}\langle b_1 \rangle + \lambda_{12}\langle b_2 \rangle$$

$$\langle c_{20} \rangle = \lambda_{21}\langle b_1 \rangle + \lambda_{22}\langle b_2 \rangle$$

and C_1 is given by $-L^{-1}RC_0$. The elements of R are given, but we will represent them simply as ρ_{ij}; then $L^{-1}RC_0$ is

$$\begin{pmatrix} \lambda_{11} & \lambda_{21} \\ \lambda_{21} & \lambda_{22} \end{pmatrix} \cdot \begin{pmatrix} \rho_{11} & \rho_{12} \\ \rho_{21} & \rho_{22} \end{pmatrix} \cdot \begin{pmatrix} \lambda_{11} & \lambda_{12} \\ \lambda_{21} & \lambda_{22} \end{pmatrix} \cdot \begin{pmatrix} b_1 \\ b_2 \end{pmatrix}$$

or

$$\cdot \begin{pmatrix} \lambda_{11} & \lambda_{12} \\ \lambda_{21} & \lambda_{22} \end{pmatrix} \cdot \begin{pmatrix} \rho_{11} & \rho_{12} \\ \rho_{21} & \rho_{22} \end{pmatrix} \cdot \begin{pmatrix} \lambda_{11}b_1 + \lambda_{12}b_2 \\ \lambda_{21}b_1 + \lambda_{22}b_2 \end{pmatrix}$$

etc., to evaluate all the components.

We can get the correlation matrix of the c's by writing $\langle c_1 c_1 \rangle$ or $\langle \sum_{n=0}^{\infty} c_{1n} \cdot \sum_{n=0}^{\infty} c_{1n} \rangle = \langle c_{10}c_{10} \rangle + \langle c_{10}c_{11} \rangle + \langle c_{11}c_{10} \rangle + \langle c_{11}c_{11} \rangle + \cdots$, where the first term is a zeroth-order correlation given by

$$\langle c_{10}c_{10} \rangle = \langle (\lambda_{11}b_1 + \lambda_{12}b_2)(\lambda_{11}b_1 + \lambda_{12}b_2) \rangle$$
$$= \lambda_{11}^2 \langle b_1 b_1 \rangle + \lambda_{12}^2 \langle b_2 b_2 \rangle + 2\lambda_{11}\lambda_{12}\langle b_1 b_2 \rangle$$

Since we have c_1 given by

$$\begin{pmatrix} \lambda_{11} & \lambda_{12} \\ \lambda_{21} & \lambda_{22} \end{pmatrix} \cdot \begin{pmatrix} \rho_{11} & \rho_{12} \\ \rho_{21} & \rho_{22} \end{pmatrix} \cdot \begin{pmatrix} c_{10} \\ c_{20} \end{pmatrix}$$

or

$$\begin{pmatrix} \lambda_{11}\rho_{11} + \lambda_{12}\rho_{21} & \lambda_{11}\rho_{12} + \lambda_{12}\rho_{22} \\ \lambda_{21}\rho_{11} + \lambda_{22}\rho_{22} & \lambda_{21}\rho_{12} + \lambda_{22}\rho_{22} \end{pmatrix} \cdot \begin{pmatrix} c_{10} \\ c_{20} \end{pmatrix}$$

then, for example,

$$(\lambda_{11}\rho_{11} + \lambda_{12}\rho_{21})c_{10} + (\lambda_{11}\rho_{12} + \lambda_{12}\rho_{22})c_{20} = c_{11}$$

where the elements ρ_{ij} are, in general, stochastic, and to get $\langle c_{11} \rangle$, for example, we must average. Or we can find $\langle c_{10}c_{11} \rangle$, etc.

It is clear that desired statistical measures can be found (at least the first- and second-order statistical measures in which we are primarily interested) for linear equations with random inhomogeneous term and random boundary conditions (with randomness both in the boundary operators and the inhomogeneous term).

We can increase the generality further by letting the original equation become a nonlinear stochastic operator equation or $Lu + \mathscr{R}u + Nu = g(t, \omega)$, or $Lu + Ru + \mathscr{R}u + Nu = g(t, \omega)$. Since the Nu is replaced by $\sum_{n=0}^{\infty} A_n$ and we can solve such equations, our conclusions apply also here.

12.8.   STOCHASTIC OPERATOR EQUATIONS WITH LINEAR BOUNDARY CONDITIONS

We now consider a linear stochastic operator equation $Lu + \mathcal{R}u = g$, with $L = d^2/dt^2$, $g = 0$, and boundary conditions $B_1 u = b_1$ and $B_2 u = b_2$, where B_1 and B_2 are stochastic boundary operators, i.e., they involve random coefficients and b_1, b_2 are also stochastic. The solution is found from

$$y = c_1 + c_2 t - L^{-1}\mathcal{R}y$$

or $y = \sum_{n=0}^{\infty} y_n$, where $y_0 = c_1 + c_2 t$, $y_1 = -L^{-1}\mathcal{R}y_0, \ldots$, and

$$B_1(c_1 + c_2 t)|_{\tau_1} = b_1$$

$$B_2(c_1 + c_2 t)|_{\tau_2} = b_2$$

To evaluate c_1 and c_2, i.e., the C vector, we need to compute the inverse of the matrix coefficient $(L + R)$. We are only approximating c_1, c_2 (we are not calculating an infinite set of components either), but results are as accurate as desired. Since

$$C = \begin{pmatrix} c_1 \\ c_2 \end{pmatrix} = \sum_0^{\infty} (-1)^n (L^{-1}R)^n L^{-1} \begin{pmatrix} b_1 \\ b_2 \end{pmatrix}$$

$$c_1 = c_1(b_1, b_2; \tau_1, \tau_2)$$

$$c_2 = c_2(b_1, b_2; \tau_1, \tau_2)$$

i.e., the c_1 and c_2 depend on the inhomogeneous boundary terms b_1 and b_2 and also of course on the chosen interval τ_1, τ_2.

EXAMPLE: Consider $Lu = 0$, where $L = d^2/dt^2$. Hence, $u = c_1 + c_2 t$. For boundary conditions, choose

$$B_1 u = (d/dt + 1)u|_{\tau_1} + \alpha u|_{\tau_1} = b_1$$

$$B_2 u = (d/dt + 1)u|_{\tau_2} + \beta u|_{\tau_2} = b_2$$

We have then

$$\dot{u}(\tau_1) + u(\tau_1) + \alpha u(\tau_1) = b_1$$

$$\dot{u}(\tau_2) + u(\tau_2) + \beta u(\tau_2) = b_2$$

Applying these conditions, we get

$$c_2 + c_1 + c_2\tau_1 + \alpha(c_1 + c_2\tau_1) = b_1$$

$$c_2 + c_1 + c_2\tau_2 + \beta(c_1 + c_2\tau_2) = b_2$$

Then

$$\begin{pmatrix} 1 + \alpha & 1 + \tau_1 + \alpha\tau_1 \\ 1 + \beta & 1 + \tau_2 + \beta\tau_2 \end{pmatrix} \cdot \begin{pmatrix} c_1 \\ c_2 \end{pmatrix} = \begin{pmatrix} b_1 \\ b_2 \end{pmatrix}$$

EXERCISES

1. Complete the example for α, β, b_1, and b_2 constants by inverting the matrix coefficient of the c vector.

2. Repeat for the case in which α, β, b_1, b_2 are zero-mean processes by considering the matrix on the left to be

$$\begin{pmatrix} 1 & 1 + \tau_1 \\ 1 & 1 + \tau_2 \end{pmatrix} + \begin{pmatrix} \alpha & \alpha\tau_1 \\ \beta & \beta\tau_2 \end{pmatrix} \equiv L + \mathscr{R}$$

and solving for the C vector. (The first term is $L^{-1}B$, etc.)

12.9. LINEAR STOCHASTIC EQUATIONS WITH NONLINEAR BOUNDARY CONDITIONS

In the equation we have just studied with solution $c_1 + c_2 t$, we include in $B_1 u$ the nonlinear term $N_1 u$ and in B_2 we include the nonlinear term $N_2 u$. Evaluating $c_1 + c_2 t$ at the boundaries τ_1, τ_2 we get $N_1(c_1, c_2)$ and $N_2(c_1, c_2)$. To be specific let $N_1 u = N_2 u = u^2$. Now $N_1(c_1, c_2) = (c_1 + c_2 \tau_1)^2$, since it is evaluated at $t = \tau_1$, and $N_2(c_1, c_2) = (c_1 + c_2 \tau_2)^2$.

Since $Nu = u^2 = \sum_{n=0}^{\infty} A_n$ in terms of our polynomials with $A_0 = u_0^2$, $A_1 = 2u_0 u_1$, $A_2 = u_1^2 + 2u_0 u_2$, etc., we have

$$A_0 = (c_{10} + c_{20}\tau_1)^2$$

$$A_1 = 2(c_{10} + c_{20}\tau_1)$$
$$\vdots$$

The matrix equation is now

$$\begin{pmatrix} 1 + \alpha & 1 + \tau_1 + \alpha\tau_1 \\ 1 + \beta & 1 + \tau_2 + \beta\tau_2 \end{pmatrix} \cdot \begin{pmatrix} c_1 \\ c_2 \end{pmatrix} = \begin{pmatrix} b_1 \\ b_2 \end{pmatrix} - \begin{pmatrix} (c_1 + c_2\tau_1)^2 \\ (c_1 + c_2\tau_2)^2 \end{pmatrix}$$

and if α and β are stochastic as well (or even if they are not, to get a simpler deterministic L operator to invert), we write

$$\begin{pmatrix} 1 & 1 + \tau_1 \\ 1 & 1 + \tau_2 \end{pmatrix} \cdot \begin{pmatrix} c_1 \\ c_2 \end{pmatrix} = \begin{pmatrix} b_1 \\ b_2 \end{pmatrix} + \begin{pmatrix} \alpha & \alpha\tau_1 \\ \beta & \beta\tau_2 \end{pmatrix} \cdot \begin{pmatrix} c_1 \\ c_2 \end{pmatrix} - \begin{pmatrix} (c_1 + c_2\tau_1)^2 \\ (c_1 + c_2\tau_2)^2 \end{pmatrix}$$

Then

$$\begin{pmatrix} c_1 \\ c_2 \end{pmatrix} = \begin{pmatrix} 1 & 1 + \tau_1 \\ 1 & 1 + \tau_2 \end{pmatrix}^{-1} \cdot \begin{pmatrix} b_1 \\ b_2 \end{pmatrix} + \begin{pmatrix} 1 & 1 + \tau_1 \\ 1 & 1 + \tau_2 \end{pmatrix}^{-1} \cdot \begin{pmatrix} \alpha & \alpha\tau_1 \\ \beta & \beta\tau_1 \end{pmatrix} \cdot \begin{pmatrix} c_1 \\ c_2 \end{pmatrix}$$
$$- \begin{pmatrix} 1 & 1 + \tau_1 \\ 1 & 1 + \tau_2 \end{pmatrix}^{-1} \cdot \begin{pmatrix} (c_1 + c_2\tau_1)^2 \\ (c_1 + c_2\tau_2)^2 \end{pmatrix}$$

which is solvable by decomposition.

EXAMPLE: Consider $\ddot{u} + k^2 u = 0$ with nonlinear boundary conditions given by

$$\dot{u}(\tau_1) + \beta u(\tau_1) + u^2(\tau_1) = b_1$$
$$\dot{u}(\tau_2) + \gamma u(\tau_2) + u^2(\tau_2) = b_2$$

We assume here the problem is entirely deterministic. We have $Lu = \ddot{u}$ and $Ru = k^2 u$ and $Lu + Ru = 0$ or

$$Lu = -Ru$$
$$u = c_1 + c_2 t - L^{-1} Ru$$
$$\sum_{n=0}^{\infty} u_n = c_1 + c_2 t - L^{-1} R \sum_{n=0}^{\infty} u_n$$
$$u_0 = c_1 + c_2 t$$
$$u_1 = -L^{-1} Ru_0$$
$$u_2 = -L^{-1} Ru_1$$
$$\vdots$$

Since $u_h = c_1 + c_2 t$, the boundary conditions give us

$$c_2 + \beta(c_1 + c_2\tau_1) + (c_1 + c_2\tau_1)^2 = b_1$$
$$c_2 + \gamma(c_1 + c_2\tau_2) + (c_1 + c_2\tau_2)^2 = b_2$$

or

$$\begin{pmatrix} \beta & 1 + \beta\tau_1 \\ \gamma & 1 + \gamma\tau_2 \end{pmatrix} \cdot \begin{pmatrix} c_1 \\ c_2 \end{pmatrix} = \begin{pmatrix} b_1 \\ b_2 \end{pmatrix} - \begin{pmatrix} (c_1 + c_2\tau_1)^2 \\ (c_1 + c_2\tau_2)^2 \end{pmatrix}$$

The last term can also be written as

$$\left\{ \begin{pmatrix} 1 & \tau_1 \\ 1 & \tau_2 \end{pmatrix} \cdot \begin{pmatrix} c_1 \\ c_2 \end{pmatrix} \right\}^2$$

if, for convenience, we *define* the square of the matrix whose elements are $c_1 + c_2\tau_1$ and $c_1 + c_2\tau_2$ to mean the matrix whose elements are $(c_1 + c_2\tau_1)^2$

and $(c_1 + c_2\tau_2)^2$. This is neither an interior nor exterior product but merely a convenient symbolism.

EXERCISE

1. Find c_1 and c_2 using specific numeric constants.

EXAMPLE: Consider $Ly + Ry = x$ with $L = d^2/dt^2$ and boundary conditions

$$L_0 y_1|_{\tau_1} + \alpha y|_{\tau_1} = b_1(\omega)$$

$$L_0 y|_{\tau_2} + \beta y|_{\tau_2} = b_2(\omega)$$

where α and β are stochastic and L is an assumed linear deterministic differential operator. Then the resulting form of the matrix equation will be

$$\begin{pmatrix} \lambda_{11} & \lambda_{12} \\ \lambda_{21} & \lambda_{22} \end{pmatrix} \cdot \begin{pmatrix} c_1 \\ c_2 \end{pmatrix} = \begin{pmatrix} b_1 \\ b_2 \end{pmatrix} - \begin{pmatrix} \rho_{11} & \rho_{12} \\ \rho_{21} & \rho_{22} \end{pmatrix} \cdot \begin{pmatrix} c_1 \\ c_2 \end{pmatrix}$$

or $\Lambda C = B - PC$. If $|\Lambda| \neq 0$, we write

$$\begin{pmatrix} c_1 \\ c_2 \end{pmatrix} = \Lambda^{-1} \begin{pmatrix} b_1 \\ b_2 \end{pmatrix} - \Lambda^{-1} P \begin{pmatrix} c_1 \\ c_2 \end{pmatrix}$$

Let $c_1 = \sum_{n=0}^{\infty} c_{1n}$ and $c_2 = \sum_{n=0}^{\infty} c_{2n}$ and derive the solution as before.

EXAMPLE: Write out c_{11} and c_{21}. If the elements of Λ^{-1} are given by

$$\begin{pmatrix} \lambda_{11} & \lambda_{12} \\ \lambda_{21} & \lambda_{22} \end{pmatrix}$$

$c_{10} = \lambda_{11} b_1 + \lambda_{12} b_2$ and $c_{20} = \lambda_{21} b_1 + \lambda_{22} b_2$. If elements of P are

$$\begin{pmatrix} \rho_{11} & \rho_{12} \\ \rho_{21} & \rho_{22} \end{pmatrix}$$

then PC is given by

$$\begin{pmatrix} \rho_{11} c_{10} & \rho_{12} c_{20} \\ \rho_{21} c_{10} & \rho_{22} c_{20} \end{pmatrix}$$

Suppose B is not a simple linear boundary operator such as $d/dt + a$ but a nonlinear operator, e.g.,

$$Bu = du/dt + u^2 = b \tag{12.9.1}$$

We then have

$$B_1 u(\tau_1) = \dot{u}(\tau_1) + \sum_{n=0}^{\infty} A_n(\tau_1) = b_1(\tau_1)$$

$$B_2 u(\tau_2) = \dot{u}(\tau_2) + \sum_{n=0}^{\infty} A_n(\tau_2) = b_2(\tau_2) \tag{12.9.2}$$

if we suppose $B_1 \equiv B_2$. If not we could have u^3 instead of u^2 in B_2 and the A_n in the second condition would be different. Now the problem is reduced to the linear problem since the A_n are additive. Adding randomness now presents no further difficulty.

EXERCISE

1. Consider $d^2u/dt^2 = 0$ with conditions

$$B_1 u(t) = \mathscr{L}_{\tau_1} u(\tau_1) + a_1 u^2(\tau_1) = b_1$$

$$B_2 u(t) = \mathscr{L}_{\tau_2} u(\tau_2) + a_2 u^2(\tau_2) = b_2$$

Take $\mathscr{L}_{\tau_1}$ simply as $d/d\tau_1$ and $\mathscr{L}_{\tau_2}$ as $d/d\tau_2$. Now

$$\begin{pmatrix} u(\tau_1) \\ u(\tau_2) \end{pmatrix} = \begin{pmatrix} \mathscr{L}_{\tau_1}^{-1} b_1 \\ \mathscr{L}_{\tau_2}^{-1} b_2 \end{pmatrix} - \begin{pmatrix} \mathscr{L}_{\tau_1}^{-1} a_1 u^2(\tau_1) \\ \mathscr{L}_{\tau_2}^{-1} a_2 u^2(\tau_2) \end{pmatrix}$$

Calculate the A_n for u^2 and complete the problem.

12.10. LINEAR DIFFERENTIAL EQUATIONS WITH NONLINEAR BOUNDARY CONDITIONS

Consider the equation

$$\ddot{u} + k^2 u = 0$$

$$B_1 u(\tau_1) = \dot{u}(\tau_1) + \beta u(\tau_1) + u^2(\tau_1) = b_1$$

$$B_2 u(\tau_2) = \dot{u}(\tau_2) + \gamma u(\tau_2) + u^2(\tau_2) = b_2$$

The equation is in the form $Lu + Ru = 0$ with $L = d^2/dt^2$ and $R = k^2$. Therefore $Lu = -Ru$ and $u = \Phi - L^{-1}Ru$ or $\sum_{n=0}^{\infty} u_n = \Phi - L^{-1}R \sum_{n=0}^{\infty} u_n$. We have

$$u_0 = \Phi = c_1 + c_2 t$$

$$u_1 = -L^{-1}Ru_0$$

$$u_2 = -L^{-1}Ru_1$$
$$\vdots$$

Since u_0 satisfies the boundary conditions,

$$c_2 + \beta(c_1 + c_2\tau_1) + (c_1 + c_2\tau_1)^2 = b_1$$

$$c_2 + \gamma(c_1 + c_2\tau_2) + (c_1 + c_2\tau_2)^2 = b_2$$

which can be written

$$\begin{pmatrix} \beta & 1 + \beta\tau_1 \\ \gamma & 1 + \gamma\tau_2 \end{pmatrix} \cdot \begin{pmatrix} c_1 \\ c_2 \end{pmatrix} + \begin{pmatrix} c_1 + c_2\tau_1 \\ c_1 + c_2\tau_2 \end{pmatrix}^2 = \begin{pmatrix} b_1 \\ b_2 \end{pmatrix}$$

or

$$\begin{pmatrix} \beta & 1 + \beta\tau_1 \\ \gamma & 1 + \gamma\tau_2 \end{pmatrix} \cdot \begin{pmatrix} c_1 \\ c_2 \end{pmatrix} = \begin{pmatrix} b_1 \\ b_2 \end{pmatrix} - \begin{pmatrix} c_1 + c_2\tau_1 \\ c_1 + c_2\tau_2 \end{pmatrix}^2$$

and finally

$$\begin{pmatrix} \beta & 1 + \beta\tau_1 \\ \gamma & 1 + \gamma\tau_2 \end{pmatrix} \cdot \begin{pmatrix} c_1 \\ c_2 \end{pmatrix} = \begin{pmatrix} b_1 \\ b_2 \end{pmatrix} - \left\{ \begin{pmatrix} 1 & \tau_1 \\ 1 & \tau_2 \end{pmatrix} \cdot \begin{pmatrix} c_1 \\ c_2 \end{pmatrix} \right\}^2$$

Inverting the first matrix (which we might view as a matrix representation of L in our general format), we get

$$\begin{pmatrix} c_1 \\ c_2 \end{pmatrix} = \begin{pmatrix} \beta & 1 + \beta\tau_1 \\ \gamma & 1 + \gamma\tau_2 \end{pmatrix}^{-1} \cdot \begin{pmatrix} b_1 \\ b_2 \end{pmatrix}$$

$$- \begin{pmatrix} \beta & 1 + \beta\tau_1 \\ \gamma & 1 + \gamma\tau_2 \end{pmatrix}^{-1} \cdot \left\{ \begin{pmatrix} 1 & \tau_1 \\ 1 & \tau_2 \end{pmatrix} \cdot \begin{pmatrix} c_1 \\ c_2 \end{pmatrix} \right\}^2$$

EXERCISE

1. Evaluate the inverse matrix for specific constants using decomposition.

If we write the matrix above as

$$\begin{pmatrix} l_{11} & l_{12} \\ l_{21} & l_{22} \end{pmatrix}$$

then

$$c_1 = l_{11}b_1 + l_{12}b_2 - [l_{11}(c_1 + c_2\tau_1)^2 + l_{12}(c_1 + c_2\tau_2)^2]$$
$$c_2 = l_{21}b_1 + l_{22}b_3 - [l_{21}(c_1 + c_2\tau_1)^2 + l_{22}(c_1 + c_2\tau_2)^2]$$

Call $l_{11}b_1 + l_{12}b_2 = (c_1)_0$. Then

$$c_1 = (c_1)_0 - l_{11}(c_1^2 + 2c_1c_{21} + c_2^2\tau_2^2) - l_{12}(c_1^2 + 2c_1c_2\tau_2 + c_2^2\tau_2^2)$$

and a similar equation can be written for c_2. Thus,

$$c_2 = (c_2)_0 - l_{21}(c_1^2 + 2c_1c_2\tau_1 + c_2^2\tau_2^2) - l_{22}(c_1^2 + 2c_1c_2\tau_2 + c_2^2\tau_2^2).$$

Now write $c_1 = \sum_{n=0}^{\infty} (c_1)_n$, where $(c_1)_0$ is specified and $c_2 = \sum_{n=0}^{\infty} (c_2)_n$ with $(c_2)_0$ specified. Now components are easy to calculate as we did coupled equations, i.e.,

$$(c_1)_1 = -l_{11}[(c_1)_0^2 + 2(c_1)_0(c_2)_0 \tau_1 + (c_2)_0^2 \tau_2^2]$$
$$\qquad -l_{12}[(c_1)_0^2 + 2(c_1)_0(c_2)_0 \tau_2 + (c_2)_0^2 \tau_2^2]$$
$$\vdots$$

EXERCISES

1. Complete several terms to approximate c_1 and c_2.

2. We can consider a direct decomposition of the matrix equation. The column vector of c_1 and c_2 will simply be called C and we consider C to be $\sum_{n=0}^{\infty} C_n$; B will represent the column vector of b_1 and b_2; and τ will represent the 2×2 matrix which multiplies C. (We might write $LC = B - (\tau C)^2$ and $C = L^{-1}B - L^{-1}[\tau C]^2$.) Let $C_0 = L^{-1}B$. Then $C_1 = -L^{-1}[\tau C_0]^2$, etc.

Now let us return to the original boundary conditions and try another approach.

$$B_1 u(\tau_1) = \dot{u}(\tau_1) + \beta u(\tau_1) + \sum_{n=0}^{\infty} A_n = b_1$$

$$B_2 u(\tau_2) = \dot{u}(\tau_2) + \beta u(\tau_2) + \sum_{n=0}^{\infty} A_n = b_2$$

where the A_n in both equations are generated for $u^2(t)$ (thus $A_0 = u_0^2(t)$, $A_1 = 2u_0 u_1$, etc.); but in the B_1 equation they are evaluated at τ_1, and in the B_2 equation they are evaluated at τ_2.

Two Examples of Nonlinear Boundary Conditions: We consider the linear equation

$$d^2u/dt^2 + k^2 u = 0$$

with nonlinear homogeneous boundary conditions at τ_1, and τ_2 specified by the boundary operator $Bu = \dot{u} - \sqrt{u}$. Thus,

$$B_1 u = (d/d\tau_1)u(\tau_1) - \sqrt{u(\tau_1)} = 0$$
$$B_2 u = (d/d\tau_2)u(\tau_2) - \sqrt{u(\tau_2)} = 0 \tag{12.10.1}$$

or, the boundary conditions specified by the boundary operator $Bu = \dot{u}(t) - u^{-m}(t)$, where m is a positive integer. Thus

$$B_1 u = (d/d\tau_1)u(\tau_1) - u^{-m}(\tau_1) = 0$$
$$B_2 u = (d/d\tau_2)u(\tau_2) - u^{-m}(\tau_2) = 0 \tag{12.10.2}$$

To solve these two systems we first write the solution of $Lu = 0$ with $L = d^2/dt^2 + k^2$. (Since in this case it is not necessary to use a simpler L, our u_0 term will be a better result from the standpoint of improved convergence.) This gives us

$$u = c_1 \phi_1(t) + c_2 \phi_2(t)$$

or specifically since $\phi_1 = \cos kt$ and $\phi_2 = (\sin kt)/k$,

$$u = c_1 \cos kt + (c_2/k) \sin kt.$$

Using the boundary conditions of (12.10.1),

$$(d/d\tau_1)u(\tau_1) - \sqrt{u(\tau_1)} = 0$$
$$(d/d\tau_2)u(\tau_2) - \sqrt{u(\tau_2)} = 0$$

These are nonlinear equations with $L_{\tau_1} = d/d\tau_1$ and $L_{\tau_2} = d/d\tau_2$ and they are solved using $L_{\tau_1}^{-1}$ and $L_{\tau_2}^{-1}$ thus using decomposition. The $A_n(\sqrt{u})$ for $Nu = \sqrt{u}$ are given by

$$A_0 = u_0^{1/2}$$
$$A_1 = \tfrac{1}{2}u_0^{-1/2}u_1$$
$$A_2 = -\tfrac{1}{8}u_0^{-3/2}u_1^2 + \tfrac{1}{2}u_0^{-1/2}u_2$$
$$A_3 = \tfrac{1}{16}u_0^{-5/2}u_1^3 - \tfrac{1}{4}u_0^{-3/2}u_1 u_2 + \tfrac{1}{2}u_0^{-1/2}u_3$$

Now calculating $u_0, u_1, u_2, \ldots$, we find

$$u_0(\tau_1) = \beta_1, \quad u_1(\tau_1) = L^{-1}\sqrt{u_0(\tau_1)} = \sqrt{\beta_1}\,\tau_1, \quad u_2(\tau_1) = \tau_1^2/4,$$

and $u_n(\tau_1) = 0$ for $n \geq 3$. Hence,

$$u(\tau_1) = \beta_1 + \sqrt{\beta_1}\,\tau_1 + \tau_1^2/4 = [\sqrt{\beta_1} + (\tau_1/2)]^2$$
$$u(\tau_2) = \beta_2 + \sqrt{\beta_2}\,\tau_2 + \tau_2^2/4 = [\sqrt{\beta_2} + (\tau_2/2)]^2$$

where β_1 and β_2 are the arbitrary constants arising on the $L_{\tau_1}^{-1}$ and $L_{\tau_2}^{-1}$ integrations. Since $u(\tau_1) = c_1 \phi_1(\tau_1) + c_2 \phi_2(\tau_1)$ and $u(\tau_2) = c_1 \phi_1(\tau_2) + c_2 \phi_2(\tau_2)$,

$$\begin{pmatrix} \phi_1(\tau_1) & \phi_1(\tau_2) \\ \phi_2(\tau_1) & \phi_2(\tau_2) \end{pmatrix} \cdot \begin{pmatrix} c_1 \\ c_2 \end{pmatrix} = \begin{pmatrix} u(\tau_1) \\ u(\tau_2) \end{pmatrix}$$

or

$$\begin{pmatrix} c_1 \\ c_2 \end{pmatrix} = \begin{pmatrix} \phi_1(\tau_1) & \phi_1(\tau_2) \\ \phi_2(\tau_1) & \phi_2(\tau_2) \end{pmatrix}^{-1} \cdot \begin{pmatrix} u(\tau_1) \\ u(\tau_2) \end{pmatrix}$$

$$= \begin{pmatrix} \phi_1(\tau_1) & \phi_1(\tau_2) \\ \phi_2(\tau_1) & \phi_2(\tau_2) \end{pmatrix}^{-1} \cdot \begin{pmatrix} [\sqrt{\beta_1} + (\tau_1/2)]^2 \\ [\sqrt{\beta_2} + (\tau_2/2)]^2 \end{pmatrix}$$

which evaluates c_1 and c_2 if

$$\begin{vmatrix} \phi_1(\tau_1) & \phi_2(\tau_1) \\ \phi_1(\tau_2) & \phi_2(\tau_2) \end{vmatrix} \neq 0$$

Now let us consider the second problem. The boundary conditions are in the form

$$L_{\tau_1} u(\tau_1) = u^{-m}(\tau_1), \qquad L_{\tau_2} u(\tau_2) = u^{-m}(\tau_2)$$

where L_τ means $d/d\tau$. Operate on the first equation with $L_{\tau_1}^{-1}$ and the second equation with $L_{\tau_1}^{-1}$. For example,

$$L_{\tau_1}^{-1} L_{\tau_1} u(\tau_1) = L_{\tau_1}^{-1} u^{-m}(\tau_1)$$

Consider

$$\frac{d}{d\tau_1} u(\tau_1) - u^{-m}(\tau_1) = 0$$

$$L_{\tau_1}^{-1} u(\tau_1) = L_{\tau_1}^{-1} u^{-m}(\tau_1)$$
$$u(\tau_1) = \beta_1 + L_{\tau_1}^{-1} u^{-m}(\tau_1)$$

$$\sum_{n=0}^{\infty} u_n(\tau_1) = \beta_1 + L_{\tau_1}^{-1} A_n [u^{-m}(\tau_1)]$$

i.e., we have $Nu = u^{-m} = \sum_{n=0}^{\infty} A_n(u^{-m})$

$$A_0 = u_0^{-m}$$
$$A_1 = -m u_0^{-(m+1)} u_1$$
$$A_2 = \tfrac{1}{2} m(m+1) u_0^{-(m+2)} u_1^2 - m u_0^{-(m+1)} u_2$$
$$A_3 = -\tfrac{1}{6} m(m+1)(m+2) u_0^{-(m+3)} u_1^3$$
$$\qquad + m(m+1) u_0^{-(m+2)} u_1 u_2 - m u_0^{-(m+1)} u_3$$
$$\vdots$$
$$u_0(\tau_1) = \beta_1$$
$$u_1(\tau_1) = L_{\tau_1}^{-1} A_0 = L_{\tau_1}^{-1} u_0^{-m}(\tau_1)$$
$$u_1(\tau_1) = \beta_1^{-m} \tau_1$$

$$u_2(\tau_1) = L_{\tau_1}^{-1} A_1 = L_{\tau_1}^{-1}[-m u_0^{-(m+1)}(\tau_1) u_1(\tau_1)]$$
$$= L_{\tau_1}^{-1}[(-m\beta_1^{-(m+1)})(\beta_1^{-m}\tau_1)]$$
$$= -m\beta_1^{-(2m+1)}\tau_1^2/2$$

The final result for $u(\tau_1)$ and $u(\tau_2)$ is

$$u(\tau_1) = [(m+1)\tau_1 + \beta_1^{m+1}]^{1/(m+1)}$$

$$u(\tau_2) = [(m+1)\tau_2 + \beta_2^{m+1}]^{1/(m+1)}$$

Knowing $u(\tau_1)$ and $u(\tau_2)$ we can now find c_1 and c_2 since

$$u(\tau_1) = c_1 \phi_1(\tau_1) + c_2 \phi_2(\tau_1)$$

$$u(\tau_2) = c_1 \phi_1(\tau_2) + c_2 \phi_2(\tau_2)$$

Thus,

$$\begin{pmatrix} \phi_1(\tau_1) & \phi_1(\tau_2) \\ \phi_2(\tau_1) & \phi_2(\tau_2) \end{pmatrix} \cdot \begin{pmatrix} c_1 \\ c_2 \end{pmatrix} = \begin{pmatrix} u(\tau_1) \\ u(\tau_2) \end{pmatrix}$$

$$\begin{pmatrix} c_1 \\ c_2 \end{pmatrix} = \begin{pmatrix} \phi_1(\tau_1) & \phi_1(\tau_2) \\ \phi_2(\tau_1) & \phi_2(\tau_2) \end{pmatrix}^{-1} \cdot \begin{pmatrix} u(\tau_1) \\ u(\tau_2) \end{pmatrix}$$

which determines the constants c_1 and c_2.

We can consider many variations, e.g., an operator equation $d^2u/dt^2 + k^2 u = 0$ and boundary conditions such as

$$\frac{du(\tau_1)}{d\tau_1} + \beta_1 u(\tau_1) u(\tau_2) = b_1$$

$$\frac{du(\tau_2)}{d\tau_2} + \beta_2 u(\tau_1) u(\tau_2) = b_2$$

i.e., coupled nonlinear mixed boundary conditions. The nonlinearities need not be simple nonlinearities; they can be composite nonlinearities as we have discussed. The composite nonlinearities can appear in the boundary conditions $B_1 u|_{\tau_1} = b_1$ and $B_2 u|_{\tau_2} = b_2$ as well as in the original operator equation. For example, if we have $\exp\{-\sin[(\pi/2)u(\tau_1)]\}$ in $B_1 u$ and $\exp\{-\cos[(\pi/2)u(\tau_2)]\}$ in $B_2 u$, we can generate the appropriate A_n polynomials for the nonlinearities.

We might also consider the same equation and conditions involving trigonometric functions

$$\frac{du(\tau_1)}{d\tau_1} + \beta_1 u(\tau_1) + \sin u(\tau_1) = b_1$$

$$\frac{du(\tau_2)}{d\tau_2} + \beta_2 u(\tau_2) + \cos u(\tau_2) = b_2$$

or exponential functions

$$\frac{du(\tau_1)}{d\tau_1} + \beta_1 e^{-u(\tau_1)} = b_1$$

$$\frac{dy(\tau_2)}{d\tau_2} + \beta_2 e^{-u(\tau_2)} = b_2$$

12.11. COUPLED NONLINEAR STOCHASTIC DIFFERENTIAL EQUATIONS

We have seen that such equations are readily solvable by decomposition. We can consider, as an example, two coupled equations in u and v in which coefficient terms may be nonlinear (possibly stochastic as well), and the forcing functions g_1 and g_2 can be stochastic, with boundary conditions containing nonlinear coupled terms, in the form

$$B_1[u(\tau_1), v(\tau_1)] = L_{11}u|_{t=\tau_1} + L_{12}v|_{t=\tau_2} + N_1[u(\tau_1), v(\tau_1)] = b_1$$

$$B_2[u(\tau_2), v(\tau_2)] = L_{21}u|_{t=\tau_2} + L_{22}v|_{t=\tau_2} + N_2[u(\tau_2), v(\tau_2)] = b_2$$

in which the L's may all be different.

Now we can consider coupled equations such as:

$$L_1 u + L_{11}v + N_1(u, v) + N_{11}(u) + N_{12}(v) + R_1 u + R_{11}v = g_1(t, \omega)$$

$$L_2 u + L_{21}v + N_2(u, v) + N_{21}(u) + N_{22}(v) + R_2 u + R_{21}v = g_2(t, \omega)$$

with boundary operator equations

$$\begin{cases} B_1(u, v) = Lu|_{\tau_1} + Lv|_{\tau_1} + N(u, v)|_{\tau_1} = b_1 \\ B_2(u, v) = Lu|_{\tau_2} + Lv|_{\tau_2} + N(u, v)|_{\tau_2} = b_2 \end{cases}$$

$$\begin{cases} B_3(u, v) = Lu|_{\tau_1} + Lv|_{\tau_1} + N(u, v)|_{\tau_1} = b_3 \\ B_4(u, v) = Lu|_{\tau_2} + Lv|_{\tau_2} + N(u, v)|_{\tau_2} = b_4 \end{cases}$$

where all the L's and N's may be different.

The possibilities are clear. We can get coupled differential equations with coupled boundary conditions such as

$$\begin{cases} L_1 u + N_1(u, v) + L_3 v = g_1 \\ L_2 v + N_2(u, v) + L_4 u = g_2 \end{cases}$$

$$\begin{cases} B_1(u, v) = b_1 \\ B_2(u, v) = b_2 \end{cases}$$

$$\begin{cases} B_3(u, v) = b_3 \\ B_4(u, v) = b_4 \end{cases}$$

or the equations can uncouple but have coupled boundary conditions, such as

$$\begin{cases} Lu + Nu = g_1 \\ Lv + Nv = g_2 \end{cases}$$

$$\begin{cases} B_1(u, v) = b_1 \\ B_2(u, v) = b_2 \end{cases}$$

$$\begin{cases} B_3(u, v) = b_3 \\ B_4(u, v) = b_4 \end{cases}$$

Or, we can get coupled equations and uncoupled boundary conditions

$$\begin{cases} L_1u + N_1(u, v) + L_3v = g_1 \\ L_2v + N_2(u, v) + L_4u = g_2 \end{cases}$$

$$\begin{cases} B_1u = b_1 \\ B_2u = b_2 \end{cases}$$

$$\begin{cases} B_3v = b_3 \\ B_4v = b_4 \end{cases}$$

or independent (uncoupled) equations and uncoupled boundary conditions (the trivial limiting case)

$$\begin{cases} Lu + Nu = g_1 \\ Lv + Nv = g_2 \end{cases}$$

and assuming L is second-order,

$$\begin{cases} B_1u = b_1 \\ B_2u = b_2 \end{cases}$$

$$\begin{cases} B_3v = b_3 \\ B_4v = b_4 \end{cases}$$

In all of these the B's and b's can be time dependent or even stochastic.

12.12. COUPLED LINEAR DETERMINISTIC EQUATIONS WITH COUPLED BOUNDARY CONDITIONS

Let us consider first an example of coupled (linear deterministic) differential equations with coupled (linear deterministic) boundary conditions, which will show our approach (avoiding the customary uncoupling at this point). For the coupled equations let us take

$$\frac{d^2}{dt^2} u + v = 0 \tag{12.12.1}$$

$$\frac{d^2}{dt^2} v + u = 0 \tag{12.12.2}$$

on the interval $[\pi/4, \pi/2]$. With (12.12.1) are associated the boundary conditions

$$B_1(u, v) = \frac{d}{dt} u(\pi/4) + \tfrac{1}{2}u(\pi/4) + 2v(\pi/4) = 3 \tag{12.12.3}$$

$$B_2(u, v) = \frac{d}{dt} u(\pi/2) + \tfrac{1}{3}u(\pi/2) + 4v(\pi/2) = 5 \tag{12.12.4}$$

and with (12.12.2) we have the boundary conditions

$$B_3(u, v) = \frac{d}{dt} v(\pi/4) + \tfrac{1}{4}v(\pi/4) + 8u(\pi/4) = 7 \tag{12.12.5}$$

$$B_4(u, v) = \frac{d}{dt} v(\pi/2) + \tfrac{1}{5}v(\pi/2) + 16u(\pi/2) = 11 \tag{12.12.6}$$

From (12.12.1) and (12.12.2), if $L = d^2/dt^2$, $Lu = -v$ and $Lv = -u$ hence,

$$u = c_1 + c_2 t - L^{-1}v$$
$$v = k_1 + k_2 t - L^{-1}u$$

Thus, since L^{-1} is a double integration

$$\begin{cases} u_0 = c_1 + c_2 t \\ v_0 = k_1 + k_2 t \end{cases}$$

$$\begin{cases} u_1 = -L^{-1}[k_1 + k_2 t] = -k_1 t^2/2 - k_2 t^3/3! \\ v_1 = -L^{-1}[c_1 + c_2 t] = -c_1 t^2/2 - c_2 t^3/3! \end{cases}$$
$$\vdots$$

i.e.,

$$u = c_1 + c_2 t - k_1 t^2/2! - k_2 t^3/3! + \cdots$$
$$v = k_1 + k_2 t - c_1 t^2/2! - c_2 t^3/3! + \cdots$$

Now differentiating u we have

$$\ddot{u} = -k_1 - k_2 t + c_1 t^2/2! + c_2 t^3/3! - \cdots$$

Adding $\ddot{u}$ to v we see (12.12.1) is satisfied for any k_1, k_2, c_1, and c_2 satisfying conditions (12.12.3)–(12.12.6). Similarly,

$$\ddot{v} = -c_1 - c_2 t + k_1 t^2/2! + k_2 t^3/3! - \cdots$$

$$u = c_1 + c_2 t - k_1 t^2/2! + k_2 t^3/3! + \cdots$$

so $\ddot{v} + u = 0$, thus satisfying (12.12.2).

Now it is only necessary to determine the four arbitrary constants by using the given (coupled) boundary conditions. These (deterministic) conditions (12.12.3) − (12.12.6) can be written more generally as

$$B_1(u, v) = \dot{u}(\tau_1) + \beta_1 u(\tau_1) + \gamma_1 v(\tau_1) = b_1$$

$$B_2(u, v) = \dot{u}(\tau_2) + \beta_2 u(\tau_2) + \gamma_2 v(\tau_2) = b_2$$

$$B_3(u, v) = \dot{v}(\tau_1) + \beta_3 v(\tau_1) + \gamma_3 u(\tau_1) = b_3$$

$$B_4(u, v) = \dot{v}(\tau_2) + \beta_4 v(\tau_2) + \gamma_4 u(\tau_2) = b_4$$

where b_i ($i = 1, 2, 3, 4$) are constants in our example although we can easily generalize further. Our objective is to make the approach clear so we have made the problem simple.

Now we use for u the approximate solution $\phi_n = \sum_{i=0}^{n-1} u_n$ and for v the approximate solution $\theta_n = \sum_{i=0}^{n-1} v_n$. Now ϕ_n and θ_n are used for u and v in the four coupled boundary operator equations on the interval $[\tau_1, \tau_2]$.

For our solutions we will take three-term approximations i.e., we use ϕ_3 and θ_3. Consequently,

$$\phi_3(t) = \sum_{n=0}^{2} u_n(t)$$

$$= (c_1 + c_2 t) - \left(k_1 \frac{t^2}{2!} + k_2 \frac{t^3}{3!}\right) + \left(c_1 \frac{t^4}{4!} + c_2 \frac{t^5}{t!}\right)$$

$$\theta_3(t) = \sum_{n=0}^{2} v_n(t)$$

$$= (k_1 + k_2 t) - \left(c_1 \frac{t^2}{2!} + c_2 \frac{t^3}{3!}\right) + \left(k_1 \frac{t^4}{4!} + k_2 \frac{t^5}{5!}\right)$$

or

$$\phi_3(t) = c_1\left(1 + \frac{t_4}{4!}\right) + c_2\left(t + \frac{t^5}{5!}\right) + k_1\left(-\frac{t^2}{2!}\right) + k_2\left(-\frac{t^3}{3!}\right)$$

$$\theta_3(t) = k_1\left(1 + \frac{t^4}{4!}\right) + k_2\left(t + \frac{t^5}{5!}\right) + c_1\left(-\frac{t^2}{2!}\right) + c_2\left(-\frac{t^3}{3!}\right)$$

Now for our particular problem, the interval $[\tau_1, \tau_2]$ is $[\pi/4, \pi/2]$ and we have the constants

$$b_1 = 3, \qquad \beta_1 = 0.500, \qquad \gamma_1 = 2$$
$$b_2 = 5, \qquad \beta_2 = 0.333, \qquad \gamma_2 = 4$$
$$b_3 = 7, \qquad \beta_3 = 0.250, \qquad \gamma_3 = 8$$
$$b_4 = 11, \qquad \beta_4 = 0.200, \qquad \gamma_4 = 16$$

We have deliberately chosen coupling coefficients that are not "small" so usual uncoupling procedures fail.

Since we will need the derivatives, we now write

$$\dot\phi_3(t) = c_1\left(\frac{t^3}{3!}\right) + c_2\left(1 + \frac{t^4}{4!}\right) + k_1(-t) + k_2\left(-\frac{t^2}{2!}\right)$$

$$\dot\phi_3(t) = k_1\left(\frac{t^3}{3!}\right) + k_2\left(1 + \frac{t^4}{4!}\right) + c_1(-t) + c_2\left(-\frac{t^2}{2!}\right)$$

Now

$$\phi_3(\tau_1) = \phi_3(\pi/4) = (1.0159)c_1 + (0.7879)c_2 + (-0.3084)k_1 + (-0.0808)k_2$$
$$\phi_3(\tau_1) = \dot\phi_3(\pi/4) = (0.0808)c_1 + (1.0159)c_2 + (-0.7854)k_1 + (-0.3084)k_2$$
$$\dot\phi_3(\tau_2) = \phi_3(\pi/2) = (1.2538)c_1 + (1.6507)c_2 + (-1.234)k_1 + (-0.6462)k_2$$
$$\dot\phi_3(\tau_2) = \dot\phi_3(\pi/2) = (0.6462)c_1 + (1.2538)c_2 + (-1.571)k_1 + (-1.234)k_2$$

and

$$\theta_3(\tau_1) = \theta_3(\pi/4) = (1.0159)k_1 + (0.7879)k_2 + (-0.3084)c_1 + (-0.0808)c_2$$
$$\dot\theta_3(\tau_1) = \dot\theta_3(\pi/4) = (0.0808)k_1 + (1.0159)k_2 + (-0.7854)c_1 + (-0.3084)c_2$$
$$\theta_3(\tau_2) = \theta_3(\pi/2) = (1.2538)k_1 + (1.6507)k_2 + (-1.234)c_1 + (-0.6462)c_2$$
$$\dot\theta_3(\tau_2) = \dot\theta_3(\pi/2) = (0.6462)k_1 + (1.2538)k_2 + (-1.571)c_1 + (-1.234)c_2$$

[It is worth noting the patterns of numbers comparing $\phi_3(\tau_2)$ and $\dot\phi_3(\tau_2)$ with $\theta_3(\tau_2)$ and $\dot\theta_3(\tau_2)$.]

The B_1 condition becomes

$$(-0.0280)c_1 + (1.2483)c_2 + (1.0922)k_1 + (1.227)k_2 = 3$$

The B_2 condition becomes

$$(-3.8723)c_1 + (-0.7813)c_2 + (3.0333)k_1 + (5.1536)k_2 = 5$$

The B_3 condition becomes

$$(-2.1324)k_1 + (0.5665)k_2 + (7.2647)c_1 + (5.9746)c_2 = 7$$

The B_4 condition becomes

$$(-18.8470)k_1 + (-8.7553)k_2 + (18.2430)c_1 + (25.0480)c_2 = 11$$

Rearranging in c_1, c_2, k_1, and k_2 order, we get

$$(-0.0280)c_1 + (1.2483)c_2 + (1.0922)k_1 + (1.227)k_2 = 3$$
$$(-3.8723)c_1 + (-0.7813)c_2 + (3.0333)k_1 + (5.1536)k_2 = 5$$
$$(7.2647)c_1 + (5.9746)c_2 + (-2.1324)k_1 + (0.5665)k_2 = 7$$
$$(18.2430)c_1 + (25.0480)c_2 + (-18.8470)k_1 + (-8.7553)k_2 = 11$$

In matrix form,

$$\begin{pmatrix} -0.0280 & 1.2483 & 1.0922 & 1.227 \\ -3.8723 & -0.7813 & 3.0333 & 5.1536 \\ 7.2647 & 5.9746 & -2.1324 & 0.5665 \\ 18.2430 & 25.0480 & -18.8470 & -8.7553 \end{pmatrix} \cdot \begin{pmatrix} c_1 \\ c_2 \\ k_1 \\ k_2 \end{pmatrix} = \begin{pmatrix} 3 \\ 5 \\ 7 \\ 11 \end{pmatrix}$$

Solving the matrix equation, we get

$$\begin{pmatrix} c_1 \\ c_2 \\ k_1 \\ k_2 \end{pmatrix} = \begin{pmatrix} 0.20300 \\ 1.00769 \\ 0.49390 \\ 0.98480 \end{pmatrix}$$

To verify the solutions

B_1 condition: $\dot{u}(\pi/4) + (0.500)u(\pi/4) + 2v(\pi/4) \overset{?}{=} 3$

B_2 condition: $\dot{u}(\pi/2) + (0.333)u(\pi/2) + 4v(\pi/2) \overset{?}{=} 5$

B_3 condition: $\dot{v}(\pi/4) + (0.250)v(\pi/4) + 8u(\pi/4) \overset{?}{=} 7$

B_4 condition: $\dot{v}(\pi/2) + (0.200)v(\pi/2) + 16u(\pi/2) \overset{?}{=} 11$

B_1 gives $0.3484 + 0.3842 + 2.2676$ $= 3.000$

B_2 gives $-0.5965 + 0.2238 + 5.3720$ $= 5.000$

B_3 gives $0.5701 + 0.28345 + 6.1464$ $= 6.9999 \simeq 7.00$

B_4 gives $-0.00853 + 0.26864 + 10.7536 = 11.02 \simeq 11.00$

The accuracy is certainly remarkable since we used only three terms of the decomposition series and the B_4 condition involved strong couplings. (If a computer had been available it would have been easy to carry ϕ_n and θ_n a few terms further.)

Actually, we can get the complete solution very easily and verify it as well. We proceed as follows:

Our coupled equations were

$$\ddot{u} + v = 0, \qquad \ddot{v} + u = 0$$

and we wrote three-term approximations. By inspection we can now see that we can write the rest of the series and consequently the complete solutions are given by

$$u(t) = c_1\phi_1(t) + c_2\phi_2(t) - k_1\phi_3(t) - k_2\phi_4(t)$$

$$v(t) = k_1\phi_1(t) + k_2\phi_2(t) - c_1\phi_3(t) - c_2\phi_4(t)$$

where

$$\phi_1(t) = \sum_{m=0}^{\infty} \frac{t^{4m}}{(4m)!}, \qquad \phi_2(t) = \sum_{m=0}^{\infty} \frac{t^{4m+1}}{(4m+1)!}$$

$$\phi_3(t) = \sum_{m=0}^{\infty} \frac{t^{4m+2}}{(4m+2)!}, \qquad \phi_4(t) = \sum_{m=0}^{\infty} \frac{t^{4m+3}}{(4m+3)!}$$

Now

$$\ddot{u} = c_1\ddot{\phi}_1 + c_2\ddot{\phi}_2 - k_1\ddot{\phi}_3 - k_2\ddot{\phi}_4$$

$$\ddot{v} = k_1\ddot{\phi}_1 + k_2\ddot{\phi}_2 - c_1\ddot{\phi}_3 - c_2\ddot{\phi}_4$$

We note that in this example

$$\ddot{\phi}_1 = \sum_{m=1}^{\infty} \frac{t^{4m+2}}{(4m-2)!} = \sum_{m-1=0}^{\infty} \frac{t^{4m-2}}{(4m-2)!}$$

letting $m = n + 1$,

$$\ddot{\phi}_1 = \sum_{n=0}^{\infty} \frac{t^{4n+2}}{(4n+2)!} \equiv \phi_3(t)$$

and

$$\ddot{\phi}_2 = \sum_{m=1}^{\infty} \frac{t^{4m-1}}{(4m-1)!} = \sum_{m-1=0}^{\infty} \frac{t^{4m-1}}{(4m-1)!}$$

letting $m = n + 1$,

$$\ddot{\phi}_2 = \sum_{n=0}^{\infty} \frac{t^{4n+3}}{(4n+3)!} \equiv \phi_4(t)$$

Similarly,

$$\ddot{\phi}_3(t) \equiv \phi_1(t), \qquad \ddot{\phi}_4(t) \equiv \phi_2(t)$$

Thus, we have a periodicity after two derivative operations and can now write

$$\ddot{u} = c_1\ddot{\phi}_1 + c_2\ddot{\phi}_2 - k_1\ddot{\phi}_3 - k_2\ddot{\phi}_4 = c_1\phi_3 + c_2\phi_4 - k_1\phi_1 - k_2\phi_2$$

and

$$v = k_1\phi_1 + k_2\phi_2 - c_1\phi_3 - c_2\phi_4$$

Hence, it is clear that the equation $\ddot{u} + v = 0$ is satisfied. Similarly

$$\ddot{v} = k_1\ddot{\phi}_1 + k_2\ddot{\phi}_2 - c_1\ddot{\phi}_3 - c_2\ddot{\phi}_4 = k_1\phi_3 + k_2\phi_4 - c_1\phi_1 - c_2\phi_2$$

and

$$u = c_1\phi_1 + c_2\phi_2 - k_1\phi_3 - k_2\phi_4$$

Therefore it is clear that $\ddot{v} + u = 0$ is also satisfied and we have derived the *complete* or *exact* solutions of the coupled system rather than an n-term approximation (and very rapidly convergent solutions).

The boundary conditions, as we have seen, determine the constants c_1, c_2, k_1, and k_2.

EXERCISE

1. For the given three coupled differential equations

$$\ddot{u} + v + w = 0$$

$$\ddot{v} + u + w = 0$$

$$\ddot{w} + u + v = 0$$

and six associated coupled boundary conditions, verify that we can write

$$u(t) = \sum_{i=1}^{6} c_i^{(1)}\phi_i^{(1)}(t)$$

$$v(t) = \sum_{i=1}^{6} c_i^{(2)}\phi_i^{(2)}(t)$$

$$w(t) = \sum_{i=1}^{6} c_i^{(3)}\phi_i^{(3)}(t)$$

and that for this specific example,

$$c_1^{(1)} = c_3^{(2)} = c_5^{(3)}$$

$$c_2^{(1)} = c_4^{(2)} = c_6^{(3)}$$

$$c_3^{(1)} = c_5^{(2)} = c_1^{(3)}$$

$$c_4^{(1)} = c_6^{(2)} = c_2^{(3)}$$

$$c_5^{(1)} = c_1^{(2)} = c_3^{(3)}$$

$$c_6^{(1)} = c_2^{(2)} = c_4^{(3)}$$

$$u_i(t) = \sum_{j=1}^{2m} c_j^{(i)} \phi_j^{(i)}(t)$$

and for m coupled equations we have

$$u_i(t) = \sum_{j=1}^{2m} c_j^{(i)} \phi_j^{(i)}(t)$$

(*Question:*   Do we get faster convergence for higher m?)

12.13.   COUPLED EQUATIONS AND COUPLED BOUNDARY CONDITIONS

We can consider equations such as

$$L_1 u + R_1 v + N_1(u, v) = g_1$$

$$L_2 v + R_2 v + N_2(u, v) = g_2$$

Preferably, let us make the linear terms interdependent as well; thus,

$$L_1 u + N_1(u, v) + L_3 v = g_1 \tag{12.13.1}$$

$$L_2 v + N_2(u, v) + L_4 u = g_2 \tag{12.13.2}$$

where the order of L_1 is greater than the order of L_3 and the order of L_2 is greater than the order of L_4.

We consider boundary conditions

$$B_1(u, v) = b_1 \tag{12.13.3}$$

$$B_2(u, v) = b_2 \tag{12.13.4}$$

for (12.13.1) and

$$B_3(u, v) = b_3 \tag{12.13.5}$$

$$B_4(u, v) = b_4 \tag{12.13.6}$$

for (12.13.2). In the case the boundary conditions are uncoupled, they can be written

$$B_1 u = b_1, \qquad B_2 u = b_2$$

$$B_3 v = b_3, \qquad B_4 v = b_4$$

Let us uncouple the equations as well. Then we have

$$L_1 u + N_1 u = g_1, \qquad L_2 v + N_2 v = g_2$$

$$B_1 u = b_1, \qquad B_2 u = b_2$$

$$B_3 v = b_3, \qquad B_4 v = b_4$$

where

$$B_1 u(a) = \dot{u}(a) + \beta_1 u(a) = b_1$$

$$B_2 u(b) = \dot{u}(b) + \beta_2 u(b) = b_2$$

$$B_3 v(a) = \dot{v}(a) + \beta_3 v(a) = b_3$$

$$B_4 v(b) = \dot{v}(b) + \beta_4 v(b) = b_4$$

where the β's and b's are constants.

12.14. BOUNDARY CONDITIONS FOR PARTIAL DIFFERENTIAL EQUATIONS

We can begin with a partial differential equation such as $u_{xx} + u_{yy} = g(x, y)$. We have seen in Chapter 9 and recent work (particularly Bellman and Adomian [1] that we can solve equations involving partial differential operators in the nonlinear stochastic case which includes the special general cases such as the above linear deterministic equation.

In order to have a complete and unique mathematical description of a problem, conditions must also be specified which the required solution must satisfy. The reason, of course, is that differential and partial differential equations can have infinitely many solutions. The added conditions ensure a unique characterization of the physical problem. They may be given as initial conditions or as boundary conditions.

In the first case, we need to specify the initial values at $t = t_0$ or $t = 0$ of the function and of a number of derivatives, depending on the order of the differential operator (i.e., n initial values of an nth order ordinary differential operator).

In the second case, we must specify the function at two distinct points a and b. We can have both initial boundary conditions in a partial differential equation. Thus, for the equation $u_{tt} = a^2 u_{xx}$ we could specify initial conditions (initial displacement and initial velocity, for example) given by

$$u(x, 0) = \phi(x), \qquad u_t(x, 0) = \phi(x)$$

and boundary conditions at the ends a and b of an interval

$$u(a, t) = u(b, t) = 0$$

or

$$u(a, t) = \alpha(t), \qquad u(b, t) = \beta(t)$$

etc. Other possibilities could be prescription of the motion of an endpoint with $u(a, t) = f(t)$ or prescription of a force at an endpoint with $u_x(b, t) = g(t)$. We can also have nonlinear boundary conditions such as $u_x(b, t) = f(u(b, t)) = Nu(b, t)$, where N is a nonlinear operator.

We can now define appropriate (partial differential) boundary operators such as

$$B_1 u = [u_x + u_y + \beta_1 u]|_{x, y = \xi_1, \eta_1} = b_1$$

$$B_2 u = [u_x + u_y + \beta_2 u]|_{x, y = \xi_2, \eta_2} = b_2$$

and proceed to generalizations in x, y, z, or position and time. For instance,

$$\nabla^2 u = g(x, y, z)$$

$$B_1 u = [u_x + u_y + u_z + \beta_1 u]|_{x, y, z = \xi_1, \eta_1, \zeta_1} = b_1$$

and, similarly, $B_2 u = b_2$ and $B_3 u = b_3$.

Again, we can consider equations such as

$$L_t u + L_x u + L_y u = g$$

where, for example, $L_t = \partial^2/\partial t^2 + \partial/\partial t$, $L_x = \partial^2/\partial x^2$, $L_y = \partial y/\partial t$, and boundary conditions are written

$$B_1 u(\tau_1) = [L_x u(x, y, t) + L_y u(x, y, t) + L_t u(x, y, t)]|_{t = \tau_1} = b_1(x, y)$$

$$B_2 u(\tau_2) = [L_x u(x, y, t) + L_y u(x, y, t) + L_t u(x, y, t)]|_{t = \tau} = b_2(x, y)$$

Since we have seen how to solve general partial differential equations, we proceed as we have previously, substituting the approximation $\phi_n = u_1 + u_2 + \cdots$ into the specified boundary operator equations. Thus the operator in the above equations can be nonlinear stochastic, e.g., $\mathscr{F} u(x, y, z) = g(x, y, z)$ where $\mathscr{F} = \nabla^2 u + ku + u^2$ and where, for example, k is stochastic.

If we consider the two-dimensional problem

$$\frac{\partial^2 u}{\partial x^2} + \frac{\partial^2 u}{\partial y^2} + k(x, y)u = g(x, y)$$

we require four boundary-condition equations for four unknowns, and we get 4×4 matrices. If we consider two such coupled equations, we get eight boundary equations and 8×8 matrices. A simple illustrative case can be taken as $(L_x + L_y)u = g$ or

$$\frac{\partial^2 u}{\partial x^2} + \frac{\partial^2 u}{\partial y^2} = g(x, y)$$

$$u(x_1, y) = a_1(y)$$

$$u(x_2, y) = a_2(y)$$

$$u(x, y_1) = b_1(x)$$

$$u(x, y_2) = b_2(x)$$

Finally, we could consider systems of coupled (nonlinear stochastic) partial differential equations and coupled conditions. As an example,

$$\left(\frac{\partial^2}{\partial x^2} + \frac{\partial^2}{\partial y^2} \right) u + k_{11}u + k_{12}v = g_1(x, y)$$

$$\left(\frac{\partial^2}{\partial x^2} + \frac{\partial^2}{\partial y^2} \right) u + k_{21}u + k_{22}v = g_2(x, y)$$

(where the k's and g's may be stochastic or we might include terms such as uv^2, etc.) and boundary conditions could be given such as

$$B_1 u = b_1(y) \qquad \text{at} \qquad x = x_1$$

$$B_2 u = b_2(y) \qquad \text{at} \qquad x = x_2$$

$$B_3 u = b_3(x) \qquad \text{at} \qquad y = y_1$$

$$B_4 u = b_3(x) \qquad \text{at} \qquad y = y_2$$

12.15. SUMMARY

To summarize, our equation or system of equations can be linear, nonlinear, deterministic, or stochastic. The general case is a coupled system with coupled boundary conditions. We can have uncoupled equations with coupled boundary conditions, coupled equations with uncoupled boundary conditions, or simply uncoupled equations with uncoupled boundary conditions. The boundary conditions may be linear, nonlinear, or random.

As an example of nonlinear boundary conditions, consider a linear differential equation with b.c. in the form

$$B_1 y(\tau_1) = Ly|_{\tau_1} + Ny|_{\tau_2} = b_1$$

and a similar condition at τ_2. More specifically, let

$$B_1 y(\tau_1) = \frac{d}{d\tau_1} y(\tau_1) + \beta_1 y(\tau_1) + \gamma_1 y^2(\tau_1) = b_1$$

Since $y(t)$ is replaced by a finite sum of decomposition components

$$\sum_{i=0}^{n-1} \frac{d}{dt} y_i(\tau_1) + \beta_1 \sum_{i=0}^{n-1} y_i(\tau_1) + \gamma_1 \sum_{i=0}^{n-1} A_n(\tau_1) \cong b_1$$

Substituting $A_0 = y_0^2$, $A_1 = 2y_0 y_1$, $A_2 = y_1^2 + 2y_0 y_2$, etc., we have, e.g., for a two-term approximation

$$\dot{y}_0(\tau_1) + \dot{y}_1(\tau_1) + \beta_1 y_0(\tau_1) + \beta_1 y_1(\tau_1)$$
$$+ \gamma_1 y_0^2(\tau_1) + \gamma_1 (2y_0(\tau_1) y_1(\tau_1)) = b_1$$

It is interesting to look at some simple linear deterministic equations which do not require our methods. Consider one-dimensional motion of a particle with uncertain initial position moving with constant velocity. We write $\dot{x} = c$ for $0 \le t \le \infty$. In our notation this is $Lx = c$ or $x = x(0) + L^{-1}c = x(0) + ct$. Given the initial condition $Bu|_{t=0} = u(0) = \beta(\omega)$, a random variable [if we write $u(t, \omega) = \beta(t, \omega)$ and let $t = 0$, we have $\beta(0, \omega)$, which is a random variable], we have now

$$x(t, \omega) = \beta(\omega) + ct \tag{12.15.1}$$

Thus, if the initial condition (initial position) is random, $x(t)$ or $x(t, \omega)$, is also random but is given by a deterministic law $g(\beta(\omega), t)$. In other words, we have a deterministic transformation of the randomness in $x(0)$ to the randomness in $x(t)$. (The stochastic operator case is difficult in comparison since this transformation is itself stochastic.)

In this problem now, let us suppose $\beta(\omega)$ is Gaussian with zero-mean and variance σ^2. The probability that $\beta(\omega)$ has a value, say between λ and $\lambda + d\lambda$ is given by $p(\lambda)$ with

$$p(\lambda) = (1/\sqrt{2\pi}\,\sigma) \exp\{-\lambda^2/2\sigma^2\}.$$

It is well known that a deterministic linear transformation (e.g., an integral) of a Gaussian process is again a Gaussian process. Thus,

$$p\{x(t) < \xi\} = p\{x(0) + ct < \xi\} = p\{x(0) < \xi - ct\}$$
$$= \int_{-\infty}^{\xi - ct} p(\lambda)\, d\lambda = \int_{-\infty}^{\xi} p(\alpha - ct)\, d\alpha$$

where

$$p(\alpha - ct) = (1/\sqrt{2\pi}\,\sigma) \exp\{-(\alpha - ct)^2/2\lambda^2\}$$

which is again Gaussian with the same variance, but the mean has changed from 0 to ct.

Thus solving a problem with a deterministic equation and randomness only in the initial condition involves a transformation of random variables. The stochastic forcing function case (again with a deterministic operator) is similar.

Returning to (12.15.1), if we are seeking the average, we write

$$\langle x(t, \omega) \rangle = \langle x(0) + ct \rangle = \langle x(0) \rangle = \langle \beta(\omega) \rangle$$

if we seek the variance,

$$\text{var}\{x(t, \omega)\} = \text{var}\{\beta(\omega)\}$$

We are no longer concerned with distributions. We are given statistical measures of the inputs (in this case the random initial conditions), and we seek statistical measures of the solution (output).

From Newton's equation

$$\ddot{x} = F/m$$

$$Lx = F/m$$

$$x = x(0) + tx'(0) + L^{-1}F/m$$

$$x = x(0) + tx'(0) + (F/m)t^2/2$$

if F is constant or

$$x = x(0) + tx'(0) + \frac{1}{m} \int_{\infty}^{t} \int_{\infty}^{\tau} F(\gamma) \, d\gamma \, d\tau$$

if F is time varying. If the initial conditions are random, $x(0)$ and $x'(0)$ will be random variables. If $F = F(t, \omega)$ the last term will also be random. Now we can average to get the expectation or multiply $x(t_1)x(t_2)$ and average to get the correlation.

It is easy now to consider the stochastic operator equations with general boundary conditions. Thus, we have $\mathscr{F}u = g(t, \omega)$, where $\mathscr{F}$ is a stochastic operator (possibly nonlinear) and boundary conditions

$$B_1 u(t, \omega)|_{t=\tau_1} = \beta_1(t, \omega)|_{t=\tau_1}$$

$$B_2 u(t, \omega)|_{t=\tau_2} = \beta_2(t, \omega)|_{t=\tau_2}$$

where, for example, each of these may be specified as

$$B_i u = Lu|_{t=\tau_1} + a_1 u|_{t=\tau_1}$$

where $L = d/dt$ and a_1 may be stochastic. Suppose we have simply

$$B_1 u|_{t=0} = u(0) = b_1(t, \omega)|_{t=0} \qquad \text{and} \qquad B_2 u|_{t=1} = u(1) = b_2(t, \omega)|_{t=1}.$$

We find the solution $\phi_n = \sum_{i=0}^{n-1} u_i$ of the equation for some n (a few terms) and substitute ϕ_n into the boundary conditions, e.g.,

$$u_0(0) + u_1(0) + u_2(0) = b_1(\omega)$$

$$u_0(1) + u_1(0) + u_2(1) = b_2(\omega)$$

to fix the constants in the u_0 term.

Suppose $\mathscr{F}u = g$ is further specified as $du/dt + \alpha u = g$. Let L be du/dt. Then $\sum_{n=0}^{\infty} u_n = u(0) + L^{-1}g - L^{-1}\alpha \sum_{n=0}^{\infty} u_n$, where $u_0 = u(0) + L^{-1}g$, $u_1 = -L^{-1}\alpha u_0, \dots$.

We have

$$u(t) = \sum_{n=0}^{\infty} u_n(t)$$

where

$$u_0 = \beta_1 + L^{-1}g$$

$$u_1 = -L^{-1}\alpha u_0$$

$$u_2 = -L^{-1}\alpha u_1$$

$$\vdots$$

The condition $u|_{t=0}$ yields $u(0) = \beta_1$ since the remaining terms vanish (they involve integrations from 0 to t with t now equal to 0).

Given the condition $\dot{u}(0) + au = b_1$ we get $\phi_n(0) + a\phi_n = b_1$. A second-order equation for $\mathscr{F}u = g$ such as $d^2u/dt^2 + Nu = g$ requires evaluation of two constants from given conditions.

EXERCISE

1. For $\ddot{u} + \pi^2 \sin \pi t = 0$ with $u(0) = u(1) = 0$ show that $u = \sin \pi t$.

A final, interesting question is that of statistical separability in stochastic systems. Consider the equation $Ly(t) = x(t, \omega)$, where L is a second-order linear deterministic differential operator. The solution is $y = y_h + y_p$, where $Ly_h = 0$ and $Ly_p = x$. Suppose the boundary conditions are specified at τ_1 and τ_2 by

$$B_1 y|_{\tau_1} = \dot{y}|_{\tau_1} + \alpha y|_{\tau_1} = b_1|_{\tau_1}$$

$$B_2 u|_{\tau_2} = \dot{y}|_{\tau_2} + \beta y|_{\tau_2} = b_2|_{\tau_2}$$

where α, β, b_1 and b_2 are stochastic processes. Let $L = d^2/dt^2$. Then $Ly_h = 0$ gives us $y_h = c_1 + c_2 t$, which we can substitute into $B_1 y$ and $B_2 y$. Thus

$$c_2 + \alpha(c_1 + c_2 \tau_1) = b_1$$

$$c_2 + \beta(c_1 + c_2 \tau_2) = b_2$$

By replacing the process α by $\langle \alpha \rangle + \alpha$ (where α is now a zero-mean process) and similarly replacing β by $\langle \beta \rangle + \beta$, we now have

$$\begin{pmatrix} \langle \alpha \rangle & 1 + \tau_1 \langle \alpha \rangle \\ \langle \beta \rangle & 1 + \tau_2 \langle \beta \rangle \end{pmatrix} \cdot \begin{pmatrix} c_1 \\ c_2 \end{pmatrix} + \begin{pmatrix} \alpha & \tau_1 \alpha \\ \beta & \tau_2 \beta \end{pmatrix} \cdot \begin{pmatrix} c_1 \\ c_2 \end{pmatrix} = \begin{pmatrix} b_1 \\ b_2 \end{pmatrix}$$

(the α, β, b_1, and b_2 are stochastic). This matrix equation can be written as $[\Lambda + P] \cdot C = B$ or $C = \Lambda^{-1} B - \Lambda^{-1} PC$ so that

$$\begin{pmatrix} c_1 \\ c_2 \end{pmatrix} = \sum_{n=0}^{\infty} (-1)^n [\Lambda^{-1} P]^n \Lambda^{-1} \begin{pmatrix} b_1 \\ b_2 \end{pmatrix}$$

Let Λ^{-1} be given by the matrix

$$\begin{pmatrix} \lambda_{11} & \lambda_{12} \\ \lambda_{21} & \lambda_{22} \end{pmatrix}$$

Since the zeroth component of C is $\Lambda^{-1} B$ we have $c_{10} = \lambda_{11} b_1 + \lambda_{12} b_2$ and $c_{20} = \lambda_{21} b_1 + \lambda_{22} b_2$. Since the λ's are deterministic but the b's are stochastic, we have

$$\langle c_{10} \rangle = \lambda_{11} \langle b_1 \rangle + \lambda_{12} \langle b_2 \rangle$$

$$\langle c_{20} \rangle = \lambda_{21} \langle b_1 \rangle + \lambda_{22} \langle b_2 \rangle$$

Components with subscript "1" are now found from

$$\begin{pmatrix} c_{11} \\ c_{21} \end{pmatrix} = \begin{pmatrix} \lambda_{11} & \lambda_{12} \\ \lambda_{21} & \lambda_{22} \end{pmatrix} \cdot \begin{pmatrix} \rho_{11} & \rho_{12} \\ \rho_{21} & \rho_{22} \end{pmatrix} \cdot \begin{pmatrix} \lambda_{11} & \lambda_{12} \\ \lambda_{21} & \lambda_{22} \end{pmatrix} \cdot \begin{pmatrix} b_1 \\ b_2 \end{pmatrix}$$

The "2" components (c_{12}, c_{22}) are then calculated and similarly for all the c_{1n}, c_{2n} column vector. If we now wish to calculate the correlation (assuming real quantities)

$$\langle c_1 c_1 \rangle = \left\langle \sum_{n=0}^{\infty} c_{1n} \sum_{n=0}^{\infty} c_{1n} \right\rangle$$

$$\langle c_2 c_2 \rangle = \left\langle \sum_{n=0}^{\infty} c_{2n} \sum_{n=0}^{\infty} c_{2n} \right\rangle$$

The zeroth order correlation for c_1 is $\langle c_{10}c_{10}\rangle$. The next term is $\langle c_{10}c_{11}\rangle +$ $\langle c_{11}c_{10}\rangle$ etc. The zeroth term is specifically given by

$$\langle c_{10}c_{10}\rangle = \lambda_{11}^2\langle b_1b_1\rangle + \lambda_{12}^2\langle b_2b_2\rangle + 2\lambda_{11}\lambda_{12}\langle b_1b_2\rangle$$

EXERCISES

1. Verify the expression for $\langle c_{10}c_{10}\rangle$.

2. Show that

$$\begin{aligned}
\langle c_{11}\rangle &= (\lambda_{11}\langle\rho_{11}\rangle + \lambda_{12}\langle\rho_{21}\rangle)(\lambda_{11}\langle b_1\rangle + \lambda_{12}\langle b_2\rangle) \\
&\quad + (\lambda_{11}\langle\rho_{12}\rangle + \lambda_{12}\langle\rho_{22}\rangle)(\lambda_{21}\langle b_1\rangle + \lambda_{22}\langle\langle b_2\rangle)
\end{aligned}$$

3. Calculate $\langle c_{10}c_{11}\rangle$

It is clear from these examples that statistical measures of interest (first- and second-order) are calculable for linear stochastic differential equations with random boundary conditions, and we have no statistical separability problems such as those occurring in hierarchy methods, where we get averages involving system parameters and outputs which do not separate into products of averages.

REFERENCES

1. R. E. Bellman and G. Adomian, The stochastic Riccati equation, *J. Nonlinear Anal. Theory, Meth. Appl.* **4**(6), 1131–1133 (1980).

SUGGESTED FURTHER READING

G. Adomian and R. Rach, Coupled differential equations and coupled boundary conditions, *J. Math. Anal. Appl.* **112**(1), 129–140.

G. Adomian, L. H. Sibul, and R. Rach, Coupled nonlinear stochastic differential equations, *J. Math. Anal. Appl.* **92**(2), 427–434 (1983).

K. S. Miller, "Linear Differential Equations." Norton, New York, 1963.

T. L. Saaty, "Modern Nonlinear Equations." McGraw-Hill, New York, 1967.

CHAPTER 13

Integral and Integro-Differential Operators

We have dealt with generic modeling in the standard form $\mathscr{F}y = x(t)$, or in the deterministic case $Fy = x$, where $Fy = Ly + Ry + Ny$ considering L to be a linear differential operator d^n/dt^n, R to represent the remainder of the linear operator, and Ny to be a nonlinear term for which the A_n polynomials are generated. We have emphasized that these operator equations need not be differential equations and can, for example, be algebraic equations. They can also be integral equations involving an operator I, which symbolizes one or more (n-fold) integrations from 0 to t. (If we need to be specific, we can write subscripts to indicate the number of integrations.) Thus

$$Ly + Iy = x(t)$$

is an *integro-differential* equation. As before, we first write $Ly = x - Iy$. (Suppose that $L = d/dt$, $I = I_1$, and $y(0)$ is specified.) Then operating with $L^{-1} \equiv I$ on both sides yields

$$y = y(0) + I_1 x - I_2 y$$

or

$$\sum_{n=0}^{\infty} y_n = y_0 - I_2 \sum_{n=0}^{\infty} y_n$$

with $y_0 = y(0) + I_1 x(t)$. Then $y_{n+1} = -I_2 y_n$ for $n \geq 0$ and $y(t) = \sum_{n=0}^{\infty} y_n$.

If L is of order n (i.e., d^n/dt^n), we can write L_n, and if I is of order m we write I_m, then $y = [\Phi + I_n x] - I_{n+m} y$, where $L_n \Phi = 0$. Just as we dealt with general nth order differential operators $\mathscr{L} = \sum_{v=0}^{n} \alpha_v \, d^v/dt^v$, where $\alpha_n = 1$, we can now define nth order integral operators

$$I = \sum_{v=0}^{n} \alpha_v(t) I_v, \qquad \alpha_n = 1$$

and integral equations

$$Iy = x(t)$$

275

The operator I_v may even involve deterministic kernels $\int_0^t G(t, \tau)[\cdot]\, d\tau$ or even stochastic kernels, in which case we write $\mathscr{I}_v$ with our usual script letters for stochastic operators. All sorts of combinations can be considered, e.g.,

$$\frac{d^2y}{dt^2} + \frac{dy}{dt} + \beta y + \gamma I_1 y + \delta I_2 y = x(t)$$

where $L = d^2/dt^2$ and $R = \alpha\, d/dt + \beta$ or nonlinear integral equations like

$$y + (Iy)^2 = x(t)$$

by using the A_n polynomials and the idea of composite nonlinearities.

EXERCISES

1. Verify that $y = ke^t$ is the solution of $I_1 y - y = -k$ by writing

$$y = k + \int_0^t \sum_{n=0}^{\infty} y_n\, dt \qquad \text{with} \qquad y_0 = k$$

2. Show that the solution of $I_2 y + y = k$ is $y(t) = \sum_{n=0}^{\infty}(-1)^n kt^{2n}/(2n)!$.

3. Consider $Ly - Iy = x(t)$, where $x(t) = -1$ and $y(0) = 1$; show that the solution is $y = e^{-t}$. (Hint: $y_0 = 1 - t,\ y_1 = -I_2 y_0,\ldots$.)

Consider the equation $d^2u/dt^2 + (du/dt)(\int_0^t u\, dt) = 0$ or $u'' + u'I_1 u = 0$ with $u(0) = c_1$ and $u'(0) = c_2$. With our L_n and I_n operators, we can also write it as

$$L_2 u + (L_1 u)(I_1 u) = 0$$

$$L_2 u = -(L_1 u)(I_1 u)$$

$$u = u_0 - L_2^{-1} \sum_{n=0}^{\infty} A_n$$

where $u_0 = c_1 + c_2 t$ and

$$A_0 = Lu_0 Iu_0$$

$$A_1 = Lu_0 Iu_1 + Lu_1 Iu_0$$

$$A_2 = Lu_1 Iu_1 + Lu_0 Iu_2 + Lu_2 Iu_0$$

$$\vdots$$

where we have dropped the subscript 1 on L and I. Hence,

$$u_0 = c_1 + c_2 t$$

$$u_1 = -L_2^{-1}A_0 = -I_2 A_0 = -I_2(u_0' Iu_0)$$

but $u_0' = c_2$ and $Iu_0 = c_1 t + c_2 t^2/2!$, so

$$u_1 = -c_1 c_2 t^3/3! - c_2^2 t^4/4!,\ldots$$

EXERCISES

1. Show that the solution of $L_2u + (L_1u)(I_1u) = t$ with $u(0) = u'(0) = 0$ is given by $u = (t^3/3!) - (15t^7/7!) + \cdots$.

2. Verify that the solution of $u' + I_1u = t$ with $u(0) = 0$ is given by $u = (t^2/2!) - (t^4/4!) + (t^6/6!) - \cdots$.

3. Show that the solution of $u' + I_1u = 0$ with $u(0) = k$ is

$$u = k \sum_{m=0}^{\infty} (-1)^m t^{2m}/(2m)!$$

When a difficult nonlinearity is present in the differential equation of interest, such as a convolution product $y * y = \int_0^t y(t)y(t - \tau)\,d\tau$, it may be useful in some cases to transform the differential equation into an algebraic equation by use of the Laplace transform, then solve the algebraic equation in the transform variable by the same techniques (decomposition and use of the A_n polynomials). A study of this possibility is being carried out presently of the equation $Ly + y * y = f(t)$, where $L = d^n/dt^n$ and $y^{(n)}(0) = c_n$ for $0 \le n \le m - 1$. For the equation $y' + y * y = 0$ with $y(0) = c_0$, the transform equation is $sY(s) - c_0 + Y^2(s)$. By decomposition $\sum_{n=0}^{\infty} Y_n(s) = (c_0/s) - (1/s)\sum_{n=0}^{\infty} A_n(s)$ and $Y(s) = (c_0/s) - (c_0^2/s^3) + (2c_0^3/s^5) - \cdots$. Then $y(t) = \sum_{n=0}^{\infty} y_n(t) = \sum_{n=0}^{\infty} \mathscr{L}^{-1}\{Y_n(s)\}$, and finally $y(t) = c_0 - c_0^2 t^2/2! + 2c_0^3 t^4/4! - \cdots$ provides a solution in a convergent series.

The interesting possibility now occurs that inverses of Laplace (or other) transforms can be determined by decomposition more easily than by conventional methods and is being investigated in a forthcoming paper by Adomian and Rach.

The possibility is suggested by the solution of the algebraic equation in series form (decomposition method) and the relatively simple inverse transform applied to *each* term. To generalize the preceding—we need not restrict our attention to Laplace transforms—write T for the transform operator (whether Laplace, Fourier, Hankel, etc.). Now considering the differential equation $Ly + Ry = x$, where $L = d^n/dt^n$ and R is the remaining linear operator, and assuming zero initial conditions $y(0) = y'(0) = \cdots = y^{(n)} = 0$ we write

$$T\{Ly\} + T\{Ry\} = T\{x\}$$

$$T\{Ly\} \to L_T Y$$

where L_T is now a linear *algebraic* operator in the transform space and Y the transform of y. Similarly $T\{Ry\} \to R_T Y$ and $T\{x\} \to X$ in transform space. Hence

$$L_Y Y = R_T Y = X$$

Solving this algebraic equation by decomposition, we get

$$L_T Y = X - R_T Y$$

$$Y = L_T^{-1} X - L_T^{-1} R_T \sum_{n=0}^{\infty} Y_n$$

$$Y = \sum_{n=0}^{\infty} (-1)^n (L_T^{-1} R_T)^n (L_T^{-1} X)$$

Finally, we obtain y from $T^{-1} Y$ or

$$T^{-1} Y = T^{-1} \sum_{n=0}^{\infty} (-1)^n (L_T^{-1} R_T)^n (L_T^{-1} X)$$

$$= \sum_{n=0}^{\infty} (-1)^n T^{-1} \{ (L_T^{-1} R_T)^n (L_T^{-1} X) \}$$

$$= \sum_{n=0}^{\infty} (-1)^n (L^{-1} R)^n L^{-1} x$$

It appears that it often may be easier to compute the inverse of each term $T^{-1}\{(L_T^{-1} R_T)^n (L_T^{-1} X)\}$ for each n than to compute $T^{-1} Y$ even if we have the exact Y. With the rapid convergence of the decomposition method, it appears that it may be a superior technique in the very difficult problem of finding inverse transforms. (Suggestion: It may be a good dissertation topic.) An analogue of this is the way we have used the decomposition method itself in computing Green's functions. In earlier work, we decomposed a linear stochastic operator into $L + \mathcal{R}$ assuming L^{-1} could be found. However since it was sometimes quite difficult, we then wrote $L = d^n/dt^n$, i.e., we chose for L the highest ordered derivative and wrote R for the remainder of the linear deterministic operator and $\mathcal{R}$ for any random part in the operator. We were then required only to find a Green's function for the simpler L, and the rest was found in series form. The simpler Green's function made our computation of successive terms all very simple compared with what they would have been. It slowed up convergence, but it was a cheap price to pay for the easy integrations. Using this idea for inverse transforms may make numerical calculation of inverse transforms unnecessary.

CHAPTER 14

On Systems of Nonlinear Partial Differential Equations

The decomposition method has now been demonstrated to solve a wide class of equations $[1, 2]$. These have included differential equations, systems of differential equations, and partial differential equations. Consider now a system of nonlinear partial differential equations given by

$$u_t = uu_x + vu_y \tag{14.1}$$

$$v_t = uv_x + vv_y \tag{14.2}$$

$$u(x, y, 0) = f(x, y)$$

$$v(x, y, 0) = g(x, y)$$

We wish to investigate the solution by the decomposition technique. Let $L_t = \partial/\partial t$, $L_x = \partial/\partial x$, $L_y = \partial/\partial y$ and write (14.1) and (14.2) in the form

$$L_t u = uu_x + vu_y$$

$$L_t v = uv_x + vv_y$$

Let $L_t^{-1} = \int_0^t [\cdot] \, dt$ and operate on both sides with L_t^{-1}:

$$u = u(x, y, 0) + L_t^{-1} uu_x + L_t^{-1} vu_y$$

$$v = v(x, y, 0) + L_t^{-1} uv_x + L_t^{-1} vv_y$$

Let $u = \sum_{n=0}^{\infty} u_n$ and $v = \sum_{n=0}^{\infty} v_n$ and using (14.4) let

$$u_0 = u(x, y, 0) = f(x, y)$$

$$v_0 = v(x, y, 0) = g(x, y)$$

so that the first term of u and of v are known. We now have

$$u = u_0 + L_t^{-1} uu_x + L_t^{-1} vu_y$$

$$v = v_0 + L_t^{-1} uv_x + L_t^{-1} vv_y$$

279

We can use the A_n polynomials for the nonlinear terms. Thus,

$$u = u_0 + L_t^{-1} \sum_{n=0}^{\infty} A_n(uu_x) + L_t^{-1} \sum_{n=0}^{\infty} A_n(vu_y)$$

$$v = v_0 + L_t^{-1} \sum_{n=0}^{\infty} A_n(uv_x) + L_t^{-1} \sum_{n=0}^{\infty} A_n(vv_y)$$

[The notation $A_n(uL_x u)$ means the A_n generated for uu_x.] Therefore,

$$A_0(uL_x u) = u_0 L_x u_0$$

$$A_1(uL_x u) = u_0 L_x u_1 + u_1 L_x u_0$$

$$A_2(uL_x u) = u_0 L_x u_2 + u_1 L_x u_1 + u_2 L_x u_0$$

$$\vdots$$

A simple rule here is that the sum of the subscripts of each term is the same as the subscript of A. Consequently, we can write

$$u_1 = L_t^{-1} u_0 L_x u_0 + L_t^{-1} v_0 L_y u_0$$

$$v_1 = L_t^{-1} u_0 L_x v_0 + L_t^{-1} v_0 L_y v_0$$

which yields the next component of u and v. Then

$$u_2 = L_t^{-1}[u_0 L_x u_1 + u_1 L_x u_0] + L_t^{-1}[v_0 L_y u_1 + v_1 L_y u_0]$$

$$v_2 = L_t^{-1}[u_0 L_x v_1 + u_1 L_x v_0] + L_t^{-1}[v_0 L_y v_1 + v_1 L_y v_0]$$

$$u_3 = L_t^{-1}[u_0 L_x u_2 + u_1 L_x u_1 + u_2 L_x u_0] + L_t^{-1}[v_0 L_y u_2 + v_1 L_y u_1 + v_2 L_y u_0]$$

$$v_3 = L_t^{-1}[u_0 L_x v_2 + u_1 L_x v_1 + u_2 L_x v_0] + L_t^{-1}[v_0 L_y v_2 + v_1 L_y v_1 + v_2 L_y v_0]$$

up to some u_n and v_n. We then have the n-term approximations $\sum_{i=0}^{n-1} u_i$ for u and $\sum_{i=0}^{n-1} v_i$ for v as our approximate solutions.

Since the solution of (14.1) and (14.2) can exhibit a shock phenomenon for finite t, we select f and g such that the shock occurs for a value of t far from our region of interest. Let $f(x, y) = g(x, y) = x + y$. Therefore, $u_0 = v_0 = x + y$; then u_1 and v_1 can be calculated as

$$\begin{aligned} u_1 &= L_t^{-1} u_0 L_x u_0 + L_t^{-1} v_0 L_y u_0 \\ &= L_t^{-1}(x + y)L_x(x + y) + L_t^{-1}(x + y)L_y(x + y) \\ &= xt + yt + xt + yt \\ &= 2xt + 2yt \end{aligned}$$

$$\begin{aligned} v_1 &= L_t^{-1} u_0 L_x v_0 + L_t^{-1} v_0 L_y v_0 \\ &= 2xt + 2yt \end{aligned}$$

and u_2 and v_2 are calculated as

$$u_2 = L_t^{-1}[(x + y)L_x(2xt + 2yt) + (2xt + 2yt)L_x(x + y)]$$
$$+ L_t^{-1}[(x + y)L_y(2xt + 2yt) + (2xt + 2yt)L_y(x + y)]$$
$$u_2 = 4t^2(x + y)$$
$$v_2 = 4t^2(x + y)$$

Thus

$$u = (x + y) + 2t(x + y) + 4t^2(x + y) + \cdots$$
$$v = (x + y) + 2t(x + y) + 4t^2(x + y) + \cdots$$

which we can write also as

$$u(x, y) = (x + y)/(1 - 2t)$$
$$v(x, y) = (x + y)/(1 - 2t)$$

Now suppose the initial functions are changed to

$$f(x, y) = x^2, \qquad g(x, y) = y$$

Now

$$u_0 = x^2$$

$$v_0 = y$$

$$u_1 = L_t^{-1}(x^2)L_x(x^2) + L_t^{-1}(y)L_y(x^2) = L_t^{-1}(2x^3) = 2x^3t$$

$$v_1 = L_t^{-1}(x^2)L_x(y) + L_t^{-1}yL_y y = yt$$

$$u_2 = L_t^{-1}[(x^2)L_x(2x^3t) + (2x^3t)L_x(x^2)] + L_t^{-1}[yL_y(2x^3t) + (yt)L_y(x^2)]$$
$$= 3x^4t^2 + 2x^4t^2 = 5x^4t^2$$

$$v_2 = L_t^{-1}[x^2L_x(yt) + (2x^3t)L_x(y)] + L_t^{-1}[yL_y(yt) + (yt)L_y(y)]$$
$$= yt^2/2 + yt^2/2 = yt^2$$

$$\vdots$$

$$u = x^2 + 2x^3t + 5x^4t^2 + \cdots$$

$$v = y + yt + yt^2 + \cdots$$

or

$$u = x^2(1 + 2tx + 5t^2x^2 + \cdots)$$
$$v = y(1 + t + t^2 + \cdots) = y/(1 - t)$$

(A shock occurs at $t = \frac{1}{4}x$.) Clearly we can calculate $u(x, y, t)$ and $v(x, y, t)$ when explicit solutions exist for given initial functions. More important, the methodology does have potential application to systems of nonlinear partial differential equations and clearly in the case of stochastic parameters as well.

REFERENCES

1. G. Adomian, "Stochastic Systems." Academic, New York, 1983.
2. R. E. Bellman and G. Adomian, "Partial Differential Equations—New Methods for Their Treatment and Application." Reidel, Dordrecht, Netherlands, 1985.

CHAPTER 15

Postlude

We have discussed solving equations by the decomposition method and, a useful corollary, the asymptotic decomposition method. We have shown that the method applies to a wide class of equations including algebraic (transcendental, matrix, polynomial), differential, coupled differential, delay-differential, and partial differential equations. It applies to linear or nonlinear, deterministic or stochastic equations without smallness assumptions. The method is more general than perturbation theories and more desirable than numerical methods. The Picard method can be cumbersome and works only if the equation satisfies a uniform Lipschitz condition. The convergence is sufficiently fast only if the Lipschitz constant is small. Bellomo and Monaco [1] have shown various significant advantages of decomposition over perturbation. Nonlinearities need not be small in the decomposition approach, and linearization is not necessary; also, no closure approximations are necessary. Boundary conditions can be quite complicated involving derivatives, nonlinear and stochastic terms, and random inhomogeneous terms. Furthermore, boundary conditions can be coupled. Thus, we can deal with coupled differential (nonlinear stochastic) equations with coupled (nonlinear stochastic) boundary conditions.

Since very complicated equations can be solved accurately and continuously, existing computer methods would seem to require reexamination.

Computers have not replaced understanding and are not a substitute but an aid for the methodology. A numerical printout provides little insight into the character of a solution. In general, it provides discrete sets of numbers whereas it should be providing continuous differentiable functions as approximations that satisfy the differential equation, and whose derivatives constitute satisfactory approximations to derivatives of the solution function. When the possible solutions for a range of parameters are calculated, the data become excessive. Our n-term approximate solution ϕ_n can be verified by substitution for any n; it is easily computable and accurate. The expressions for each term do show the dependences and effect of changes and will provide numerical results when we wish. Such an analytical approximation method, yielding insight into relationships, without linearization or perturbation, applications to frontier problems.

Special restrictive assumptions on the nature of stochastic processes are eliminated, and stochasticity can be present in coefficients of the differential or partial differential equation, in coefficients of boundary operators, or in inhomogeneous terms of the equation or the boundary conditions.

If we consider a differential equation such as $y' + Ny = 0$ with $y(0) = k$ (which is in our standard form $Ly + Ny = x$ with $x = 0$ and $L = d/dt$), we have $y = kL^{-1} \sum_{n=0}^{\infty} A_n$ or $\sum_{n=0}^{\infty} y_n = k - L^{-1} \sum_{n=0}^{\infty} A_n$. If we consider the algebraic equation $Ly + Ny = x$ with L a constant and x a constant, we again have $\sum_{n=0}^{\infty} y_n = k - L^{-1} \sum_{n=0}^{\infty} A_n$. If we have the same nonlinearity in both, the real difference is that in one case the A_n are integrated, and, on the other, they are divided by a constant. In Chapter 13 we show that we can also extend the work to integral equations. Thus, interesting possibilities arise for research.

The generally rapid convergence (see footnote—Section 11.4) and the broad applicability of the method should make it broadly useful in applications in many fields, especially so, since it requires essentially only calculus and some elementary linear algebra.

It is hoped that this book will be useful as a textbook and as a research monograph in the mathematical sciences.

REFERENCE

1. N. Bellomo and R. Monaco, *J. Math. Anal. Appl.*, **110** (2), 49–502 (1985).

Index

STOCHASTIC SYSTEMS
by George Adomian

ERRATA

Pages 232–233

Equation (8.2.6) on p. 232 should read

$$F^{-1}x = y_0 + L^{-1} \sum_{n-0}^{x} A_n$$

The last three equations on p. 232 should read

$$y_1 = F_1^{-1}x = L^{-1}A_0$$
$$y_2 = F_2^{-1}x = L^{-1}A_1$$
$$y_3 = F_3^{-1}x = L^{-1}A_2$$

The signs of the A_n on p. 233 are incorrect. They should read

$$A_0 = y_0^2$$
$$A_1 = 2y_0y_1$$
$$A_2 = y_1^2 + 2y_0y_2$$

The expression for ϕ_4 on p. 233 should be

$$y = 1 + t + t^2 + \tfrac{4}{3}t^3 + \cdots$$

The paragraph following the example should read

Adomian's terms are clearly far less cumbersome to compute. To comment on the relative accuracy of the two methods, one must relate the approximate solutions to an analytic expression for the exact solution. If this is done, the superior accuracy becomes evident as well. (The function $t^2 + y^2$ is an entire function and the solution is analytic in a neighborhood, so we can get a Taylor series yielding the same answer for y for the four terms calculated.)

287